Editorial Director: Cynthia Tripp
Cover Designer and Illustrator: Matt Pollock
Illustrator: Sam Valentino
Photography Credit: wk1003mike/Shutterstock (front cover background)

ISBN 978-0-7609-9226-5
©2015—Curriculum Associates, LLC
North Billerica, MA 01862

NOT FOR RESALE

No part of this book may be reproduced
by any means without written permission
from the publisher.
All Rights Reserved. Printed in USA.
30 29 28 27 26 25 24 23 22 21 20 19 18 17 16

Table of Contents

Family Letter available with every lesson.

©Curriculum Associates, LLC   Copying is not permitted.

Table of Contents

Family Letter available with every lesson.

©Curriculum Associates, LLC   Copying is not permitted.

Dear Family,

This week your child is exploring place value in whole numbers and decimal numbers.

We use a number system called base ten. It is based on a pattern of tens. The models below show the pattern of tens in whole numbers and decimals. Each place value is 10 times the place value to its right.

Thousands	Hundreds	Tens	Ones
1 thousand is 10 times 1 hundred	1 hundred is 10 times 1 ten	1 ten is 10 times 1 one	1 one
1,000	100	10	1

Ones	Tenths	Hundredths
1 whole is 10 times 1 tenth	1 tenth is 10 times 1 hundredth	1 hundredth
1	0.1	0.01

Understanding place value helps your child think about and use different ways to add, subtract, multiply, and divide numbers.

Invite your child to share what he or she knows about place value by doing the following activity together.

©Curriculum Associates, LLC   Copying is not permitted.

Lesson 1 Understand Place Value   1

Work together with your child to shade models to understand decimal place value.

- Have your child shade in the models below to represent the number that is shown below each model.

- Ask your child to explain the pattern that he or she sees in the models. (The models on the right have 10 times as many squares shaded as the models on the left.)

Each grid represents 1 whole.

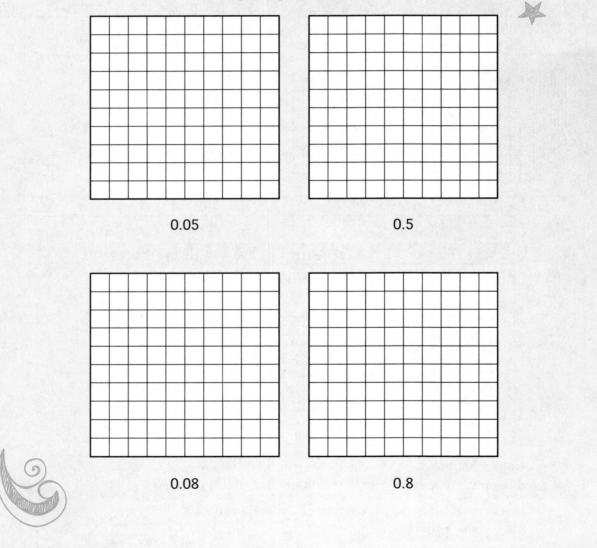

0.05

0.5

0.08

0.8

    ©Curriculum Associates, LLC   Copying is not permitted.

Name: _____

Prerequisite: How do you show decimals with place-value models and charts?

Study the example modeling a decimal using a place-value model and chart. Then solve problems 1–6.

Example

How can you model the decimal 0.25 two different ways?

The grid represents 1 whole.

Ones	.	Tenths	Hundredths
0	.	2	5

1 Complete the sentences to show the value of the digits in the decimal 0.25 from the example problem above.

The 2 has a value of 2 _____ , or 0.2.

The 5 has a value of 5 _____ , or 0.05.

2 Write the decimal 0.25 in words.

_____

3 Write a number from the box to complete each model.

| 0.08   0.88   0.8 |

_____   _____   _____

Solve.

4 How is shading a grid to show 1 tenth different from shading a grid to show 1 hundredth?

_____

_____

_____

5 Model A shows the decimal 1.4. Shade Model B to show the decimal 1.04.

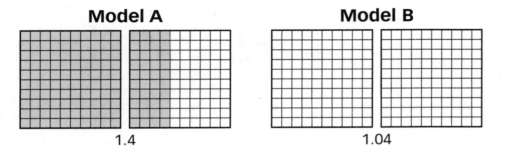

Model A

1.4

Model B

1.04

6 Trent and Lex each shaded a grid to show the decimal 0.53.

Their grids are shown below.

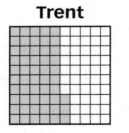

Trent   Lex

Do both grids show the decimal 0.53? Which grid is faster to check? Explain.

_____

_____

_____

_____

©Curriculum Associates, LLC   Copying is not permitted.

Name: _____

Work with Place-Value Patterns

Study how the example shows place-value patterns. Then solve problems 1–8.

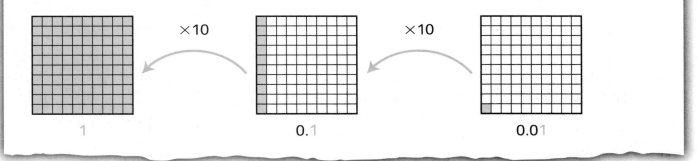

Example

Show how the numbers 1, 0.1, and 0.01 are related.

×10   ×10

1   0.1   0.01

1 Use the ×10 pattern from the example to complete each equation.

_____ = 1 × 10

1 = _____ × 10

0.1 = _____ × 10

2 The pattern can also be described using division. Use the grids in the example to complete the equations.

10 ÷ 10 = _____

1.0 ÷ 10 = _____

0.1 ÷ 10 = _____

3 Use the ÷10 pattern to fill in the blanks.

400   _____   _____   0.4   _____

4 How are the decimals 0.009 and 0.09 related? Explain.

_____

_____

_____

Solve.

5 Choose *Yes* or *No* to tell whether the expression is equivalent to 0.07.

   a. 0.007×10 ☐ Yes   ☐ No

   b. $0.7 \div 10$ ☐ Yes   ☐ No

   c. 0.07×10 ☐ Yes   ☐ No

   d. $0.007 \div 10$ ☐ Yes   ☐ No

6 Describe the shaded section of the model two different ways. Fill in the missing information below.

   a.   8 tenths = _____

   b.   _____ hundredths = 0.80

7 Choose a symbol from the box to show the relationship between 0.8 and 0.80.

   | < | > | = |

   0.8 ◯ 0.80

8 Shade some or all of the grids to show that 2 ones is the same as 20 tenths. Explain.

   _____

   _____

   _____

   _____

©Curriculum Associates, LLC   Copying is not permitted.

Name: _____

Reason and Write

Study the example. Underline two parts that you think make it a particularly good answer and a helpful example.

Example

Clara knows that each time a digit moves one place to the right in a whole number, the value of the digit is one-tenth as much.

Describe an example you would show to Clara to demonstrate that this is true for decimal numbers also.

Show your work. Use pictures, words, or numbers to explain.

I would show Clara an example using the decimal 0.2.

If you move the digit 2 in 0.2 one place to the right, the decimal is now 0.02.

The digit 2 in the decimal 0.02 has a value that is one tenth as much as the digit 2 in the decimal 0.2. I can show this to Clara using models.

0.2   0.02

0.2 has 20 shaded squares and 0.02 has 2 shaded squares. Since 2 squares are one tenth of 20 squares, the models show that 0.02 is one tenth the value of 0.2.

Where does the example . . .

- use a picture to explain?
- use words to explain?
- use numbers to explain?

©Curriculum Associates, LLC   Copying is not permitted.

Solve the problem. Use what you learned from the example.

Leo knows that each time a digit moves one place to the left in a whole number, the value of the digit is 10 times as much.

Describe an example you would show to Leo to demonstrate that this is true for decimal numbers also.

Show your work. Use pictures, words, or numbers to explain your answer.

Did you . . .

• use a picture to explain?

• use words to explain?

• use numbers to explain?

©Curriculum Associates, LLC Copying is not permitted.

Dear Family,

This week your child is exploring the powers of ten.

Your child is learning that numbers such as 10, 100, or 1,000 can be written as products of the number 10.

These numbers are called powers of ten.

$$10 = 10 = 10^1$$
$$100 = 10 \times 10 = 10^2$$
$$1,000 = 10 \times 10 \times 10 = 10^3$$

> An **exponent** tells how many times to multiply 10.
>
> 10^3 ← exponent

When you multiply a decimal by a power of ten, the decimal point moves right.

$$0.43 \times 10 = 4.3$$

> Multiply by 10. Move the decimal point **one** place to the right. The digit in the tenths place is now in the ones place.

$$0.075 \times 100 = 7.5$$

> Multiply by 100 (10 × 10). Move the decimal point **two** places to the right. The digit in the hundredths place is now in the ones place.

When you divide a decimal by a power of ten, the decimal point moves left.

$$4.3 \div 10 = 0.43$$

> Divide by 10. Move the decimal point **one** place to the left. The digit in the ones place is now in the tenths place.

$$7.5 \div 100 = 0.075$$

> Divide by 100 (10 × 10). Move the decimal point **two** places to the left. The digit in the ones place is now in the hundredths place.

Invite your child to share what he or she knows about powers of ten by doing the following activity together.

NEXT

©Curriculum Associates, LLC   Copying is not permitted.

Powers of Ten Activity

Work together with your child to show how the decimal point moves when you multiply a decimal number by a power of ten.

- Have your child write the number 12345 with large digits on a separate sheet of paper or use the number below.

- Have your child place his or her finger between the 3 and 4. Your child's finger represents the decimal point.

- Ask your child to multiply the number by 10 and show the answer by moving the decimal point. (Your child should move his or her finger one place to the right.)

- Ask your child to divide by 100 and show the answer by moving the decimal point. (Your child should move his or her finger two places to the left.)

- Ask your child to show you another multiplication or division by a power of 10. Have your child explain how he or she knows where to move the decimal point.

   ©Curriculum Associates, LLC   Copying is not permitted.

Prerequisite: How can you multiply and divide decimals by 10?

Study the example problem showing multiplying a decimal by 10. Then solve problems 1–6.

Example

Find 0.05×10. Check your answer using a model.

When you multiply the value of a digit by 10, the digit moves one place to the left, so $0.05 \times 10 = 0.5$.

$$\begin{array}{c} \\ 0.05 \end{array} \quad \times 10 = \quad \begin{array}{c} \\ 0.5 \end{array}$$

$\times 10 =$

1 Use the example to help you complete each equation.

  a. $0.005 \times 10 =$ _____

  b. $0.05 \times$ _____ $= 0.5$

  c. _____ $\times 10 = 5$

  d. $5 \times 10 =$ _____

2 How could you rewrite $0.05 \times 10 = 0.5$ as a division equation? Explain how you know.

_____

_____

_____

_____

Solve.

3 Each grid below represents a whole. Shade Models A, B, and C to match the number and decimals.

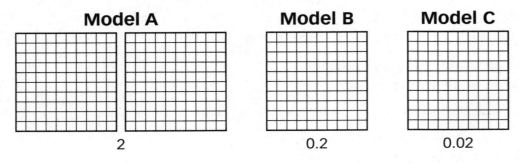

Model A	**Model B**	**Model C**
2	0.2	0.02

4 Use the shaded grids in problem 3 to complete the multiplication sentences that show how the models are related.

a. Look at Model A and Model B.

$0.2 \times 10 =$ _____

b. Look at Model B and Model C.

_____ $\times 10 =$ _____

5 Use the shaded grids in problem 3 to write division sentences that show how the models are related.

a. Look at Model A and Model B.

_____ $\div 10 =$ _____

b. Look at Model B and Model C.

_____ $\div 10 =$ _____

6 Look at problem 3. Imagine a Model D that shows 0.002. Write a multiplication equation and a division equation that show how Model C and Model D are related. Is there more than one possible answer? Explain.

_____

_____

_____

©Curriculum Associates, LLC   Copying is not permitted.

Name: _____

Multiply and Divide with Powers of Ten

Study the example showing how the decimal point moves when you multiply a decimal number by a power of ten. Then solve problems 1–7.

Example

Find 100×0.004.

Break 100 into the product of 10s.

The decimal point moves one place to the right for each factor of ten.

$$100 \times 0.004 = 10 \times 10 \times 0.004$$

$$= 10 \times 0.04$$

$$= 0.4$$

$$100 \times 0.004 = 0.4$$

1 Write the missing power of ten.

  a. $0.04 \times$ _____ $= 0.4$ $0.004 \times$ _____ $= 4$

  b. _____ $\times 0.006 = 0.6$ _____ $\times 0.006 = 6$

  c. $0.007 \times$ _____ $= 7$ $0.07 \times$ _____ $= 7$

2 When you multiply a decimal by a power of ten, what is the relationship between the number of places the decimal point moves and the number of zeros in the power of ten? Give an example.

_____

_____

_____

_____

_____

3 Complete the equations.

  a. $0.03 \times 1,000 =$ _____

  b. $0.008 \times 100 =$ _____

Vocabulary

power of ten a number that can be written as a product of tens.

$10 = 10$

$100 = 10 \times 10$

$1,000 = 10 \times 10 \times 10$

©Curriculum Associates, LLC   Copying is not permitted.

Solve.

4 Complete the table below to show dividing by powers of ten.

Ones	.	Tenths	Hundredths	Thousandths	
9	.	0	0	0	
					$9 \div 10$
					$9 \div 100$
					$9 \div 1{,}000$

5 Write the quotient.

a. $0.03 \div 10 =$ _____

b. $0.3 \div 100 =$ _____

c. $3 \div 1{,}000 =$ _____

6 How is the way the decimal point moves when you divide a decimal number by a power of ten the same as when you multiply? How is it different?

_____

_____

_____

_____

7 Complete the equations showing powers of tens using exponents.

a. $8 \times 100 = 8 \times 10^2 =$ _____

b. $8 \times 1{,}000 = 8 \times$ _____ $=$ _____

c. $2 \times$ _____ $= 2 \times 10^1 =$ _____

d. $0.02 \times 100 = 0.02 \times$ _____ $=$ _____

Vocabulary

exponent the number in a power that tells how many times to use the base as a factor.

$10^2 \longleftarrow$ **exponent**
$\uparrow$
base

$10^2 = 10 \times 10$, or 100

   ©Curriculum Associates, LLC   Copying is not permitted.

Reason and Write

Study the example. Underline two parts that you think make it a particularly good answer and a helpful example.

Example

Becca was finding the products of decimals and powers of ten.

Here is what Becca wrote for two problems:

$0.07 \times 10^2 = 70 \qquad 0.07 \times 10^3 = 700$

What did Becca do correctly? What did she do wrong? What can you tell her to help her multiply correctly with powers of ten the next time?

Show your work. Use pictures, words, or numbers to explain.

Becca moved the decimal point the correct way, to the right for multiplying by a power of ten. She showed that the value of 0.07 increases when you multiply by a power of ten.

Her mistake is that she multiplied by the wrong number of 10s, or didn't move the decimal point the correct number of places.

She should have multiplied by two tens, or 100, for 10^2, and three tens, or 1,000, for 10^3, like this:

$0.07 \times 10^2 = 0.07 \times 100 = 7$

$0.07 \times 10^3 = 0.07 \times 1,000 = 70$

I would tell her to remember that the exponent shows the number of zeros in the power of ten that you multiply by. This number of zeros is also the number of places that you move the decimal point to the right.

> Where does the example . . .
> - answer each question?
> - use words to explain?
> - use pictures or numbers to explain?

Solve the problem. Use what you learned from the example.

Stefan was finding the quotients of decimals and powers of ten.

Here is what Stefan wrote for two problems:

$0.2 \div 100 = 20$ $0.02 \div 10 = 0.2$

What did Stefan do correctly? What did he do wrong? What can you tell him to help him divide correctly with powers of ten the next time?

Show your work. Use pictures, words, or numbers to explain.

Did you . . .

• answer each question?

• use words to explain?

• use pictures or numbers to explain?

©Curriculum Associates, LLC   Copying is not permitted.

Dear Family,

This week your child is learning how to read and write decimals.

The chart below shows different ways to represent the number 5.387.

Standard Form	5.387
Words	five and three hundred eighty-seven thousandths
Place-Value Chart	see chart below
Decimal Expanded Form	$5 + 0.3 + 0.08 + 0.007$
Fraction Expanded Form	$5 + \frac{3}{10} + \frac{8}{100} + \frac{7}{1,000}$
Mixed Number	$5\frac{387}{1,000}$

Ones	.	Tenths	Hundredths	Thousandths
5	.	3	8	7

Understanding different ways to read and write decimals helps prepare your child for comparing decimals and solving problems with decimals.

Invite your child to share what he or she knows about reading and writing decimals by doing the following activity together.

NEXT

©Curriculum Associates, LLC   Copying is not permitted.

Decimal Place Value Activity

Materials: number cube

- Use the place-value charts below. Have your child roll the number cube. You and your child each write the digit shown on the cube in one place in your place-value chart. You can each write the digit in a different place in your chart.

- Have your child roll the number cube three more times. Write each digit rolled in your place-value charts. For example, if the digits 1, 3, 5, and 6 are rolled, you might write 3.615 and your child might write 5.361.

- Now, write the decimal in words and in standard form in your charts.

- Ask your child to explain why the order of the digits matters when writing decimals.

Place-Value Chart	Ones	.	Tenths	Hundredths	Thousandths
		.			
Words					
Standard Form					

Place-Value Chart	Ones	.	Tenths	Hundredths	Thousandths
		.			
Words					
Standard Form					

    ©Curriculum Associates, LLC   Copying is not permitted.

Read and Write Decimals

Name: _____

Prerequisite: Write Fractions as Decimals

Study the example showing how to write a fraction as a decimal. Then solve problems 1–8.

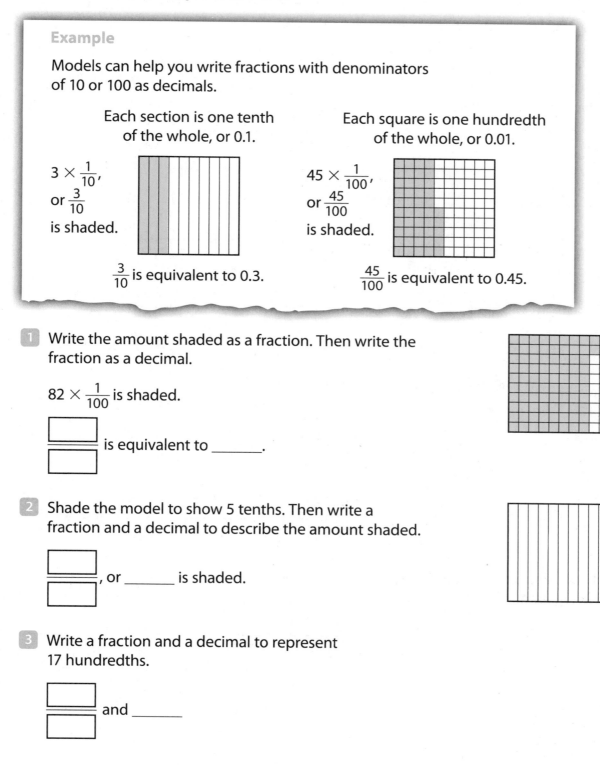

Example

Models can help you write fractions with denominators of 10 or 100 as decimals.

Each section is one tenth of the whole, or 0.1.

$3 \times \frac{1}{10}$, or $\frac{3}{10}$ is shaded.

$\frac{3}{10}$ is equivalent to 0.3.

Each square is one hundredth of the whole, or 0.01.

$45 \times \frac{1}{100}$, or $\frac{45}{100}$ is shaded.

$\frac{45}{100}$ is equivalent to 0.45.

1 Write the amount shaded as a fraction. Then write the fraction as a decimal.

$82 \times \frac{1}{100}$ is shaded.

☐/☐ is equivalent to _____.

2 Shade the model to show 5 tenths. Then write a fraction and a decimal to describe the amount shaded.

☐/☐ , or _____ is shaded.

3 Write a fraction and a decimal to represent 17 hundredths.

☐/☐ and _____

©Curriculum Associates, LLC   Copying is not permitted.

Solve.

4 How many places after the decimal point does the equivalent decimal have if:

   a. the denominator of the fraction is 10? _____

   b. the denominator of the fraction is 100? _____

5 Look at your answers to problem 4. Explain the reasoning you used to find the answers.

_____

_____

_____

_____

6 Shade the model to show 4 hundredths. Then write a fraction and a decimal to describe the amount shaded.

, or _____ is shaded.

7 Choose either *Yes* or *No* to tell if the expression or number represents 7 hundredths.

   a. $7 \times \frac{1}{10}$ ☐ Yes   ☐ No

   b. $7 \times \frac{1}{100}$ ☐ Yes   ☐ No

   c. 0.70   ☐ Yes   ☐ No

   d. 0.07   ☐ Yes   ☐ No

8 Explain how using a model can help you write a fraction with a denominator of 10 or 100 as a decimal.

_____

_____

_____

_____

©Curriculum Associates, LLC Copying is not permitted.

Name: _____

Read a Decimal

Study the example problem showing how to read a decimal. Then solve problems 1–7.

Example

To read a decimal, you name the place value of the smallest-sized unit, and tell how many of those units there are.

Ones	.	Tenths	Hundredths	Thousandths
0	.	0	7	3

The least place value of 0.073 is thousandths.

There are 73 thousandths.

To read the decimal 0.073, say: *seventy-three thousandths.*

1 Write the decimal 0.24 in the place-value chart.

Ones	.	Tenths	Hundredths	Thousandths
	.			

2 Using the chart in problem 1, what is the least place value of 0.24?

_____

3 How do you read the decimal 0.24?

_____

4 Write the word form of each decimal.

a. 0.8 _____

b. 0.08 _____

c. 0.008 _____

Solve.

5 The two grids show the same amount shaded. Is the word form of the decimals the same? Explain.

0.4 is shaded.   0.40 is shaded.

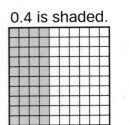

_____

_____

_____

_____

_____

6 Write the expanded form of 0.68 with decimals.

0.68 = 0.6 + _____

= _____ × 0.1 + 8 × _____

7 Write the expanded form of 0.031 with fractions.

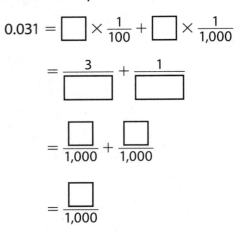

$0.031 = \boxed{} \times \frac{1}{100} + \boxed{} \times \frac{1}{1,000}$

$= \dfrac{3}{\boxed{}} + \dfrac{1}{\boxed{}}$

$= \dfrac{\boxed{}}{1,000} + \dfrac{\boxed{}}{1,000}$

$= \dfrac{\boxed{}}{1,000}$

> ### Vocabulary
>
> **expanded form** a way to show the value of each digit in a number.
>
> For example, $34.56 = (3 \times 10) + (4 \times 1) + \left(5 \times \frac{1}{10}\right) + \left(6 \times \frac{1}{100}\right)$

Name: _____

Write a Mixed Number as a Decimal

Study the example showing a number written in multiple forms. Then solve problems 1–6.

Example

words	one and forty-six thousandths
mixed number	$1\frac{46}{1,000}$
expanded form	$1 + \frac{46}{1,000}$ $1 + \frac{40}{1,000} + \frac{6}{1,000}$ $1 + \frac{4}{100} + \frac{6}{1,000}$
decimal	1.046

1 In the example, what does the 0 in 1.046 mean?

_____

_____

2 Fill in the missing information in the table below.

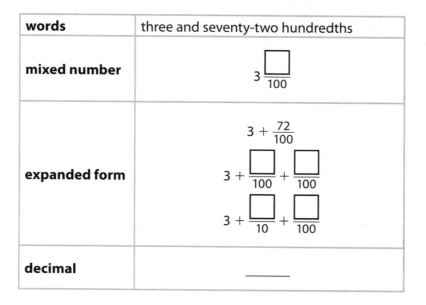

words	three and seventy-two hundredths
mixed number	$3\frac{\square}{100}$
expanded form	$3 + \frac{72}{100}$ $3 + \frac{\square}{100} + \frac{\square}{100}$ $3 + \frac{\square}{10} + \frac{\square}{100}$
decimal	_____

©Curriculum Associates, LLC   Copying is not permitted.

Solve.

3 Fill in the blanks to write numbers and words to show the values of the digits.

Four and seventy-two hundredths is _____ ones and _____ hundredths. 72 hundredths is _____ hundredths and _____ hundredths, or 7 _____ and 2 _____ .

4 Write the decimal four and seventy-two hundredths in the place-value chart and then write it in decimal form.

Ones	.	Tenths	Hundredths	Thousandths

Four and seventy-two hundredths is written _____ .

5 When a decimal is written in word form, what indicates that the equivalent form is a mixed number and not a fraction? Explain.

_____

_____

_____

6 The length of an Eastern Gray Tree Frog tadpole can be as long as five and twenty-two hundredths centimeters. What is this length written as a decimal?

Show your work.

Solution: _____

   ©Curriculum Associates, LLC   Copying is not permitted.

Read and Write Decimals

Solve the problems.

1 Sonya measured her pet mouse from the tip of its nose to the tip of its tail. Her mouse is fourteen hundredths of a meter long. Which of the following expresses this length as a decimal?

How many decimal places will this number have?

A 0.014   **C** 1.4

B 0.14   **D** 14.00

2 Choose either *Yes* or *No* to tell if each of the following represents 0.87.

What are the place values of each digit in 0.87?

a. $\frac{8}{10} + \frac{7}{100}$ ☐ Yes ☐ No

b. $\frac{8}{100} + \frac{7}{100}$ ☐ Yes ☐ No

c. 87 hundredths   ☐ Yes ☐ No

d. eighty-seven hundredths ☐ Yes ☐ No

3 $3 \times 10 + 2 \times 1 + 6 \times \frac{1}{100} + 4 \times \frac{1}{1,000}$ is the expanded form of which decimal?

Which decimal places are represented in the expanded form?

A 3.2064   **C** 32.604

B 32.064   **D** 320.064

Santo chose **C** as the correct answer. How did he get that answer?

_____

_____

_____

_____

_____

Solve.

4 Doria swam the 100-meter backstroke in 58.329 seconds. How do you express this time in words?

Show your work.

What mixed number could represent 58.329?

Solution: _____

5 Which of the following correctly represent 1.706? Circle the letter for all that apply.

What number does each answer choice represent?

A 1 + 0.7 + 0.06

B 1 + 0.7 + 0.006

C 1 + 706 × 0.1

D 1 + 7 × 0.001 + 6 × 0.001

E 1 + 7 × 0.1 + 6 × 0.001

6 A box turtle Marcos found is 0.115 of a meter long. What is this length in expanded form?

Show your work.

How is this number represented in a place-value chart?

Solution: _____

_____

©Curriculum Associates, LLC   Copying is not permitted.

Dear Family,

This week your child is learning to compare and round decimals.

One way to compare decimals is to use a place-value chart. For example, compare 7.033 and 7.02. Write a 0 in the thousandths column for 7.02. Start by comparing the ones.

Ones	.	Tenths	Hundredths	Thousandths
7	.	0	3	3
7	.	0	2	0

   7 = 7   0 = 0   3 > 2

The ones digits are the same. The tenths digits are the same. 3 hundredths > 2 hundredths. So, 7.033 > 7.02.

Another way to compare decimals is to write them as mixed numbers. Write the fractions with the same denominators.

$$7.033 = 7\frac{33}{1,000} \qquad\qquad 7.02 = 7\frac{2}{100} = 7\frac{20}{1,000}$$

$$7\frac{33}{1,000} > 7\frac{20}{1,000}$$

So, 7.033 > 7.02.

Your child is also learning to round decimals using a number line. The number line shows that 0.042 is closer to 0.04 than to 0.05.

0.042 rounded to the nearest hundredth is 0.04

Comparing and rounding decimals helps your child understand how to estimate with decimals. Estimation is a useful strategy for solving problems.

Invite your child to share what he or she knows about comparing and rounding decimals by doing the following activity together.

NEXT ➡

©Curriculum Associates, LLC   Copying is not permitted.

Comparing Decimals Activity

Work with your child to find real-life examples that involve comparing decimals.

- Look around the house or through fliers for at least 8 decimal numbers. The wrappers or labels on household items usually show a number. Make a list of the decimals as you find them. You don't need to write the units.

  - Examples: a 3.17-ounce bar of soap, an 8.5-ounce bottle of lotion, a 7.4-ounce box of snack bars, a 7.9-ounce box of crackers

- Take turns. One person marks two numbers for the other person to compare. Make a place-value chart like the one on the front of this sheet if needed. Circle the greater decimal.

- Challenge! After you've finished the activity, you now have 4 sets of decimal numbers with the greater decimal circled. Can you determine the greatest decimal of those four decimals?

     ©Curriculum Associates, LLC   Copying is not permitted.

Compare and Round Decimals

Name: _____

Study the example comparing decimals in a place-value chart. Then solve problems 1–5.

Example

Compare 0.6 and 0.59 using >, =, or <.

Write the decimals in a place-value chart.

Ones	.	Tenths	Hundredths
0	.	6	0
0	.	5	9

Remember that 6 tenths equals 60 hundredths.

Start at the leftmost place value and compare until you find digits that are different.

Ones: 0 = 0
Tenths: 6 > 5

The tenths are different. 6 > 5.

So, 0.6 > 0.59.

1 Compare 8.7 and 8.5 using >, =, or <.

_____

2 Use the place-value chart to compare the following decimals to 0.59. Find the decimals that are less than 0.59. Circle the letter of all that apply.

Ones	.	Tenths	Hundredths
0	.	**5**	**9**
0	.	0	7
0	.	4	
0	.	6	
0	.	5	5

A 0.07

B 0.4

C 0.6

D 0.55

Solve.

3 Write the decimals 1.24 and 1.3 in the chart.

Ones	.	Tenths	Hundredths

Compare 1.24 and 1.3 using >, =, or <.

_____

4 Look at problem 3. In which places do you need to compare digits? In which place do you *not* need to compare digits? Explain.

_____

_____

_____

_____

_____

_____

_____

5 Which change would make the statement below true? Circle the letter of the correct answer.

   3.7 < 3.56

A Put a 0 in the hundredths place to change 3.7 to 3.70.

B Change the hundredths digit in 3.56 to 8.

C Change the tenths digit in 3.7 to 6.

D Change the tenths digit in 3.56 to 8.

What new statement would result from each change?

©Curriculum Associates, LLC   Copying is not permitted.

Name: _____

Compare Decimals Written as Mixed Numbers

Study the example problem comparing decimals rewritten as mixed numbers. Then solve problems 1–6.

Example

Package A weighs 1.401 kilograms. Package B weighs 1.29 kilograms. Write an inequality statement comparing the weights of the packages.

Express the weights as mixed numbers with like denominators. Then compare.

$$1.401 = 1\frac{401}{1,000} \qquad\qquad 1.29 = 1\frac{29}{100} = 1\frac{290}{1,000}$$

$$1\frac{401}{1,000} \text{ is greater than } 1\frac{290}{1,000}.$$

So, 1.401 > 1.29. The weight of Package A is greater than the weight of Package B.

---

1 Complete the steps to write an inequality statement comparing 2.087 and 2.15 using mixed numbers.

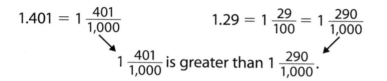

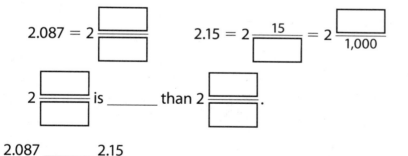

2.087 _____ 2.15

2 Which statement and reasoning is true about the decimals 0.4 and 0.06? Circle the letter of all that apply.

A $0.4 > 0.06$ because $\frac{40}{100} > \frac{6}{100}$.

B $0.4 > 0.06$ because 4 tenths is greater than 6 hundredths.

C $0.4 < 0.06$ because $\frac{4}{10} < \frac{6}{10}$.

D $0.4 < 0.06$ because 6 hundredths is greater than 4 tenths.

©Curriculum Associates, LLC   Copying is not permitted.

Solve.

3 Write a number from the box to make each statement true.

a. $0.07 = $ _____

b. $0.07 > $ _____

c. $0.07 < $ _____

0.007	0.070	0.072
	0.068	0.608

4 Compare 5.269 and 5.038.

a. Write 5.269 and 5.038 as sums of fractions.

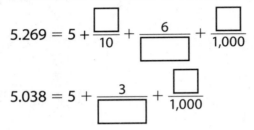

$$5.269 = 5 + \frac{\square}{10} + \frac{6}{\square} + \frac{\square}{1,000}$$

$$5.038 = 5 + \frac{3}{\square} + \frac{\square}{1,000}$$

b. Write 5.269 and 5.038 as mixed numbers.

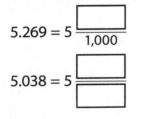

$$5.269 = 5\frac{\square}{1,000}$$

$$5.038 = 5\frac{\square}{\square}$$

c. Compare 5.269 and 5.038 using >, =, or <.

_____

5 Look at problem 4. Why is 5.269 written as the sum of four numbers and 5.038 as the sum of only three numbers?

_____

_____

6 Daslyn has a piece of rope 2.085 meters long and another piece 2.63 meters long. Which piece can she cut to make a piece that is 2.5 meters long?

Show your work.

Solution: _____

Lesson 4 Compare and Round Decimals

©Curriculum Associates, LLC   Copying is not permitted.

Name: _____

Round Decimals

Study the example problem showing how to round a decimal by plotting it on a number line. Then solve problems 1–5.

> ### Example
>
> Chiara runs 0.446 kilometer in one lap around the track. What is this distance rounded to the nearest hundredth?
>
> Place 0.446 on a number line to see its relationship to nearby hundredths.
>
>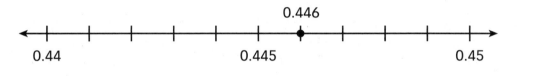
>
> 0.446 is between 0.44 and 0.45, and closer to 0.45.
>
> The distance rounded to the nearest hundredth is 0.45 kilometer.

1 Round 0.446 kilometer to the nearest tenth by following these steps:

   a. Complete the marking of the number line to show hundredths.

   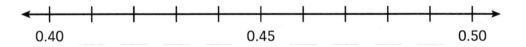

   b. Label 0.446 on the number line.

   c. Determine whether 0.446 is closer to 0.4 or 0.5. If the hundredths digit in 0.446 is 5 or greater, round up. If the hundredths digit in 0.446 is less than 5, round down. What is 0.446 kilometer rounded to the nearest tenth?

   _____

Lesson 4 Compare and Round Decimals   **33**

Solve.

2 Aubra and Tony are rounding the number 1.65 to the nearest tenth. On a number line they see 1.65 is exactly halfway between 1.6 and 1.7. Aubra says to round to the greater value, 1.7. Tony says because it is in the middle, you can round to either value. Who is right? Explain.

_____

_____

_____

_____

_____

_____

3 Complete the table to compare 4.77 to nearby tenths.

To the nearest tenth, 4.77 rounds to _____ .

Ones	.	Tenths	Hundredths
4	.	7	
4	.	7	7
4	.	8	

4 One gallon is equal to about 3.785 liters. What is this amount rounded to the nearest tenth?

Show your work.

Solution: _____

5 Look at problem 4. What is the greatest number of whole liters of water you could pour into a one-gallon container without it overflowing? Explain your answer.

_____

_____

_____

  ©Curriculum Associates, LLC   Copying is not permitted.

Name: _____

Compare and Round Decimals

Solve the problems.

1 Which of the following decimals is greater than 0.66 but less than 0.68? Circle the letter for all that apply.

How do I represent these numbers in a place-value chart?

A 0.67

B 0.57

C 0.665

D 0.695

2 A carton holds 1.248 liters of fruit juice. What is this amount rounded to the nearest tenth? Use the number line below.

Which digits do I need to look at? Which digits can I ignore?

Show your work.

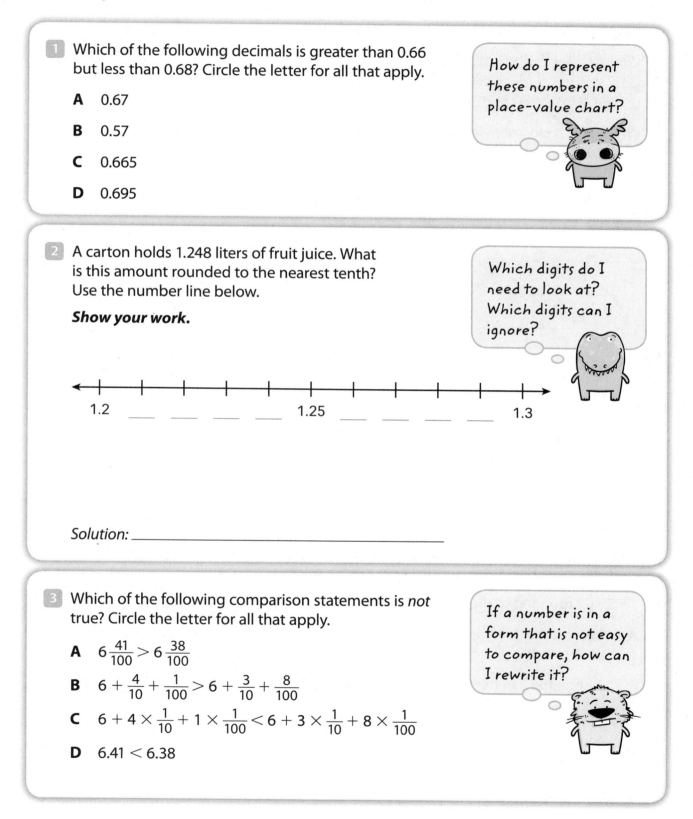

Solution: _____

3 Which of the following comparison statements is *not* true? Circle the letter for all that apply.

If a number is in a form that is not easy to compare, how can I rewrite it?

A $6\frac{41}{100} > 6\frac{38}{100}$

B $6 + \frac{4}{10} + \frac{1}{100} > 6 + \frac{3}{10} + \frac{8}{100}$

C $6 + 4 \times \frac{1}{10} + 1 \times \frac{1}{100} < 6 + 3 \times \frac{1}{10} + 8 \times \frac{1}{100}$

D $6.41 < 6.38$

©Curriculum Associates, LLC   Copying is not permitted.

Solve.

4 The lengths of four trails are listed below.

Oak Trail	10.653 kilometers
Maple Trail	10.592 kilometers
Pine Trail	10.732 kilometers
Spruce Trail	10.484 kilometers

Which trail is closest in length to 10.5 kilometers?

A Oak Trail

C Pine Trail

B Maple Trail

D Spruce Trail

Padma chose **B**. How did she get that answer?

_____

_____

_____

_____

_____

_____

_____

Which numbers do I need to compare?

5 Which change would make the statement below true? Circle the letter of all that apply.

2.309 rounded to the nearest tenth is 2.4.

A Take out the 0 in the hundredths place to change 2.309 to 2.39.

B Change the 3 in the tenths place of 2.309 to 4.

C Change the 4 in the tenths place of 2.4 to 3.

D Change the 0 in the hundredths place of 2.309 to 4.

How does each change affect the numbers in the statement?

©Curriculum Associates, LLC   Copying is not permitted.

Dear Family,

This week your child is learning to multiply three-digit numbers by two-digit numbers.

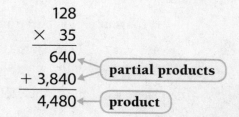

One way to multiply 128 × 35 is to set up the problem vertically.

First multiply each digit in 128 by the 5 ones in 35: 5 × 128 = 640.

Then multiply each digit in 128 by the 3 tens in 35: 30 × 128 = 3,840.

$$\begin{array}{r} 128 \\ \times\ \ 35 \\ \hline 640 \\ +\ 3{,}840 \\ \hline 4{,}480 \end{array}$$

partial products

product

Add the partial products to find the product: 640 + 3,840 = 4,480.

Another way your child is learning to multiply is with an area model. An area model gives a visual representation of the multiplication.

The area model below shows 128 × 35.
    The length of the rectangle represents 128: 100 + 20 + 8.
    The width of the rectangle represents 35: 30 + 5.
    Multiply. Add the partial products to find the product.

	100	20	8
30	30 × 100 = 3,000	30 × 20 = 600	30 × 8 = 240
5	5 × 100 = 500	5 × 20 = 100	5 × 8 = 40

128 × 35 = 3,000 + 600 + 240 + 500 + 100 + 40 = 4,480

Invite your child to share what he or she knows about multiplying whole numbers by doing the following activity together.

NEXT

Lesson 5 Multiply Whole Numbers   **37**

Multiplication Activity

Materials: magazine or newspaper

Work with your child to find a real-life example of using multiplication that involves the number of words in a magazine or newspaper article.

Sometimes a reporter has to write a story with a certain number of words, for example, 500 words. Multiplication is a good way to find the number of words in a story.

- Have your child choose an article from a magazine or newspaper.
- Ask your child to count the number of words in one paragraph and record the number on a sheet of paper.
- Then count the number of paragraphs in the article.
- Suppose each paragraph had the same number of words. How many words are in the article? (Multiply the number of words in a paragraph by the number of paragraphs.)
- If each paragraph has a different number of words, is the answer to the previous question an exact answer or an estimate for the total number of words in the article? (It's an estimate because the number of words in each paragraph varies.)

My article had 189 words in a paragraph, and 23 paragraphs. How many words in the article?

©Curriculum Associates, LLC   Copying is not permitted.

Multiply Whole Numbers

Name: _____

Prerequisite: Multiply Two-Digit Numbers

Study the example showing how to multiply two-digit numbers using partial products. Then solve problems 1–5.

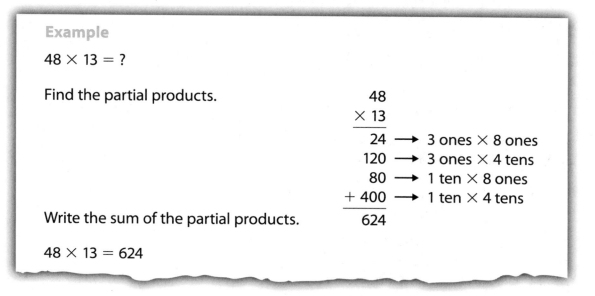

Example

$48 \times 13 = ?$

Find the partial products.

```
        48
      × 13
        24  → 3 ones × 8 ones
       120  → 3 ones × 4 tens
        80  → 1 ten × 8 ones
     + 400  → 1 ten × 4 tens
       624
```

Write the sum of the partial products.   624

$48 \times 13 = 624$

---

1 Complete the steps to find the product of 52×16.

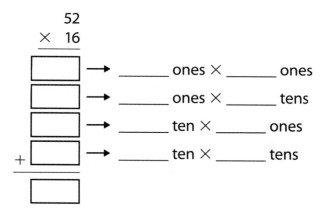

```
        52
      × 16
```

[____] → _____ ones × _____ ones

[____] → _____ ones × _____ tens

[____] → _____ ten × _____ ones

+ [____] → _____ ten × _____ tens

[____]

2 How can you check if your answer to problem 1 is reasonable?

_____

_____

_____

_____

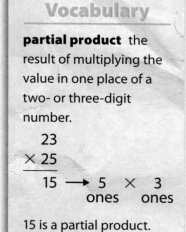

Vocabulary

partial product the result of multiplying the value in one place of a two- or three-digit number.

```
     23
   × 25
     15  → 5  ×  3
         ones  ones
```

15 is a partial product.

©Curriculum Associates, LLC   Copying is not permitted.

Solve.

3 You can also use an area model to multiply.

$16 \times 52 =$ ☐ ?

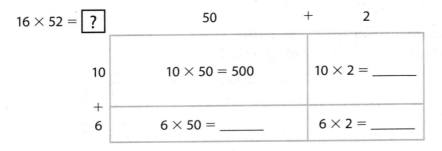

a. Write the missing partial products in the area model.

b. Then, write the partial products to complete the equation below. Find the sum.

$16 \times 52 = 500 +$ _____ $+$ _____ $+$ _____ $=$ _____

4 Look at problem 3. Would the product change if $50 + 2$ on the top of the area model was changed to $20 + 30 + 2$? Explain.

_____

_____

_____

_____

_____

5 Roy is going on a 12-day bike trip. He plans to ride 35 miles a day. How many miles will Roy ride on the trip?

Show your work.

Solution: _____

©Curriculum Associates, LLC   Copying is not permitted.

Name: _____

Multiply Three-Digit Numbers

Study the example showing how to multiply a three-digit number by a two-digit number using the distributive property. Then solve problems 1–3.

Example

Find 132 × 26.

Use the distributive property.

$$132 \times 26 = 132(20 + 6)$$
$$= (132 \times 20) + (132 \times 6)$$

Find the partial products.

132		132	
× 20		× 6	
40	(20 × 2)	12	(6 × 2)
600	(20 × 30)	180	(6 × 30)
+ 2,000	(20 × 100)	+ 600	(6 × 100)
2,640		792	

Write the sum of the partial products.   2,640 + 792 = 3,432

132 × 26 = 3,432

---

1 Complete the steps to find 253 × 34.

253 × 34 = 253(30 + 4) = (_____ × 30) + (_____ × 4)

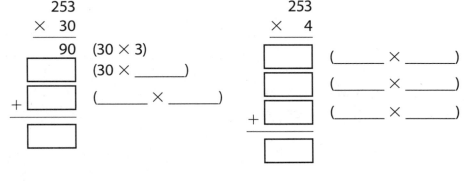

```
      253                       253
   ×  30                     ×    4
      90  (30 × 3)         ____
   ____   (30 × ____)      ____   (____ × ____)
 + ____   (____ × ____)    ____   (____ × ____)
   ____                  + ____   (____ × ____)
                           ____
```

253 × 34 = 7,590 + 1,012 = _____

©Curriculum Associates, LLC   Copying is not permitted.   **Lesson 5** Multiply Whole Numbers

Solve.

2 You can also use an area model to find the product of 253 × 34.

   a. Write the missing partial products in the area model.

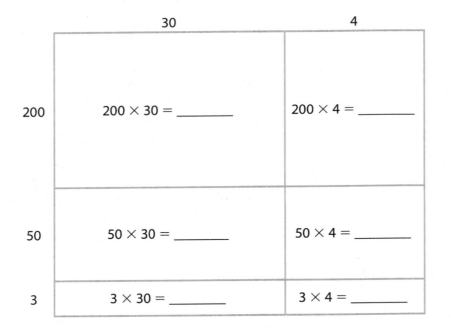

	30	4
200	200 × 30 = _____	200 × 4 = _____
50	50 × 30 = _____	50 × 4 = _____
3	3 × 30 = _____	3 × 4 = _____

   b. Write the partial products to complete the equations below.

     First column: _____ + _____ + _____ = _____

     Second column: _____ + _____ + _____ = _____

   c. 253 × 34 = _____

3 Nate's mother drives 225 miles back and forth to work each month. How many miles does she drive back and forth to work in one year?

Show your work.

There are twelve months in one year.

Solution: _____

©Curriculum Associates, LLC   Copying is not permitted.

Name: _____

Multiply Whole Numbers

Solve the problems.

1 Which expression shows the numbers multiplied for the partial product 12,480?

$$\begin{array}{r} {}^{1}_{1} \\ 416 \\ \times\ \ 32 \\ \hline 832 \\ +\ 12{,}480 \\ \hline 13{,}312 \end{array}$$

In what step is the partial product 12,480 written?

A 3 × 410   **C** 30 × 410

B 3 × 416   **D** 30 × 416

2 There are 28 tables in the cafeteria. Each table has 12 students sitting at it. Fourth graders sit at 13 of the tables. Fifth graders sit at the rest of the tables. How many fifth graders are there?

How do you find the number of tables fifth graders are sitting at?

A 156   **C** 336

B 180   **D** 700

Yuri chose **C** as the correct answer. How did he get that answer?

_____

_____

_____

_____

_____

_____

©Curriculum Associates, LLC   Copying is not permitted.

Solve.

3 A small bottle contains 177 milliliters of strawberry yogurt smoothie. One box holds 24 bottles. Are there more or less than 4,000 milliliters of the smoothie in one box? Explain.

I think there is more than one step to solving this problem.

Show your work.

Solution: _____

_____

4 Jeff and Kayla are finding the product of 178 × 56. They both are using the distributive property to find partial products. Look at their work below.

How did each student break up the factor 56?

Jeff		Kayla		
178	178	178	178	178
× 50	× 6	× 20	× 30	× 6

a. Explain why each student's work shows a way to find the product of 178 × 56.

_____

_____

_____

_____

b. Would you use one of these methods or a different method to find the product of 178 × 56? Why?

_____

_____

 ©Curriculum Associates, LLC   Copying is not permitted.

Dear Family,

This week your child is learning to divide whole numbers by a two-digit number.

One way to solve a division problem such as 624 ÷ 12 is to set it up vertically.

First divide the hundreds in 624 by 12.
There are 50 groups of 12 in 600.

Then divide the tens in 624 by 12.
There are 2 groups of 12 in 24.

Add the partial quotients to find the quotient.
50 + 2 = 52

624 ÷ 12 = 52

$$
\begin{array}{r}
52 \leftarrow \text{quotient} \\
2 \\
50 \\
12\overline{)624} \\
-600 \\
\hline
24 \\
-24 \\
\hline
0
\end{array}
$$

quotient
partial quotients

Another way your child is learning to divide is with an area model, similar to the model used in multiplication.

The area model below shows 624 ÷ 12.
Since multiplication and division are inverse, or opposite, operations, use the relationship between them to divide.

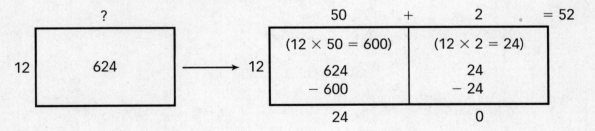

624 ÷ 12 = 52

Both methods result in the same quotient, 52. Notice that 50 and 2 appear as partial quotients in each way of dividing.

Invite your child to share what he or she knows about dividing whole numbers by doing the following activity together.

NEXT ➡

©Curriculum Associates, LLC   Copying is not permitted.

Work with your child to solve real-life problems involving division.

- Choose a favorite book with your child and look at the total number of pages in it. The book should have more than 100 pages. Pick a number of pages to read each day (a two-digit number). How many days would it take to read the entire book?

- Use division to find the answer.
  - Example: Suppose the book has 286 pages and the number of pages to be read each day is 15. Divide 286 by 15.

- Work together to write and solve the division problem about the book.

- Decide what to do if there is a remainder. Will you read the remaining number of pages on the next day, or will you read the remaining number of pages on the last day of reading?

 ©Curriculum Associates, LLC   Copying is not permitted.

Divide Whole Numbers

Name: _____

Study the example problem showing division with a one-digit divisor using partial quotients. Then solve problems 1–4.

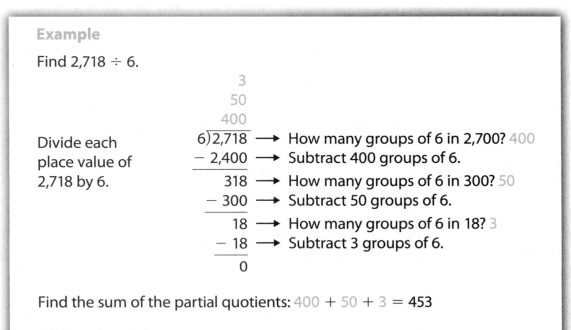

Example

Find 2,718 ÷ 6.

Divide each place value of 2,718 by 6.

$$\begin{array}{r} 3 \\ 50 \\ 400 \\ 6)\overline{2,718} \\ -2,400 \\ \hline 318 \\ -300 \\ \hline 18 \\ -18 \\ \hline 0 \end{array}$$

→ How many groups of 6 in 2,700? 400
→ Subtract 400 groups of 6.
→ How many groups of 6 in 300? 50
→ Subtract 50 groups of 6.
→ How many groups of 6 in 18? 3
→ Subtract 3 groups of 6.

Find the sum of the partial quotients: 400 + 50 + 3 = **453**

2,718 ÷ 6 = 453

1 Complete the steps to find 4,830 ÷ 5.

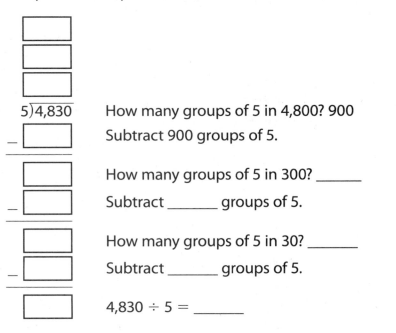

5)4,830   How many groups of 5 in 4,800? 900
           Subtract 900 groups of 5.

           How many groups of 5 in 300? _____
           Subtract _____ groups of 5.

           How many groups of 5 in 30? _____
           Subtract _____ groups of 5.

           4,830 ÷ 5 = _____

©Curriculum Associates, LLC   Copying is not permitted.

Solve.

2 Quinn and Jewel are finding the quotient of 336 ÷ 8. Look at their work to the right.

How are Quinn's and Jewel's ways of finding the quotient similar? How are they different?

_____

_____

_____

_____

_____

Quinn	Jewel
2	2
10	40
30	8)336
8)336	− 320
− 240	16
96	− 16
− 80	0
16	
− 16	
0	

3 A game store has 2,540 video games on 4 racks. Each rack holds the same number of video games. How many video games are on each rack?

Show your work.

Solution: _____

4 A sports team donates 157 tickets to a sporting event, with tickets to be shared equally among 9 classrooms. How many tickets does each classroom receive? How many tickets are left over?

Show your work.

Solution: Each classroom receives _____ tickets.

There are _____ tickets left over.

 ©Curriculum Associates, LLC Copying is not permitted.

Name: _____

Divide by Two-Digit Numbers

Study the example showing division with a two-digit divisor using partial quotients. Then solve problems 1–5.

Example

Find $1,386 \div 22$.

To divide using partial quotients, estimate a number that can be multiplied by the divisor to get a product less than or equal to the dividend, and then subtract the product from the dividend. Repeat these steps until there is nothing left over.

$$
\begin{array}{r}
63 \\
\hline
3 \\
60 \\
22\overline{)1,386} \\
-\ 1,320 \\
\hline
66 \\
-\ 66 \\
\hline
0
\end{array}
$$

→ How many groups of 20 in 1,200? 60
→ 22×60

→ How many groups of 22 in 66? 3
→ 22×3

$1,386 \div 22 = 63$

---

1 Look at the example. For the first step, Jaime thought, "How many groups of 20 in 1,400? There are 70." If he continues with the division steps, when will he know that his first estimate of 70 is too high?

_____

_____

_____

2 Multiply 14 by multiples of 10 to complete the table.

Multiples of 10	10	20	30	40	50	60
× 14	140	280			700	

Write a multiple of 10 from the table to show the best partial quotient to start with for each division problem below.

a. $14\overline{)462}$ **b.** $14\overline{)350}$ **c.** $14\overline{)798}$ **d.** $14\overline{)588}$

©Curriculum Associates, LLC   Copying is not permitted.

Solve.

3 Complete the steps for using an area model to solve 504 ÷ 14.

504 ÷ 14 is the same as _____ × ? = _____ .

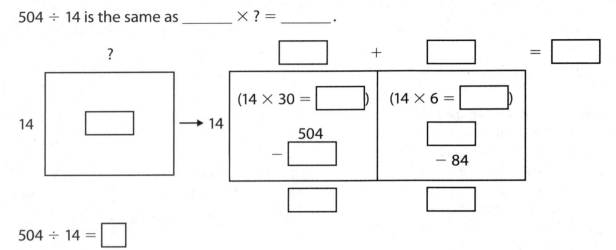

504 ÷ 14 = ☐

4 Solve 504 ÷ 14 using the partial quotient method shown in the example problem.

Show your work.

Solution: _____

5 Food for a hunger relief program is shipped in 25-pound boxes. How many boxes will 2,350 pounds of food fill?

Show your work.

Solution: _____

 ©Curriculum Associates, LLC   Copying is not permitted.

Name: _____

Divide Whole Numbers

Solve the problems.

1   The Mini Muffin Company bakes 1,872 muffins. The large Mini Muffin boxes hold a dozen muffins. How many large boxes are needed to package the muffins?

Show your work.

What will be the greatest place in the quotient?

Solution: _____

2   Look at problem 1. Suppose the Mini Muffin Company packs 6 muffins in each small box. Which of the following describes the number of small boxes they will fill? Circle the letter for all that apply.

A   It will be more than the number of large boxes.

B   It will be double the number of large boxes.

C   It will be fewer than the number of large boxes.

D   It will be half the number of large boxes.

If you make the number in each group smaller, do you get more groups or fewer?

3   The Best Bagel Company bakes 1,872 bagels. They put a baker's dozen, or 13 bagels, into each bag. How many bags do they fill?

Show your work.

How is this problem similar to problem 1?

Solution: _____

Lesson 6 Divide Whole Numbers

Solve.

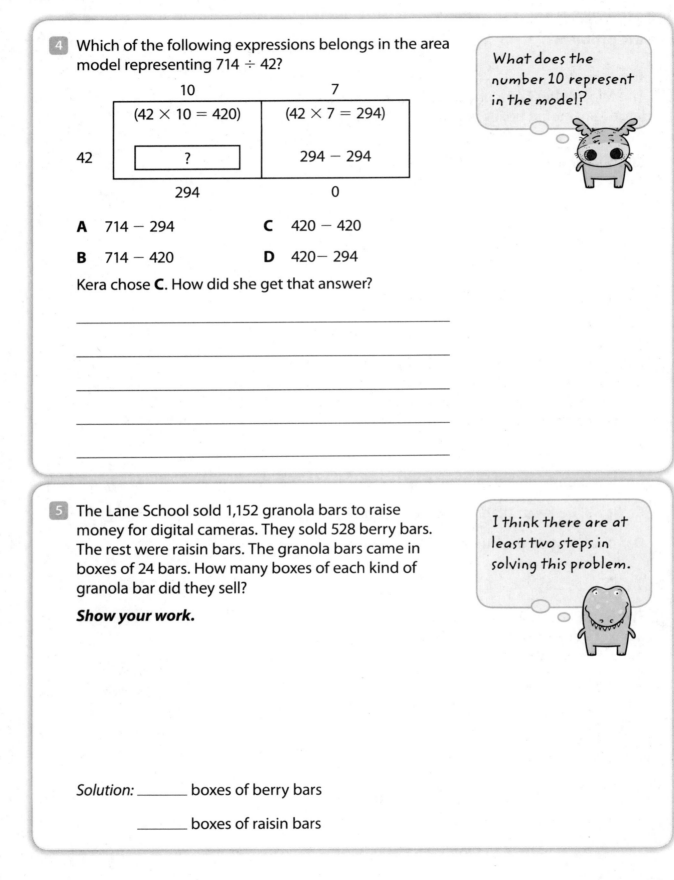

4 Which of the following expressions belongs in the area model representing 714 ÷ 42?

	10	7
42	(42 × 10 = 420)	(42 × 7 = 294)
	[?]	294 − 294
	294	0

A 714 − 294   **C** 420 − 420

B 714 − 420   **D** 420 − 294

Kera chose **C**. How did she get that answer?

_____

_____

_____

_____

_____

What does the number 10 represent in the model?

5 The Lane School sold 1,152 granola bars to raise money for digital cameras. They sold 528 berry bars. The rest were raisin bars. The granola bars came in boxes of 24 bars. How many boxes of each kind of granola bar did they sell?

Show your work.

I think there are at least two steps in solving this problem.

Solution: _____ boxes of berry bars

_____ boxes of raisin bars

 ©Curriculum Associates, LLC   Copying is not permitted.

Dear Family,

This week your child is learning to add and subtract decimals.

Your child can use what he or she knows about adding and subtracting whole numbers to add and subtract decimals.

To add 3.82 + 0.4, it's useful to show the numbers in a place-value chart.

Ones	.	Tenths	Hundredths
3	.	8	2
0	.	4	0

> Write a 0 in the hundredths column of 0.4, since $\frac{4}{10}$ is equivalent to $\frac{40}{100}$.

Line up the decimal points and add as you do with whole numbers. Remember to write a decimal point in the sum.

$$\begin{array}{r} {\scriptstyle 1} \\ 3.82 \\ +\ 0.40 \\ \hline 4.22 \end{array}$$

To subtract 2.05 from 4.6, write 4.6 as a hundredths decimal, 4.60. You need to write both decimals as hundredths decimals in order to subtract.

Line up the decimal points and subtract as you do with whole numbers.

$$\begin{array}{r} {\scriptstyle 5\ 10} \\ 4.\cancel{6}0 \\ -\ 2.05 \\ \hline 2.55 \end{array}$$

Another way your child can add and subtract decimals is to picture a number line or base-ten models. Jump forward on the number line for addition and jump backward for subtraction. Combine base-ten models for addition and remove base-ten models for subtraction.

Invite your child to share what he or she knows about adding and subtracting decimals by doing the following activity together.

Lesson 7 Add and Subtract Decimals · **53**

Adding and Subtracting Decimals Activity

Materials: calculator (optional)

Work with your child to make up and solve real-life problems involving decimals.

- Take turns finding or making up some Amazing Stories with decimal numbers for the other person to solve.

- First try to solve the problems with a paper and pencil. Then check your answers with a calculator.

- Here are some examples:

A large fish measured 284.56 centimeters long. At one time, the world's longest goldfish was 47.4 centimeters long. If you put those two fish end to end, what would the total length be?

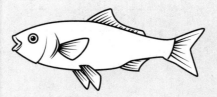

A dog jumped 1.72 meters, and its human owner jumped 1.81 meters. How much higher did the owner jump than the dog?

- Be on the lookout for other real-life examples of adding and subtracting decimals. For example, a grocery receipt shows decimal addition. Challenge your child to estimate the sum, then look at the receipt to check.

 ©Curriculum Associates, LLC   Copying is not permitted.

Add and Subtract Decimals

Name: _____

Study the example showing subtracting whole numbers using regrouping. Then solve problems 1–6.

Example

Find $8,305 - 4,267$.

Write the problem vertically. Align places and regroup as needed.

$$\begin{array}{r} \overset{2\ 10}{8,3\cancel{0}5} \\ -\ 4,267 \end{array}$$ 3 hundreds = 2 hundreds + 10 tens

$$\begin{array}{r} \overset{9}{\underset{2\ 10\ 15}{8,\cancel{3}\cancel{0}\cancel{5}}} \\ -\ 4,267 \end{array}$$ 10 tens = 9 tens + 10 ones
5 ones + 10 ones = 15 ones

Subtract.

$$\begin{array}{r} \overset{9}{\underset{2\ 10\ 15}{8,\cancel{3}\cancel{0}\cancel{5}}} \\ -\ 4,267 \\ \hline 4,038 \end{array}$$ So, $8,305 - 4,267 = 4,038$.

---

1 Which of the equations represents regrouping needed for the problem shown? Circle the letter for all that apply.

$$\begin{array}{r} 52,134 \\ -\ 36,091 \\ \hline \end{array}$$

A 3 tens = 2 tens + 10 ones

B 1 hundred = 0 hundreds + 10 tens

C 2 thousands = 1 thousand + 10 hundreds

D 5 ten thousands = 4 ten thousands + 10 thousands

2 Find the difference for the subtraction problem in problem 1.

Show your work.

Solution: _____

Solve.

3 You can also show regrouping above addition problems. The addition to the right is partially completed. Why is there a 1 above the hundreds place?

$$\begin{array}{r} 1 \\ 627{,}643 \\ + \ 236{,}083 \\ \hline 726 \end{array}$$

_____

_____

4 Look at problem 3.

a. Estimate the sum.

_____

b. Find the sum. _____

c. Is your answer reasonable? Explain.

_____

Use the information in the chart to solve problems 5 and 6.

Mountain (Continent)	Elevation (feet)
Everest (Asia)	29,035
McKinley (North America)	20,237
Kosciuszko (Australia)	7,310

5 How much higher is the summit of Mt. McKinley than the summit of Mt. Kosciuszko?

Show your work.

Solution: _____

6 How much higher is the summit of Mt. Everest than the combined elevations of Mt. McKinley and Mt. Kosciuszko?

Show your work.

Solution: _____

©Curriculum Associates, LLC Copying is not permitted.

Name: _____

Add Decimals to Hundredths

Study the example problem showing decimal addition using a place-value chart. Then solve problems 1–5.

Example

Alana walks 3.45 miles before lunch and 5.18 miles after lunch. How many miles does she walk in all?

Ones	.	Tenths	Hundredths
3	.	4	5
5	.	1	8

3 ones + 5 ones = 8 ones
4 tenths + 1 tenth = 5 tenths
5 hundredths + 8 hundredths = 13 hundredths

Sum = 8 ones + 5 tenths + 13 hundredths
     = 8 ones + 6 tenths + 3 hundredths

Alana walks 8.63 miles in all.

---

1 Look at the example problem. Suppose Alana walks 6.6 miles the next day. Complete the steps below to find the number of miles she walks in two days.

Ones	.	Tenths	Hundredths
8	.	6	3
☐	.	☐	☐

Sum = 14 ones + _____ tenths + _____ hundredths

    = _____ ones + 2 tenths + 3 hundredths

    = _____ ten + _____ ones + _____ tenths + _____ hundredths

Alana walks _____ miles in two days.

Lesson 7 Add and Subtract Decimals   **57**

Solve.

2 You can also add decimals by writing the problem vertically, lining up the decimal points to keep track of place values.

$$\begin{array}{r} \overset{1}{14.52} \\ +\ 22.29 \\ \hline 1 \end{array}$$

The problem to the right is partially completed. Explain why there is a 1 above the tenths place.

_____

_____

_____

_____

3 Find the sum for the addition problem in problem 2. Tell whether each statement about it is *True* or *False*.

a. It is more than 36. ☐ True ☐ False

b. It is closer to 37 than 36. ☐ True ☐ False

c. It is 36.71. ☐ True ☐ False

d. It is 36.81. ☐ True ☐ False

4 The size 4 soccer ball Sean's team uses should weigh no more than 0.37 kilogram, and no less than 0.31 kilogram. A soccer bag has two balls in it. What is the most they could weigh together? The least?

Show your work.

Solution: _____

5 Look at problem 4. Will three soccer balls weigh more than 1 kilogram? Explain.

_____

_____

_____

  ©Curriculum Associates, LLC   Copying is not permitted.

Name: _____

Subtract Decimals to Hundredths

Study the example problem showing decimal subtraction using a place-value chart. Then solve problems 1–5.

Example

Last year Jeff ran the 40-yard dash in 5.8 seconds. This year he ran it in 5.48 seconds. How much faster did he run this year than last year?

Use a place-value chart to write this year's and last year's times.

Regroup as needed in order to subtract.

	Ones	.	Tenths	Hundredths
Last year's time	5	.	8	0
Is the same as	5	.	7	10
This year's time	5	.	4	8

5 ones − 5 ones = 0 ones
7 tenths − 4 tenths = 3 tenths
10 hundredths − 8 hundredths = 2 hundredths

   Difference = 0 ones + 3 tenths + 2 hundredths

Jeff ran 0.32 second faster this year than last year.

---

1 Look at the example problem. Jeff's brother Rob ran the 40-yard dash in 4.95 seconds this year. Complete the steps. How much faster did Rob run than Jeff?

	Ones	.	Tenths	Hundredths
Jeff's time	5	.	4	8
Is the same as	4	.	☐	☐
Rob's time	4	.	9	5

_____ ones − 4 ones = _____ ones

_____ tenths − 9 tenths = _____ tenths

_____ hundredths − 5 hundredths = _____ hundredths

   Difference = 0 ones + _____ tenths + _____ hundredths

Rob ran _____ second faster than Jeff.

Solve.

2 You can also subtract decimals by writing the problem vertically, lining up the decimal points to keep track of place values.

$$\begin{array}{r} 7.\overset{2\ 11}{\cancel{3}\cancel{1}} \\ -\ 5.24 \\ \hline \end{array}$$

The problem to the right is partially completed. Explain the regrouping shown.

_____

_____

_____

3 Find the difference for the subtraction problem in problem 2. Use the numbers in the box to complete the statements.

2	3	7
2.07	2.17	2.7

The difference is _____ .

The difference is closest to the whole number _____ .

4 Between 6:00 PM and 8:00 PM the temperature fell 5.25°F. At 6:00 PM the temperature was 62.4°F. What was the temperature at 8:00 PM?

A 57.25°F   **C** 10.10°F

B 57.15°F   **D** 10.9°F

5 Haley's anole lizard measures 14.5 centimeters. Caleb's anole lizard measures 12.34 centimeters. An anole lizard's tail is half its length. How much longer is the tail of Haley's lizard than the tail of Caleb's lizard?

Show your work.

Solution: _____

   ©Curriculum Associates, LLC   Copying is not permitted.

Name: _____

Add and Subtract Decimals

Solve the problems.

1 Jake bought 4.08 pounds of apples. He knows that 1.19 pounds are Gala apples and the rest are Cameo apples. How many pounds of Cameo apples did he buy?

Do you need to regroup to find the answer?

A 2.89   **C** 3.89

B 3.11   **D** 5.27

Chase chose answer **C**. How did he get that answer?

_____

_____

_____

2 Tell whether each number sentence is *True* or *False*.

Remember to line up the decimal points to keep track of place values.

a. 8.35 + 7.9 = 16.25   ☐ True ☐ False

b. 5.31 − 3 = 2.31   ☐ True ☐ False

c. 94.43 + 74.9 = 169.33   ☐ True ☐ False

d. 183.7 + 28.34 = 467.1   ☐ True ☐ False

3 How did you decide your answer to **d.** in problem 2? Explain.

*Did you estimate or compute to decide your answer to **d.**?*

_____

_____

_____

_____

_____

Solve.

4 The distance between the goals on a soccer field is 52 meters. Each goal has a box that extends 5.49 meters into the field. What is the distance from the front of the box at one end of the field to the front of the box at the other end of the field?

Show your work.

Can I draw a diagram to help understand the problem?

Solution: _____

5 Ms. Chen's fifth-grade class held bake sales on Tuesday and Thursday during lunch to raise money to buy science equipment for the classroom.

They raised $20.55 more on Thursday than on Tuesday. Use this information to fill in the data that are missing from the table.

Where do you find how much money was raised on Thursday in the table?

	1st lunch	2nd lunch	3rd lunch	TOTAL
Tuesday	$21.45		$25.90	
Thursday		$26.35		$86.70
TOTAL	$50.55		$57.15	

©Curriculum Associates, LLC   Copying is not permitted.

Dear Family,

This week your child is learning to multiply decimals.

One way your child is learning to show decimal multiplication is with an area model.

The model at right shows 1.2×1.4.

The width of the model represents 1.2.
The length of the model represents 1.4.

1   0.2

1

0.4

Multiply to find the area of each section in the model. Then add the partial products.

$1 \times 1 = 1$ $1 \times 0.2 = 0.2$

$1 + 0.2 + 0.4 + 0.08 = 1.68$

$1.2 \times 1.4 = 1.68$ $0.4 \times 1 = 0.4$ $0.4 \times 0.2 = 0.08$

To decide whether the product is reasonable, your child is learning to estimate the product of a decimal multiplication like 1.2×1.4.

Round each factor to the nearest whole number. Multiply the rounded numbers to estimate the product. The product should be about 1.

Round 1.2 to 1.
Round 1.4 to 1.
$1 \times 1 = 1$

The product 1.68 is close to the estimated product, 1.

Invite your child to share what he or she knows about multiplying decimals by doing the following activity together.

NEXT

©Curriculum Associates, LLC   Copying is not permitted.

Materials: calculator, pencil and paper

Work with your child to do an activity that involves decimal multiplication.

- On a sheet of paper, one person writes down two decimal numbers. With a calculator, multiply the two numbers without the decimal points.

- The other person estimates the product of the two numbers written on the sheet of paper. He or she then explains where the decimal point should be placed in the product shown on the calculator.

- Check the answer by multiplying the decimals with the calculator.

- Take turns and repeat the activity.

Look for real-life examples of multiplying decimals. For example, you might buy 12.5 gallons of gas at a price of $3.62 a gallon, or 2.5 pounds of apples at a price of $0.99 a pound. Work together with your child to estimate the product and then check your estimates with the receipt.

 ©Curriculum Associates, LLC   Copying is not permitted.

Multiply Decimals

Prerequisite: Multiply Whole Numbers

Study the example problem showing one way to multiply whole numbers using partial products. Then solve problems 1–6.

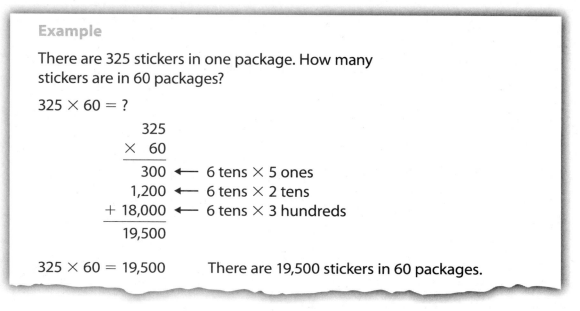

Example

There are 325 stickers in one package. How many stickers are in 60 packages?

$325 \times 60 = ?$

$$
\begin{array}{r}
325 \\
\times\ \ 60 \\
\hline
300 \\
1{,}200 \\
+\ 18{,}000 \\
\hline
19{,}500
\end{array}
$$

300 ← 6 tens × 5 ones
1,200 ← 6 tens × 2 tens
18,000 ← 6 tens × 3 hundreds

$325 \times 60 = 19{,}500$ There are 19,500 stickers in 60 packages.

1 Look at the example problem. How would the partial products and the sum of the partial products change if there were 6 packages instead of 60? Explain.

_____

_____

_____

2 Complete the steps to find the product.

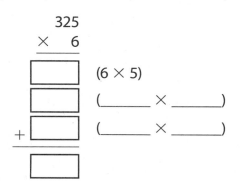

$$
\begin{array}{r}
325 \\
\times\ \ \ 6 \\
\hline
\end{array}
$$

☐ (6×5)

☐ (_____ × _____)

+ ☐ (_____ × _____)

☐

©Curriculum Associates, LLC   Copying is not permitted.

Solve.

3 Show how to find 42 × 27 using an area model.

    a. Write the missing equations in the model.

    b. Use the information from the model to complete the equation.

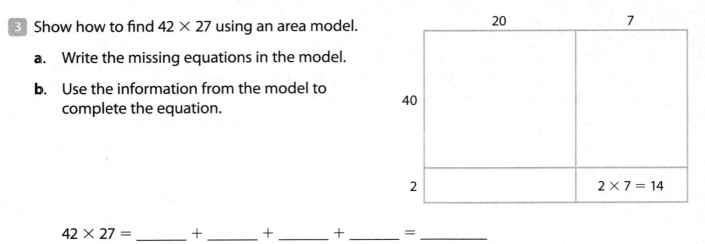

42 × 27 = _____ + _____ + _____ + _____ = _____

4 Is your answer to problem 3 reasonable? Explain your thinking.

_____

_____

5 A pet-supply store sells dog biscuits and cat treats. The store has 27 boxes of dog biscuits and 21 pouches of cat treats. Each box holds 18 dog biscuits. Each pouch holds 24 cat treats. Are there more dog biscuits or cat treats in the store?

Show your work.

Solution: _____

6 Look at problem 5. How many more boxes of dog biscuits do you need in order for there to be more dog biscuits than cat treats? Explain.

_____

_____

_____

©Curriculum Associates, LLC   Copying is not permitted.

Name: _____

Multiply Decimals by Whole Numbers

Study the example showing multiplying a decimal by a whole number using partial products. Then solve problems 1–7.

Example

$3.17 \times 4 =$? Estimate: $3 \times 4 = 12$

$$\begin{array}{r} 3.17 \\ \times \quad 4 \\ \hline \end{array}$$

28 ⟵ 4 ones × 7 hundredths   =   28 hundredths
40 ⟵ 4 ones × 1 tenth = 4 tenths   =   40 hundredths
+ 1,200 ⟵ 4 ones × 3 ones = 12 ones   = 1,200 hundredths

1,268 hundredths = 12.68

1　Look at the example. Compare the product with the estimate. Is it reasonable that the product is greater than the estimate? Explain.

_____

_____

_____

2　Complete the steps to find the product.

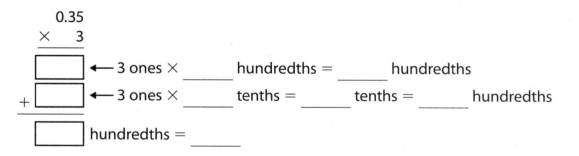

$$\begin{array}{r} 0.35 \\ \times \quad 3 \\ \hline \end{array}$$

☐ ⟵ 3 ones × _____ hundredths = _____ hundredths
+ ☐ ⟵ 3 ones × _____ tenths = _____ tenths = _____ hundredths

☐ hundredths = _____

3　Look at problem 2. Why wasn't the zero in the ones place included as a partial product?

_____

_____

_____

Solve.

4 Write the decimal point in each product so that the equation is correct.

a. $6 \times 8.29 = 4\,9\,7\,4$

c. $9.72 \times 7 = 6\,8\,0\,4$

b. $0.53 \times 5 = 2\,6\,5$

d. $3.18 \times 16 = 5\,0\,8\,8$

5 Explain how you decided where to place the decimal points in the products in problem 4.

_____

_____

_____

_____

6 Complete the steps to find 3.18×16.

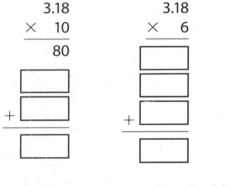

$$3.18 \times 16 = \underline{\hspace{1cm}} \text{ hundredths} + \underline{\hspace{1cm}} \text{ hundredths}$$

$$= \underline{\hspace{1cm}} \text{ hundredths} = \underline{\hspace{1cm}}$$

7 In the city where Sonya lives it rained an average of 4.05 inches each month last year. About how many inches of rain fell in all?

Show your work.

Solution: _____

©Curriculum Associates, LLC   Copying is not permitted.

Name: _____

Multiply With an Area Model

Study the example showing multiplying a decimal by a decimal using an area model. Then solve problems 1–5.

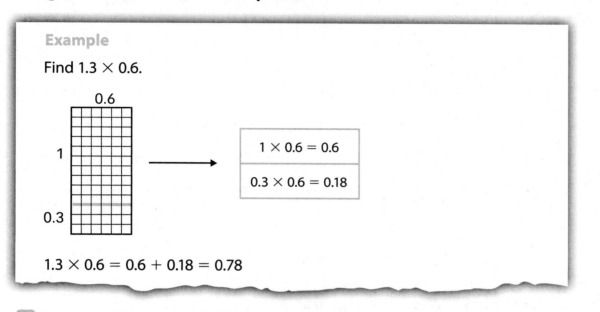

Example

Find 1.3 × 0.6.

1 × 0.6 = 0.6
0.3 × 0.6 = 0.18

1.3 × 0.6 = 0.6 + 0.18 = 0.78

1 Complete the area model. Find the product of 2.3 × 1.5.

	1	0.5
	2 × 1 = 2	

2.3 × 1.5 = _____

2 How would the area model in problem 1 need to change if the factor 2.3 was changed to 12.3?

_____

_____

_____

_____

_____

©Curriculum Associates, LLC   Copying is not permitted.   **Lesson 8** Multiply Decimals   **69**

Solve.

3 Halen wrote the product 0.4 for the problem shown. Don says that is not correct since when you multiply tenths by tenths the product will be in the hundredths. Is Don right? Explain.

$$0.5 \times 0.8 = \boxed{?}$$

_____

_____

_____

_____

_____

_____

_____

4 Use numbers from the box to complete the equations.

0.01	0.1	1
0.02	0.2	2

a. $0.5 \times 0.4 =$ _____   **c.** $0.2 \times 0.5 =$ _____

b. $0.5 \times 4 =$ _____   **d.** $2 \times 0.5 =$ _____

5 The Barga school grows lettuce and other vegetables for school lunches. The school garden is 8.4 meters long and 6.4 meters wide. The section used to grow lettuce is 2.2 meters long and 0.8 meter wide. How many square meters of ground does the garden cover? How many square meters of the garden is used to grow lettuce?

Show your work.

Solution: The garden covers _____ square

meters of ground and _____ square meters of

the garden is used to grow lettuce.

Lesson 8 Multiply Decimals   ©Curriculum Associates, LLC   Copying is not permitted.

Multiply Decimals

Solve the problems.

1 Fabiola's basketball team practices 4.25 hours each week. The basketball season is 14 weeks long. How much time does Fabiola spend in practice during the season?

Can I use an area model to solve this problem?

Show your work.

Solution: _____

2 The model represents the expression 0.7 × 0.3. Choose the product.

A 0.21   **C** 0.30

B 2.1   **D** 0.03

0.3

0.7

What does each small square in the model represent?

Val chose **C** as the correct answer. How did she get that answer?

_____

_____

_____

_____

3 Find the product of 0.6 × 0.6.

A 30.6   **C** 3.06

B 3.6   **D** 0.36

Will the product be in tenths or hundredths?

Solve.

4 One pound of red grapes costs $2.42. Ella buys 0.5 pound. How much does she spend on red grapes?

Show your work.

Will the product be greater or less than 2.42?

Solution: _____

5 Terry lives 0.9 kilometer from school. He walks back and forth to school each day. How many kilometers does he walk to and from school each week?

Show your work.

How many days in a week is Terry in school?

Solution: _____

    ©Curriculum Associates, LLC   Copying is not permitted.

Dear Family,

This week your child is learning to divide a decimal by a whole number.

Your child might see a problem like this:

> Marty is running in a 2.7 kilometer race. Water stations are set up at 9 equal sections of the race. How far apart are the water stations?

One way to understand decimal division is to use a bar model.

2.7 kilometers

?

The whole bar represents the length of the race, 2.7 kilometers. The bar has 9 equal sections. Find the length of each section to find how far apart the water stations are.

Divide 2.7 by 9 to find the length of each shorter section. $2.7 \div 9 = 0.3$

Another way your child is learning to divide decimals is to think about multiplying decimals. Division and multiplication are related operations.

To find $2.7 \div 9$, think $9 \times ? = 2.7$
$9 \times ? = 27$ tenths
9×3 tenths $= 27$ tenths

$2.7 = 27$ tenths

The answer, 3 tenths, is the same as the answer found using the bar model, 0.3. The water stations are 0.3 kilometer apart.

Invite your child to share what he or she knows about dividing decimals by doing the following activity together.

NEXT

©Curriculum Associates, LLC   Copying is not permitted.

Dividing Decimals Activity

Work with your child to solve a real-life problem involving dividing decimals.

- Think of something you spend money on for the whole family, such as the grocery bill, tickets to the movies, or a new board game.

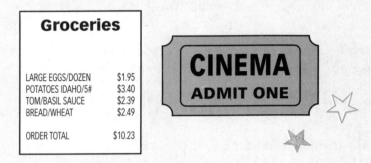

Groceries

LARGE EGGS/DOZEN	$1.95
POTATOES IDAHO/5#	$3.40
TOM/BASIL SAUCE	$2.39
BREAD/WHEAT	$2.49
ORDER TOTAL	$10.23

- Divide the cost by the number of people in the family. This will describe the cost for each family member.

  - Example: A book of puzzles cost $11.76.
    There are 4 people in the family.
    Divide 11.76 by 4 to find the cost for each family member.

- Check that the answer is reasonable. In the example above, is 29.4 a reasonable answer for 11.76 ÷ 4?

Be on the lookout for other real-life examples of dividing decimals that you can share with your child.

 ©Curriculum Associates, LLC   Copying is not permitted.

Divide Decimals

Prerequisite: Divide Whole Numbers

Study the example problem showing how to use a bar model to represent division. Then solve problems 1–5.

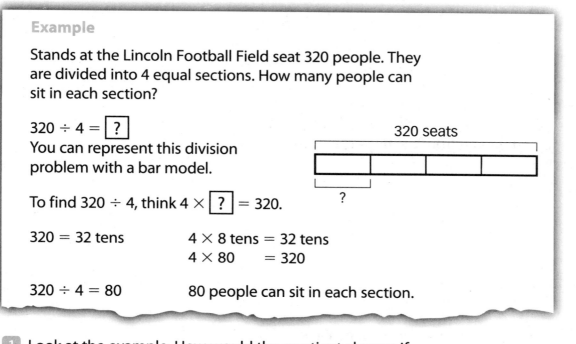

Example

Stands at the Lincoln Football Field seat 320 people. They are divided into 4 equal sections. How many people can sit in each section?

$320 \div 4 =$ ⬚?
You can represent this division problem with a bar model.

320 seats

?

To find $320 \div 4$, think $4 \times$ ⬚? $= 320$.

$320 = 32$ tens

4×8 tens $= 32$ tens
$4 \times 80 \quad = 320$

$320 \div 4 = 80$ 80 people can sit in each section.

---

1 Look at the example. How would the quotient change if the total number of seats was 3,200 instead of 320? Explain.

_____

_____

_____

_____

2 Rewrite each division problem as a multiplication problem and solve.

a. $490 \div 7 =$ ⬚?   _____ $\times$ ⬚? $=$ _____ $490 \div 7 =$ _____

b. $2,400 \div 12 =$ ⬚?   _____ $\times$ ⬚? $=$ _____ $2,400 \div 12 =$ _____

c. $350 \div 50 =$ ⬚?   _____ $\times$ ⬚? $=$ _____ $350 \div 50 =$ _____

d. $5,400 \div 90 =$ ⬚?   _____ $\times$ ⬚? $=$ _____ $5,400 \div 90 =$ _____

©Curriculum Associates, LLC   Copying is not permitted.

Solve.

3 Choose *Yes* or *No* to tell whether the expression represents the number 40.

a.	1,600 ÷ 4	☐ Yes	☐ No
b.	120 ÷ 3	☐ Yes	☐ No
c.	480 ÷ 12	☐ Yes	☐ No
d.	280 ÷ 70	☐ Yes	☐ No

4 A large drink dispenser used at a school field day holds 640 ounces of lemonade. How many glasses of lemonade can be poured from the dispenser if each glass holds 8 ounces?

Show your work.

Solution: _____

5 Each costume for a dance group in a talent show requires 2 yards of black material and 3 yards of red material. The dance group has 30 yards of black material and 60 yards of red material. What is the greatest number of costumes they can make? Explain.

Show your work.

Solution: _____

_____

_____

_____

©Curriculum Associates, LLC   Copying is not permitted.

Divide a Decimal by a Whole Number

Study the example problem showing one way to divide a decimal by a whole number. Then solve problems 1–5.

Example

The temperature rose 4.8 degrees in 6 hours. If the temperature rose by an equal amount each hour, how many degrees did it rise each hour?

You can represent this with a bar model.

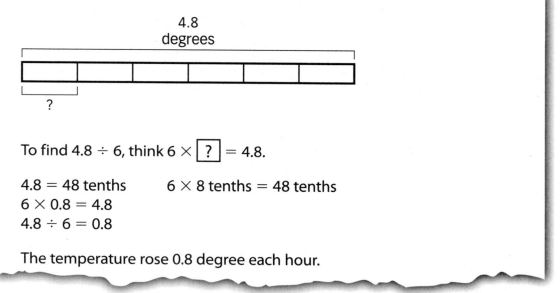

4.8 degrees

?

To find 4.8 ÷ 6, think 6 × ⎡ ? ⎤ = 4.8.

4.8 = 48 tenths   6 × 8 tenths = 48 tenths
6 × 0.8 = 4.8
4.8 ÷ 6 = 0.8

The temperature rose 0.8 degree each hour.

1 Look at the example problem. Suppose the temperature had risen 5.4 degrees in 6 hours. Complete the steps to solve 5.4 ÷ 6.

a. 5.4 ÷ 6 Think: _____ × ⎡ ? ⎤ = _____

b. 5.4 = _____ tenths _____ × ⎡ ? ⎤ = _____ tenths

c. 6 × _____ tenths = _____ tenths

d. 5.4 ÷ 6 = _____

2 Use numbers from the box. Write the number of tenths and hundredths in each decimal.

3.5	0.79	0.35
	350	35
7.9	79	790

3.5 = _____ tenths   3.5 = _____ hundredths

0.79 = _____ tenths   0.79 = _____ hundredths

©Curriculum Associates, LLC Copying is not permitted.

Solve.

3 Complete the steps for using an area model to solve 1.56 ÷ 12.

1.56 ÷ 12 is the same as _____ × [**?**] = _____.

1.56 = _____ hundredths

?

12 | 156 hundredths | → 12

12 × 10 = ☐

156

− ☐

12 × 3 = ☐

☐

− ☐

156 hundredths ÷ 12 = _____ hundredths

1.56 ÷ 12 = _____

4 Conor earns $9 an hour for yard work. He raked leaves one afternoon and earned $29.25. How many hours did he rake leaves?

Show your work.

Solution: _____

5 Look at problem 4. How much does Conor earn for each minute he does yard work?

Show your work.

There are 60 minutes in 1 hour.

Solution: _____

    ©Curriculum Associates, LLC   Copying is not permitted.

Name: _____

Divide by Tenths

Study the example showing one way to divide a decimal by a decimal. Then solve problems 1–7.

Example

What is 2.1 ÷ 0.7?

You can represent this problem with decimal grids.

Each large square represents 1 whole.

To find 2.1 ÷ 0.7, think 0.7 × ? = 2.1.

The lines separate groups of 0.7.

2.1 = 21 tenths
0.7 =   7 tenths

In words: 7 tenths × ? = 21 tenths
                7 tenths × 3 = 21 tenths

2.1 ÷ 0.7 = 3

1   Look at the example. How is the quotient, 3, represented by the grids?

_____

_____

_____

2   What other expressions are represented by the decimal grids in the example problem? Circle the letter of all that apply.

A   0.7 × 3   **C**   0.7 ÷ 3

B   3 × 0.7   **D**   2.1 ÷ 3

3   How many grids would you need to represent the problem 4.5 ÷ 0.5? Explain.

_____

_____

©Curriculum Associates, LLC   Copying is not permitted.

Solve.

4 Complete the steps to solve $4.5 \div 0.5$.

   a. $4.5 \div 0.5$ Think: _____ $\times$ $\boxed{?}$ = _____

   b. $4.5 =$ _____ tenths and $0.5 =$ _____ tenths

   c. 5 tenths $\times$ _____ $= 45$ tenths

   d. $4.5 \div 0.5 =$ _____

5 Rewrite each division problem as a multiplication problem and solve.

   a. $6.3 \div 0.9 = \boxed{?}$ _____ $\times$ $\boxed{?}$ = _____ $6.3 \div 0.9 =$ _____

   b. $3.2 \div 0.4 = \boxed{?}$ _____ $\times$ $\boxed{?}$ = _____ $3.2 \div 0.4 =$ _____

   c. $1.8 \div 0.3 = \boxed{?}$ _____ $\times$ $\boxed{?}$ = _____ $1.8 \div 0.3 =$ _____

   d. $2.4 \div 1.2 = \boxed{?}$ _____ $\times$ $\boxed{?}$ = _____ $2.4 \div 1.2 =$ _____

6 The Razdan family drinks 0.5 gallon of milk a day. Will 2.5 gallons of milk last them more than 1 week? Explain.

Show your work.

Solution: _____

_____

7 Mrs. Lang is hanging drawings for the school art show across a wall that is 2.8 meters wide. She determines each picture, along with the space needed around each picture, will take up 0.4 meter along the wall. How many pictures can she hang in one row across the wall?

Show your work.

Solution: _____

©Curriculum Associates, LLC   Copying is not permitted.

Name: _____

Divide by Hundredths

Study the example showing one way to divide by hundredths. Then solve problems 1–6.

Example

1.8 ÷ 0.04 = ?

Identify the least place. Write each decimal to the least place.

0.04 = 4 hundredths
1.8 = 180 hundredths

180 hundredths ÷ 4 hundredths = 45
1.8 ÷ 0.04 = 45

Divide as you would with whole numbers, using partial quotients or another method.

$$\begin{array}{r} 45 \\ \hline 5 \\ 40 \\ 4)\overline{180} \\ -\ 160 \\ \hline 20 \\ -\ 20 \\ \hline 0 \end{array}$$

1 Complete the steps to solve 1.02 ÷ 0.06.

   a. 1.02 ÷ 0.06

   b. 1.02 = _____ hundredths
       0.06 = _____ hundredths

   c. 102 ÷ 6 = _____

   d. 1.02 ÷ 0.06 = _____

2 Did you use partial quotients or another method to divide 102 by 6 in problem 1? Explain.

_____

_____

_____

3 Check your answer to problem 1 by writing the decimals in a multiplication equation.

_____ × _____ = _____

       Lesson 9 Divide Decimals   **81**

Solve.

4 Choose *True* or *False* for each equation.

a. $1.23 = 123$ hundredths ☐ True ☐ False

b. $0.5 = 50$ hundredths ☐ True ☐ False

c. 74 hundredths $= 7.4$ ☐ True ☐ False

d. $1,088$ hundredths $= 10.88$ ☐ True ☐ False

5 Jaden buys 1.15 pounds of cheese at the deli counter. If each slice is 0.05 pound, how many slices of cheese does she buy?

Show your work.

Solution: _____

6 Ray feeds his dog 0.12 kilogram of dry dog food each day. He wants to buy the smallest bag that has enough food to feed his dog for one month. Should he buy the bag that has 1.8 kilograms, 2.4 kilograms, or 4.2 kilograms of dog food?

Show your work.

Solution: _____

©Curriculum Associates, LLC   Copying is not permitted.

Name: _____

Divide Decimals

Solve the problems.

1 Evan walks his dog 4 times around the perimeter of a park, for a total distance of 2.8 kilometers. How many kilometers does he walk each time around? Circle the letter of the correct answer.

What basic fact can help you solve this problem?

A 0.07   **C** 0.7

B 0.12   **D** 1.2

2 How many 45¢ stamps can you buy with $9? Circle the letter of the correct answer.

How do you write 45¢ as a decimal? $9 as a decimal?

A 0.2   **C** 20

B 2   **D** 200

Da Jin chose **D** as the correct answer. How did he get that answer?

_____

_____

_____

_____

3 Which change would make the statement below true?

3.9 = 39 hundredths

It may be helpful to rewrite the equation for each change described.

A Change 3.9 to 3.90.

B Change *hundredths* to *tenths*.

C Change *hundredths* to *ones*.

D Change 3.9 to 390.

©Curriculum Associates, LLC   Copying is not permitted.

4 Choose *Yes* or *No* to tell if the expression is represented by the bar model.

9.6

?

0.6

a. $9.6 \div 0.6$ ☐ Yes ☐ No

b. $9.6 \div 6$ ☐ Yes ☐ No

c. $0.06 \div 9.6$ ☐ Yes ☐ No

d. $0.6 \div 9.6$ ☐ Yes ☐ No

What is the least place shown in the two decimals?

5 Banks sell quarters in rolls. Each roll has a value of $10.

Part A

How many quarters are in one roll?

Show your work.

What operation can you use to solve the problem?

Solution: _____

Part B

If a roll of dimes also had a value of $10, how many dimes would be in the roll?

Show your work.

Solution: _____

©Curriculum Associates, LLC   Copying is not permitted.

Unit 1 Game

Decimal Race to 100

What you need: Recording Sheet,
2 sets of Digit Cards (0–9)

Directions

- The goal of the game is to add 5 numbers to get as close as you can to 100, without going over.

- Take turns making decimal numbers. On your first turn, choose three digit cards. Write them in any order and put the decimal point before or after any digit. Write your decimal on the Recording Sheet and shuffle the cards back into the pile.

- On your second turn, pick three more cards to make another decimal in the same way. Write the second decimal on the recording sheet. Line up the decimal points and add your two numbers.

- Take turns making decimal numbers and adding the number to your sum.

- After 5 rounds, subtract your sum from 100. The player who is closest to 100 without going over is the winner.

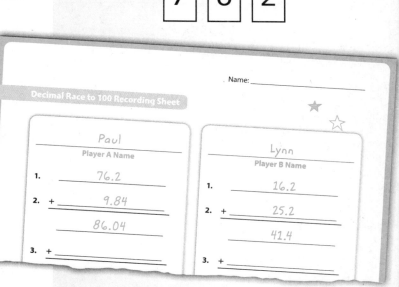

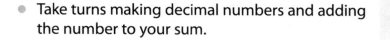

With these digits, I could make numbers from 762 (way too big!) all the way down to 0.267 (which won't get me very close to 100!).

©Curriculum Associates, LLC   Copying is not permitted.

Decimal Race to 100 Recording Sheet

_____
Player A Name

1. _____

2. + _____

    _____

3. + _____

    _____

4. + _____

    _____

5. + _____

    _____

100.00
− _____
_____

Final Score Player A [   ]

_____
Player B Name

1. _____

2. + _____

    _____

3. + _____

    _____

4. + _____

    _____

5. + _____

    _____

100.00
− _____
_____

Final Score Player B [   ]

©Curriculum Associates, LLC

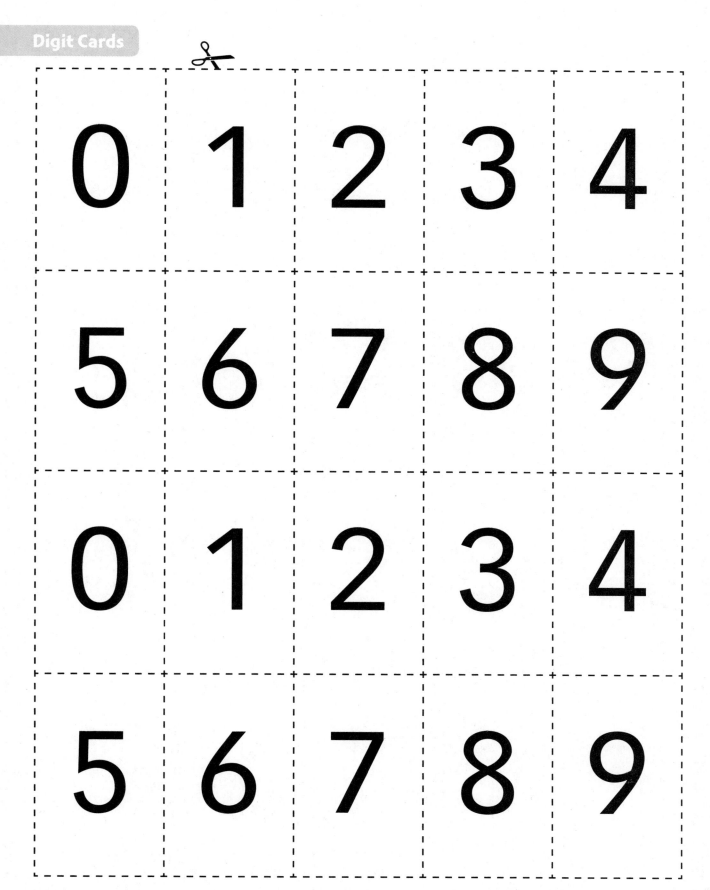

©Curriculum Associates, LLC

Unit 1 Number and Operations in Base Ten

Name: _____

Number and Operations in Base Ten

In this unit you learned to:	Lesson
read and write decimals, for example: $80.63 = 8 \times 10 + 6 \times \frac{1}{10} + 3 \times \frac{1}{100}$.	1, 3
compare decimals, for example: $3.47 > 3.096$.	1, 4
round decimals, for example: 6.274 rounded to the nearest tenth is 6.3.	4
multiply whole numbers, for example: $410 \times 16 = 6,560$.	2, 5
divide whole numbers, for example: $2,812 \div 38 = 74$.	6
add and subtract decimals, for example: $20.08 + 5.15 = 25.23$.	7
multiply decimals, for example: $7.25 \times 9.4 = 68.15$.	8
divide decimals, for example: $18.72 \div 3.6 = 5.2$.	9

Use these skills to solve problems 1–5.

1 Answer the following questions about the decimals 2.65 and 0.609.

a. Write the word form of each decimal.

2.65

_____

0.609

_____

b. Write each decimal to complete the inequality statement.

_____ > _____

2 Over one weekend The Fast Florist makes 368 deliveries of one dozen roses. Did The Fast Florist deliver more than or less than 4,000 roses? Explain.

_____

_____

_____

_____

_____

Solve.

3 An above-ground pool holds 5,310 gallons of water. How many times could the water in the pool fill a bathtub that holds 45 gallons of water?

A   85 times

B   118 times

C   122 times

D   1,018 times

4 What is 2.4 − 2.24?

A   0.16

B   0.26

C   2.24

D   24

5 Katrin is making a poster for school elections. She draws a line 20.4 centimeters long across the poster board. She starts at one end of the line and makes a mark every 3.4 centimeters along it. She plans to write the letters of her name in the spaces between the marks.

Part A

Will Katrin make enough spaces for each letter of her name to go in one space? Explain.

Show your work.

Solution: _____

_____

Part B

Katrin has 5 letters in her last name. Fill in the blanks to complete the equation to show how long the line has to be for her to have enough spaces to write both her first and last name and leave a space in between.

Equation: _____ × 3.4 = _____ centimeters

    ©Curriculum Associates, LLC   Copying is not permitted.

Name: _____

Answer the questions and show all your work on separate paper.

A fifth-grade class has a budget of $160.00 to buy props for a play. They need to buy 3 matching place settings. A place setting includes 1 plate, 1 cup, 1 bowl, 1 fork, and 1 spoon. They have a table but need to buy 3 matching chairs. The charts below show prices of different options.

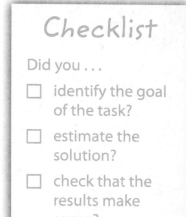

Checklist

Did you . . .

☐ identify the goal of the task?

☐ estimate the solution?

☐ check that the results make sense?

	Cost per Plate	Cost per Bowl	Cost per Cup
Patterned Dinnerware	$9.19	$8.62	$5.99
Solid Dinnerware	$6.99	$6.75	$3.12

	Basic Forks and Spoons	Fancy Forks and Spoons
Cost per Item	$0.83	$2.29

	Metal Folding Chairs	Chairs with Cloth Seats	Chairs with Wooden Seats
Cost per Chair	$19.99	$24.45	$21.22

There is a tax of 0.05 times the total purchase.

Use rounding to first help you estimate which items to buy. Then make two different plans for buying the props the students need for their play. Make sure to include the tax. Show that each plan stays within the budget. Tell how much money is left over with each plan.

Reflect on Mathematical Practices

1. **Make Sense of Problems** How did you organize your information for buying the props? What equations did you write? How do the equations represent the information in the problem?

2. **Be Precise** When you calculated the tax on the purchase, how did you handle thousandths in the decimals? Why?

Performance Task Tips

Word Bank Here are some words that you might use in your answer.

add	sum	subtract
difference	tenth	hundredth
thousandth	dollar	estimate
round	about	multiply

Models Here are some models that you might use to find the solution.

	Cost per Plate	Cost per Bowl	Cost per Cup	Cost for 1 Set	Cost for 3 Sets
Patterned Dinnerware					
Solid Dinnerware					

	Basic Forks and Spoons	Fancy Forks and Spoons
Cost per Item		
Cost for 3 Forks & 3 Spoons		

	Metal Folding Chairs	Chairs with Cloth Seats	Chairs with Wooden Seats
Cost per Chair			
Cost for 3 Chairs			

Sentence Starters Here are some sentence starters that might help explain your work.

To find the tax _____

The cost of three _____

The total cost of _____

After buying everything and paying tax _____

©Curriculum Associates, LLC   Copying is not permitted.

Unit 1 Vocabulary

Name: _____

My Examples

base ten

a ten-digit number system that uses place value to record numbers

place value

the value of a digit that depends on the digit's position in a number; ones, tens, hundreds, and so on

decimal number

a number written in base ten

tenth

one part of a whole that has been divided into 10 equal parts

©Curriculum Associates, LLC   Copying is not permitted.

hundredth

one part of a whole that has been divided into 100 equal parts

thousandth

one part of a whole that has been divided into 1,000 equal parts

expanded form

a way to show the value of each digit in a number

exponent

the number in a power that tells how many times to use the base as a factor

©Curriculum Associates, LLC   Copying is not permitted.

power of ten

a number that can be written as a product of tens

inverse

the opposite of something

expression

a group of numbers and symbols that shows a mathematical relationship

compare

to determine if one value is greater than, equal to, or less than another

division

an operation used to find the number in each group or the number of groups in equal-sized groups

multiplication

an operation used to find the total number of items in equal-sized groups

partial product

the result of multiplying the value in one place of a two- or three-digit number

factor

a number that is multiplied by another number

©Curriculum Associates, LLC   Copying is not permitted.

product

the result of multiplication

dividend

the number being divided in a division problem

divisor

the number being divided into a dividend in a division problem

quotient

the result of division

©Curriculum Associates, LLC   Copying is not permitted.

estimate

to find an answer that is close to the exact answer by rounding or using compatible numbers

difference

the result of subtraction

sum

the result of addition

standard algorithm

a step-by-step method for computing

©Curriculum Associates, LLC   Copying is not permitted.

My Words

My Examples

My Words

My Examples

_____

_____

_____

_____

_____

_____

_____

_____

_____

_____

_____

_____

_____

_____

_____

©Curriculum Associates, LLC   Copying is not permitted.

Dear Family,

This week your child is learning to add and subtract fractions.

Here's how a model can show fraction addition, such as $1\frac{2}{3} + \frac{3}{4}$.

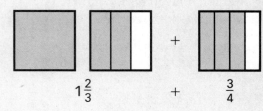

$1\frac{2}{3}$ $+$ $\frac{3}{4}$

> The denominators, 3 and 4, tell how many equal parts are in the whole. 3 and 4 are **unlike denominators**.

The parts of the whole are different sizes, thirds and fourths.

It doesn't make sense to add different-size parts, so divide the model to show equal-size parts, twelfths. Then add.

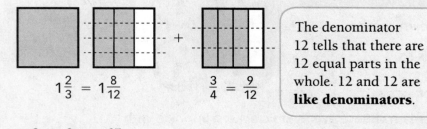

$1\frac{2}{3} = 1\frac{8}{12}$ $\qquad$ $\frac{3}{4} = \frac{9}{12}$

> The denominator 12 tells that there are 12 equal parts in the whole. 12 and 12 are **like denominators**.

$1\frac{8}{12} + \frac{9}{12} = 1\frac{17}{12}$

$1\frac{17}{12}$ can also be written as $2\frac{5}{12}$.

Some other ways your child can think about adding and subtracting fractions is to use a picture or a number line. Jump forward on the number line for addition and jump backward for subtraction.

Invite your child to share what he or she knows about adding and subtracting fractions by doing the following activity together.

©Curriculum Associates, LLC   Copying is not permitted.

Work together with your child to solve real-life problems about adding and subtracting fractions.

- Suppose you want to make some healthy snacks and have $\frac{7}{8}$ cup of cream cheese and $\frac{3}{4}$ cup raisins.

- Look at the two recipes below. Add fractions to decide if there is enough cream cheese and raisins to make both recipes.

- Subtract fractions to determine how much of each ingredient you *may* have left over.

Recipe for Creamed Crackers

Ingredients:

6 crackers (any variety)

$\frac{1}{2}$ cup cream cheese

$\frac{1}{4}$ cup raisins

Directions:

Spread cream cheese evenly on crackers. Sprinkle with raisins.

Recipe for Celery Logs

Ingredients:

6 two-inch pieces of celery

$\frac{1}{3}$ cup cream cheese

$\frac{1}{8}$ cup raisins

Directions:

Spread cream cheese evenly on celery. Sprinkle with raisins.

©Curriculum Associates, LLC   Copying is not permitted.

Add and Subtract Fractions

Name: _____

Study the example showing how you can use models and multiplication to find equivalent fractions. Then solve problems 1–7.

Example

The model is divided into 4 equal parts.

The shaded section shows the fraction $\frac{1}{4}$.

You can divide the same whole into 2 times as many equal parts. There are 2 times as many parts shaded.

You can divide the same whole into 3 times as many equal parts. There are 3 times as many parts shaded.

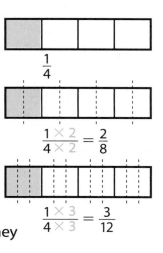

The fractions $\frac{1}{4}$, $\frac{2}{8}$, and $\frac{3}{12}$ are equivalent because they each show the same shaded part of a whole.

1   Look at the model to the right. $\frac{3}{5}$ of the whole is shaded. Divide the model into a different number of equal parts to find an equivalent fraction. Complete the equation.

$\frac{3}{5} = \dfrac{\boxed{}}{\boxed{}}$

2   Write the missing numbers to describe the equivalent fraction you found in problem 1.

There are _____ times as many equal parts.

There are _____ times as many shaded parts.

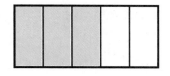

$\dfrac{3 \times \boxed{}}{5 \times \boxed{}} = \dfrac{\boxed{}}{\boxed{}}$

Solve.

3 Shade the model to show $\frac{2}{3}$. Then divide the model to show 6 equal parts.

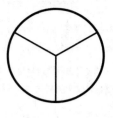

4 Look at the model in problem 3. Write the missing numbers to show the equivalent fraction you formed by dividing it into 6 equal parts.

$$\frac{2 \times \boxed{}}{3 \times \boxed{}} = \frac{\boxed{}}{\boxed{}}$$

5 Explain how you can multiply to find equivalent fractions.

_____

_____

_____

_____

6 Choose *Yes* or *No* to tell whether the fraction is equivalent to $\frac{2}{5}$.

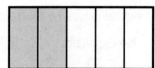

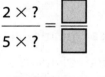

a. $\frac{4}{10}$ ☐ Yes ☐ No

b. $\frac{5}{8}$ ☐ Yes ☐ No

c. $\frac{6}{15}$ ☐ Yes ☐ No

d. $\frac{6}{20}$ ☐ Yes ☐ No

e. $\frac{10}{25}$ ☐ Yes ☐ No

7 How did you determine whether a fraction was equivalent to $\frac{2}{5}$ in problem 6? Explain.

_____

_____

_____

_____

©Curriculum Associates, LLC   Copying is not permitted.

Name: _____

Add Fractions with Unlike Denominators

Study the example showing one way to add fractions with unlike denominators. Then solve problems 1–4.

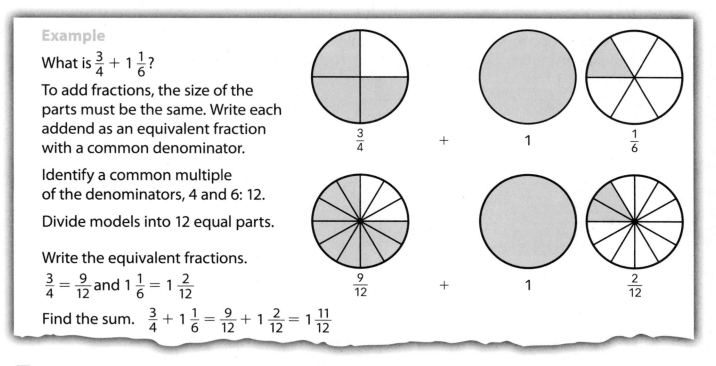

Example

What is $\frac{3}{4} + 1\frac{1}{6}$?

To add fractions, the size of the parts must be the same. Write each addend as an equivalent fraction with a common denominator.

Identify a common multiple of the denominators, 4 and 6: 12.

Divide models into 12 equal parts.

Write the equivalent fractions.

$\frac{3}{4} = \frac{9}{12}$ and $1\frac{1}{6} = 1\frac{2}{12}$

Find the sum. $\frac{3}{4} + 1\frac{1}{6} = \frac{9}{12} + 1\frac{2}{12} = 1\frac{11}{12}$

$\frac{3}{4}$ +   1 $\frac{1}{6}$

$\frac{9}{12}$ +   1 $\frac{2}{12}$

---

1 The example uses 12 as the common multiple of 4 and 6.

   a. Name a different common multiple of 4 and 6.

   _____

   b. Using the common multiple from part **a.**, how would the models be different? How would they be the same?

   _____

   _____

   _____

   c. Use the common multiple from part **a.** as the common denominator to write equivalent fractions for $\frac{3}{4}$ and $1\frac{1}{6}$.

   $\frac{3}{4} =$ _____ $1\frac{1}{6} = 1$ _____

©Curriculum Associates, LLC   Copying is not permitted.

Solve.

2 One way to find a common denominator is by multiplying the denominators of the two fractions together and using the product as the common denominator.

Use this method to find a common denominator for each pair of fractions. Write the equivalent fractions.

a. $1\dfrac{3}{5} = 1\dfrac{\boxed{}}{20}$ $1\dfrac{3}{4} = 1\dfrac{\boxed{}}{20}$

b. $2\dfrac{1}{2} = $ _____ $\dfrac{4}{5} = $ _____

c. $\dfrac{3}{8} = $ _____ $\dfrac{1}{6} = $ _____

3 Show how to add $2\dfrac{1}{2} + \dfrac{4}{5}$ using the number line below.

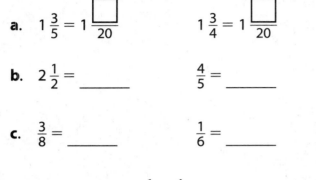

Write an equation to represent the problem.

_____

4 Maya is packing her backpack for a hike. In one pocket she puts in a $\dfrac{1}{4}$-pound bag of trail mix, a water bottle weighing $2\dfrac{1}{5}$ pounds, and a flashlight weighing $\dfrac{1}{4}$ pound. How much weight do these three items add to her backpack?

Show your work.

Solution: _____

©Curriculum Associates, LLC   Copying is not permitted.

Name: _____

Subtract Fractions with Unlike Denominators

Study the example problem showing one way to subtract fractions with unlike denominators. Then solve problems 1–5.

Example

Felicia lives $1\frac{1}{5}$ miles from school and $\frac{9}{10}$ mile from the soccer field. How much closer does she live to the field than to school?

You can show $1\frac{1}{5} - \frac{9}{10}$ using a number line.

First find the common denominator.

Identify a common multiple of 5 and 10: 10.

Rewrite the fractions as needed. $1\frac{1}{5} = 1\frac{2}{10}$

Divide the number line into tenths.

Start at the point $1\frac{2}{10}$ and jump left $\frac{9}{10}$.

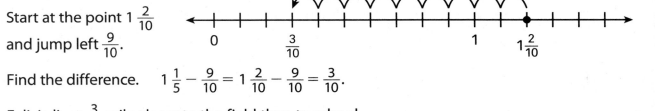

Find the difference. $1\frac{1}{5} - \frac{9}{10} = 1\frac{2}{10} - \frac{9}{10} = \frac{3}{10}$.

Felicia lives $\frac{3}{10}$ mile closer to the field than to school.

1. How would the model and answer in the example problem change if Felicia lives $\frac{7}{10}$ mile from the soccer field?

_____

_____

2. Eric says he knows $\frac{9}{10}$ is $\frac{1}{10}$ less than $\frac{10}{10}$, or 1 mile.

So, he is going to subtract 1 mile, then add $\frac{1}{10}$ back.

Can he use this method to solve the example problem? Explain.

_____

_____

©Curriculum Associates, LLC   Copying is not permitted.   **Lesson 10** Add and Subtract Fractions

Solve.

3 Sometimes it is helpful to rewrite mixed numbers that include a fraction greater than 1. Use the number line to write the missing numbers.

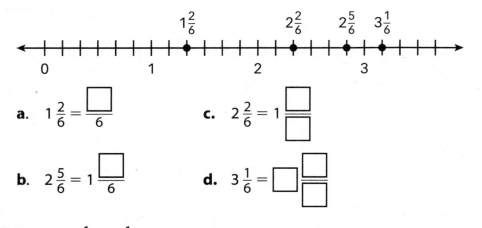

a. $1\frac{2}{6} = \dfrac{\square}{6}$

c. $2\frac{2}{6} = 1\dfrac{\square}{\square}$

b. $2\frac{5}{6} = 1\dfrac{\square}{6}$

d. $3\frac{1}{6} = \square\dfrac{\square}{\square}$

4 What is $3\frac{1}{3} - 1\frac{1}{2}$?

Show your work.

Solution: _____

5 Emil's backpack weighs $6\frac{3}{8}$ pounds. He removes a book that weighs $\frac{3}{4}$ pound. Then he removes a book that weighs $\frac{1}{2}$ pound. How much does Emil's backpack weigh now?

Show your work.

I can find the total weight of the books first and then subtract, or subtract the weight of each book separately.

Solution: _____

©Curriculum Associates, LLC   Copying is not permitted.

Name: _____

Add and Subtract Fractions with Unlike Denominators

Solve.

1 Which statement and reasoning is true for finding a common denominator for the fractions $\frac{1}{4}$ and $\frac{1}{8}$? Circle the letter of all that apply.

Can a pair of fractions have more than one common denominator?

A I can use 8 because $2 \times 4 = 8$.

B I can use 12 because $2 \times 4 = 8$ and $4 + 8 = 12$.

C I can use 16 because $4 \times 4 = 16$ and $2 \times 8 = 16$.

D I can use 24 because $6 \times 4 = 24$ and $3 \times 8 = 24$.

2 What is $3\frac{1}{4} + \frac{3}{8}$?
Show your work.

I need to find a common denominator before I can add.

Solution: _____

3 Kado spent $1\frac{2}{3}$ hours painting a fence. Then he spent $\frac{4}{5}$ of an hour walking his dog. How much longer did he spend painting than walking?

I know he spent more time walking his dog because $1\frac{2}{3}$ is greater than $\frac{4}{5}$.

A $\frac{2}{15}$ hour   **C** $1\frac{2}{15}$ hours

B $\frac{13}{15}$ hour   **D** $1\frac{13}{15}$ hours

Orleans chose **C** as the correct answer. How did she get that answer?

_____

_____

_____

Solve.

4 A piece of string is $5\frac{5}{8}$ inches long. How much should Lena cut off to make it $3\frac{1}{2}$ inches long?

Show your work.

Do I represent this problem with an addition or subtraction expression?

Solution: _____

5 Erin and Ethan add the fractions $2\frac{1}{3}$ and $1\frac{1}{2}$. Look at their work below.

How are the pictures for the two answers alike?

Erin $\quad 2\frac{1}{3} + 1\frac{1}{2}$
$2\frac{1 \times 2}{3 \times 2} = 2\frac{2}{6} \qquad 1\frac{1 \times 3}{2 \times 3} = 1\frac{3}{6}$ $2\frac{2}{6} + 1\frac{3}{6} = 3\frac{5}{6}$

Ethan $\quad 2\frac{1}{3} + 1\frac{1}{2}$
$2\frac{1 \times 4}{3 \times 4} = 2\frac{4}{12} \qquad 1\frac{1 \times 6}{2 \times 6} = 1\frac{6}{12}$ $2\frac{4}{12} + 1\frac{6}{12} = 3\frac{10}{12}$

Both Erin's and Ethan's answers are correct. Use pictures to explain why this is true.

_____

_____

©Curriculum Associates, LLC   Copying is not permitted.

Dear Family,

This week your child is learning to add and subtract fractions in word problems.

Your child is also learning to estimate the answer in order to check whether an answer is reasonable or not. He or she might see a problem like this:

> Paul used $\frac{3}{8}$ of a cup of milk to make muffins and $\frac{1}{3}$ of a cup of milk to make nut bread. How much milk did Paul use to make muffins and nut bread?

To solve the problem, add the fractions $\frac{3}{8}$ and $\frac{1}{3}$.

It's helpful to show the fractions on number lines.

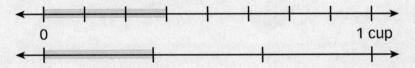

To estimate the sum, you can use benchmark fractions for each fraction in the problem. $\frac{1}{2}$ is a good benchmark fraction to use.

$\frac{3}{8}$ is less than $\frac{1}{2}$. $\frac{1}{3}$ is also less than $\frac{1}{2}$. Since $\frac{1}{2} + \frac{1}{2} = 1$, an estimate of $\frac{3}{8} + \frac{1}{3}$ is less than 1.

Now add the fractions $\frac{3}{8} + \frac{1}{3}$. The fractions need to have equal-sized parts, so write equivalent fractions with like denominators. Then add.

$$\frac{3}{8} = \frac{9}{24} \qquad \frac{1}{3} = \frac{8}{24}$$

$\frac{9}{24} + \frac{8}{24} = \frac{17}{24}$

Is the sum of $\frac{17}{24}$ a reasonable answer? Check the sum against the estimate you made. The estimate is less than 1 and $\frac{17}{24}$ is less than 1, so the sum is reasonable.

Invite your child to share what he or she knows about adding and subtracting fractions in word problems by doing the following activity together.

NEXT

©Curriculum Associates, LLC   Copying is not permitted.

Adding Fractions Activity

Work together with your child to identify some real-life situations when you might use fractions, such as when you are cooking, building, or gardening.

- Here are some examples in which you might add and subtract fractions in real life:

A recipe for soup calls for $2\frac{1}{3}$ cups of water and $1\frac{3}{8}$ cups of milk.

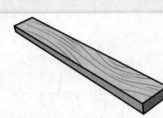

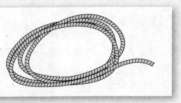

One piece of wood is $4\frac{1}{2}$ feet long and another piece is $2\frac{2}{3}$ feet long.

A string used for tomato plants is $3\frac{3}{4}$ feet long. Another string is $2\frac{1}{3}$ feet long.

Choose one of the examples above. Add the mixed numbers in that example. Work together to first make an estimate of the sum. Check your answer against the estimate to make sure your answer is reasonable.

©Curriculum Associates, LLC   Copying is not permitted.

Add and Subtract Fractions in Word Problems

Name: _____

Study the example problem showing comparing numbers by using the benchmark fraction $\frac{1}{2}$. Then solve problems 1–5.

Example

Ricci and his brother Lorenzo both have to practice for an upcoming karate tournament. Ricci practices for $\frac{3}{8}$ hour, and Lorenzo practices for $\frac{3}{4}$ hour. Which brother practices for a longer time?

Compare both numbers to the benchmark fraction $\frac{1}{2}$.

Look at the number line. It shows that $\frac{3}{8}$ is less than $\frac{1}{2}$ and $\frac{3}{4}$ is greater than $\frac{1}{2}$.
So, $\frac{3}{8} < \frac{3}{4}$ and $\frac{3}{4} > \frac{3}{8}$.

Lorenzo practices for a longer time.

1 Use the number line in the example problem to compare each fraction below to $\frac{1}{2}$. Write each fraction in the correct box.

$$\frac{6}{8} \qquad \frac{3}{4} \qquad \frac{1}{4} \qquad \frac{5}{8} \qquad \frac{2}{4} \qquad \frac{7}{8} \qquad \frac{2}{8}$$

Less than $\frac{1}{2}$	Equal to $\frac{1}{2}$	Greater than $\frac{1}{2}$

Vocabulary

benchmark fraction
a common fraction you can judge other numbers against (example: $\frac{1}{4}$, $\frac{1}{2}$, $\frac{3}{4}$).

Solve.

2 You can also use the number 1 as a benchmark. Use the fractions from the box.

Write each fraction that is

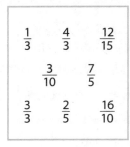

$$\frac{1}{3} \qquad \frac{4}{3} \qquad \frac{12}{15}$$
$$\frac{3}{10} \qquad \frac{7}{5}$$
$$\frac{3}{3} \qquad \frac{2}{5} \qquad \frac{16}{10}$$

a. greater than 1. _____

b. less than 1. _____

c. equal to 1. _____

3 Which fraction from problem 2 is greater than $1\frac{1}{2}$? Explain how you know.

_____

_____

4 You can also model comparisons to $\frac{1}{2}$ using fraction strips. Write $>$, $=$, or $<$ to compare each set of fractions below.

$$\frac{2}{3} \underline{\hspace{1cm}} \frac{1}{2} \qquad\qquad \frac{2}{6} \underline{\hspace{1cm}} \frac{1}{2}$$

So, $\frac{2}{3} \underline{\hspace{1cm}} \frac{2}{6}$.

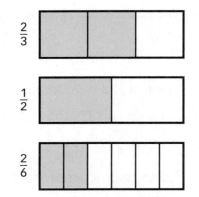

5 Josan and Andrea are on a long-distance bike ride. They decide they will stop for water if either of their water bottles is less than half full. Josan's bottle is $\frac{2}{5}$ full. Andrea's bottle is $\frac{5}{6}$ full. Should they stop? Explain.

Show your work.

Solution: _____

_____

_____

    ©Curriculum Associates, LLC   Copying is not permitted.

Name: _____

Estimate using Benchmark Fractions

Study the example problem showing how to estimate a sum using benchmark fractions. Then solve problems 1–5.

Example

David grew $1\frac{3}{4}$ inches last year and $1\frac{5}{8}$ inches this year. Estimate how much he grew in the two years.

You can estimate $1\frac{3}{4} + 1\frac{5}{8}$ using benchmark fractions. The number line below shows common fractions used as benchmark fractions to estimate sums and differences.

$1\frac{3}{4}$ is already one of the benchmark fractions, so just estimate $1\frac{5}{8}$.

$1\frac{5}{8}$ is a little greater than $1\frac{1}{2}$. Estimate using $1\frac{1}{2}$.

$1\frac{3}{4} + 1\frac{1}{2} = 1\frac{3}{4} + 1\frac{2}{4} = 2\frac{5}{4}$, or $3\frac{1}{4}$.

The sum is a little greater than $3\frac{1}{4}$, so David grew a little more than $3\frac{1}{4}$ inches.

1　Look at the example problem. Explain how you know $1\frac{5}{8}$ is a little greater than $1\frac{1}{2}$.

_____

2　Find the actual sum of $1\frac{3}{4} + 1\frac{5}{8}$ to determine how much David grew in two years. Explain how you know your answer is reasonable.

Show your work.

Solution: _____

_____

Solve.

Irene makes $4\frac{2}{3}$ cups of pancake batter. She splits the batter into 2 bowls. She mixes blueberries into $2\frac{1}{4}$ cups of batter and walnuts into the rest of the batter.

3 Estimate how much of the batter has walnuts in it. Explain your estimate.

_____

_____

4 Find the actual amount of batter that has walnuts in it. Explain how you know your answer is reasonable.

Show your work.

Solution: _____

_____

_____

5 Irene makes a second batch of $3\frac{1}{4}$ cups of pancake batter. She wants to know how much more batter she made in the first batch. She estimates that the difference between the sizes of the two batches $4\frac{2}{3} - 3\frac{1}{4}$ is $2\frac{1}{12}$. Explain why this estimate is *not* reasonable.

_____

_____

_____

_____

 ©Curriculum Associates, LLC   Copying is not permitted.

Name: _____

Add and Subtract Fractions in Word Problems

Solve the problems.

1   Write the missing numbers to show equivalent fractions for some common numbers used as benchmarks.

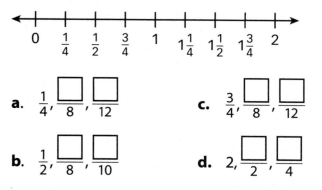

a. $\dfrac{1}{4}, \dfrac{\Box}{8}, \dfrac{\Box}{12}$

b. $\dfrac{1}{2}, \dfrac{\Box}{8}, \dfrac{\Box}{10}$

c. $\dfrac{3}{4}, \dfrac{\Box}{8}, \dfrac{\Box}{12}$

d. $2, \dfrac{\Box}{2}, \dfrac{\Box}{4}$

Remember to multiply both the numerator and denominator by the same number to show an equivalent fraction.

2   The Graf family made two pizzas. They ate $1\frac{1}{8}$ pizza before watching a movie, and $\frac{1}{2}$ pizza more after the movie. Which is a reasonable estimate for the amount of pizza left?

A   less than $\frac{1}{2}$

C   less than $1\frac{1}{4}$

B   more than $\frac{1}{2}$

D   more than $1\frac{1}{4}$

Tammy chose **A** as the correct answer. How did she get that answer?

Where is $1\frac{1}{8}$ located on the number line?

_____

_____

_____

_____

_____

_____

_____

Solve.

3 Lexi bought $1\frac{2}{5}$ pounds of green grapes and $2\frac{3}{10}$ pounds of red grapes. Grapes are $2.99 a pound. Did Lexi spend more or less than $12 on grapes? Explain.

_____

_____

_____

_____

_____

_____

> Do I need to find the actual number of pounds of grapes, or can I answer the question using an estimate?

4 On Monday Marco practiced the piano for $\frac{7}{10}$ hour. On Tuesday he practiced for $1\frac{5}{6}$ hours. He is supposed to practice $1\frac{1}{4}$ hours each day.

Use this information to write a question that involves adding or subtracting fractions.

_____

_____

> What fractions can I use to write an addition or subtraction question?

5 Look at the question you wrote in problem 4. Show how to estimate the answer. Then find the actual answer.

Show your work.

> What benchmark fractions could I use to estimate?

Solution: _____

©Curriculum Associates, LLC   Copying is not permitted.

Dear Family,

This week your child is learning how fractions and division are related.

He or she might see a problem like this:

> Three family members equally share 5 granola bars. How much does each family member receive?

This word problem can be represented as a division problem. The family equally shares 5 granola bars among 3 people, so the division problem to solve is $5 \div 3$.

A model is a useful way to show the problem.
The model below shows 5 wholes. Each whole is divided into 3 parts.

Each family member receives $\frac{1}{3}$ of each of 5 whole bars. So, the answer to the division problem $5 \div 3$ is $\frac{5}{3}$. You can say that the fraction $\frac{5}{3}$ represents the division problem $5 \div 3$.

$$\frac{1}{3} \times 5 = \frac{5}{3}$$

This shows how fractions and division are related.
You can think of fractions as the division of two numbers.

Another way to write the fraction $\frac{5}{3}$ is to show it as a mixed number. So each family member receives $\frac{5}{3}$, or $1\frac{2}{3}$, granola bars.

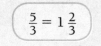

$$\frac{5}{3} = 1\frac{2}{3}$$

Invite your child to share what he or she knows about how fractions and division are related by doing the following activity together.

NEXT

©Curriculum Associates, LLC   Copying is not permitted.   **Lesson 12** Fractions as Division   **119**

Fractions as Division Activity

Work with your child to find opportunities to practice modeling a division situation as a fraction.

- Together with your child, think of things that can be shared equally among family members, such as boxes of crackers or raisins, or bags of grapes or trail mix.

- Choose one idea. Work together with your child to show how to equally divide a number of the items among the people in your family.

  - Example: 4 family members equally share 7 bags of trail mix.

- Have your child write the idea as a division problem.

  - Example: $7 \div 4 = \frac{7}{4}$

- Have your child explain how much of the item each family member will get.

  - Example: Each person will get $\frac{7}{4}$, or $1\frac{3}{4}$, bags of trail mix.

©Curriculum Associates, LLC   Copying is not permitted.

Fractions as Division

Name: _____

Study the example problem showing how to write a fraction greater than 1 as a mixed number. Then solve problems 1–5.

Example

Ms. Sud uses $\frac{3}{4}$ foot of blue ribbon on a costume she is making for a recital. How many feet of ribbon will she need to make 5 costumes?

$5 \times \frac{3}{4} = \frac{15}{4}$

You can use a number line to write $\frac{15}{4}$ as a mixed number.

$$\frac{15}{4}$$

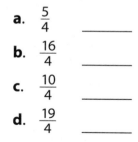

Remember that 1 whole is $\frac{4}{4}$.

$\frac{15}{4}$ is 3 wholes $+ \frac{3}{4}$ of a whole. Write this as the mixed number $3\frac{3}{4}$.

Ms. Sud will need $3\frac{3}{4}$ feet of blue ribbon.

1 Use the number line in the example problem to help you write each fraction as a mixed number or a whole number.

   a. $\frac{5}{4}$ _____

   b. $\frac{16}{4}$ _____

   c. $\frac{10}{4}$ _____

   d. $\frac{19}{4}$ _____

2 You can also use number lines to write mixed numbers as fractions greater than 1. Use the number line in the example problem. Complete the equation.

$2\frac{3}{4} = \dfrac{\boxed{}}{4}$

Solve.

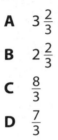 Write a mixed number and a fraction greater than 1
for each point on the number line.

a. _____, _____

b. _____, _____

c. _____, _____

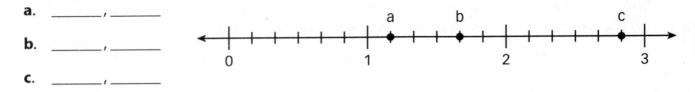

4 Which number represents the amount shaded in the
model? Circle the letter for all that apply.

A $3\frac{2}{3}$

B $2\frac{2}{3}$

C $\frac{8}{3}$

D $\frac{7}{3}$

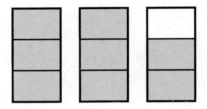

5 Brett lives $\frac{3}{10}$ mile from school. If he rides his bike to
and from school each day, Monday to Friday, how
many miles does he ride?

Show your work.

Solution: _____

©Curriculum Associates, LLC   Copying is not permitted.

Name: _____

Find Fraction Quotients

Study the example problem showing whole number division with a fraction quotient. Then solve problems 1–5.

Example

There are 4 packages of printer paper to be divided equally among 6 classrooms. How much paper will each classroom get?

There are 4 packages for 6 classrooms to share, which is $4 \div 6$.

If you divide each package into sixths, each classroom would get one sixth of each package. $\frac{1}{6}$ of each package from 4 packages is the same as $\frac{4}{6}$ of a package.

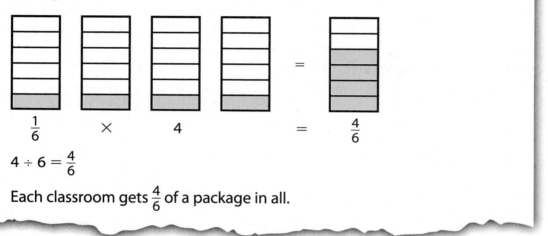

$$\frac{1}{6} \quad \times \quad 4 \quad = \quad \frac{4}{6}$$

$4 \div 6 = \frac{4}{6}$

Each classroom gets $\frac{4}{6}$ of a package in all.

1 Look at the example problem. Which statement is true about the amount of printer paper each classroom gets?

A It is more than $\frac{1}{2}$ package.

B It is less than $\frac{1}{2}$ package.

C It is equal to $\frac{1}{2}$ package.

D It is more than 1 package.

2 Suppose only 5 classrooms share 4 packages of printer paper. How would the model in the example problem change? How would the answer change?

_____

_____

Lesson 12 Fractions as Division   **123**

Solve.

3 Trish is taking care of the Han family's dogs. The Hans leave 7 cans of dog food for the 3 days they'll be away. How much food will the dogs get each day if Trish feeds them an equal amount each day?

Show your work.

Solution: _____

4 Look at problem 3. How many more cans of dog food would Trish need if she needed to feed the dogs 3 cans each day? Explain.

_____

_____

_____

_____

_____

5 Gus is making 48 ounces of spiced cider. If he serves an equal amount to 7 people, will each person get more than 1 cup of cider or less than 1 cup?

Show your work.

I know that 1 cup is the same as 8 ounces.

Solution: _____

©Curriculum Associates, LLC   Copying is not permitted.

Name: _____

Fractions as Division

Solve the problems.

1 Jack is sharing 3 bananas with 3 friends. Which expression represents the amount each one will get if they share them equally? Circle the letter for all that apply.

If Jack shares with 3 friends, how many people are sharing the bananas?

A $3 \times \frac{1}{3}$　　　　**C** $\frac{3}{4}$

B $3 \times \frac{1}{4}$　　　　**D** $1\frac{1}{3}$

2 Elaine is decorating for a party. She cuts 3 equal-length streamers from a strip of purple paper that is 8 feet long. How long is each streamer? Circle the letter of the correct answer.

If the paper was 9 feet long, each streamer would be 3 feet long. Since 8 is less than 9, they must be less than 3 feet long.

A $2\frac{2}{3}$ feet

B $1\frac{3}{8}$ feet

C $\frac{2}{3}$ feet

D $\frac{3}{8}$ feet

Zane chose **C** as the correct answer. How did he get that answer?

_____

_____

_____

_____

©Curriculum Associates, LLC　Copying is not permitted.

Solve.

3 Four 5th graders are taking turns visiting a 2nd grade classroom to read aloud from a chapter book. The book has 38 pages. If they each read the same number of pages, how many pages will each one read?

Show your work.

Will each student read more or less than 10 pages?

Solution: _____

4 Rafiq is making a fruit punch using 48 ounces of grape juice and some seltzer water. He wants to make 10 equal servings that are at least 9 ounces each. Should he add 32 or 48 ounces of seltzer water? Explain.

Show your work.

How much fruit punch will Rafiq have in all if he adds 32 ounces of seltzer water? 48 ounces?

Solution: _____

_____

_____

_____

_____

_____

 ©Curriculum Associates, LLC Copying is not permitted.

Dear Family,

This week your child is exploring products of fractions.

He or she might see a problem like this:

> If $\frac{2}{3}$ of the gym floor has been cleaned and students can play on $\frac{3}{4}$ of the cleaned floor, what part of the whole gym floor can the students play on?

To solve the problem, you multiply $\frac{3}{4} \times \frac{2}{3}$.

An area model can help you visualize the problem.

The first model shows $\frac{1}{4}$ and $\frac{1}{3}$ of the same whole.

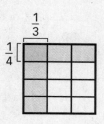

Each row shows $\frac{1}{4}$ of the whole.
Each column shows $\frac{1}{3}$ of the whole.
The part shaded dark green shows
$\frac{1}{4}$ of $\frac{1}{3}$ of the whole.

The second model shows $\frac{3}{4}$ and $\frac{2}{3}$ of the same whole.

3 rows show $\frac{3}{4}$ of the whole.
2 columns show $\frac{2}{3}$ of the whole.
The part shaded dark green shows
$\frac{3}{4}$ of $\frac{2}{3}$ of the whole.

The model is divided into 12 equal parts, 6 of which are shaded dark green.

$\frac{6}{12}$ of the whole is shaded dark green. So, $\frac{3}{4} \times \frac{2}{3} = \frac{6}{12}$.

Students can play on $\frac{6}{12}$, or $\frac{1}{2}$, of the gym floor.

Invite your child to share what he or she knows about products of fractions by doing the following activity together.

©Curriculum Associates, LLC   Copying is not permitted.

Materials: 2 different colors of crayons or colored pencils, number cube

- Together with your child, use the blank rectangle at the bottom of the page to show the product of fraction multiplication.

- One person rolls the number cube. This number tells how many equal parts to show in the rectangle. Draw vertical lines to show the equal parts.

  - Example: Roll a 6 and draw vertical lines to show 6 equal parts in the rectangle.

- The same person shades a fraction of the rectangle and names that fraction.

  - Example: Shade $\frac{5}{6}$.

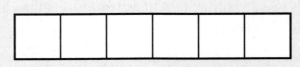

- The other person rolls the number cube. This number tells how many equal parts to show in the same rectangle. Draw horizontal lines to show the equal parts.

  - Example: Roll a 2 and draw a horizontal line to show 2 equal parts (top and bottom) of the rectangle.

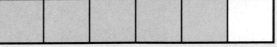

- The same person shades the parts that overlap.

- Together, write the fraction multiplication that the picture shows.

  - Example: $\frac{1}{2} \times \frac{5}{6} = \frac{5}{12}$

©Curriculum Associates, LLC   Copying is not permitted.

Name: _____

Prerequisite: How do you multiply a fraction by a whole number?

Study the example showing multiplying a fraction by a whole number. Then solve problems 1–8.

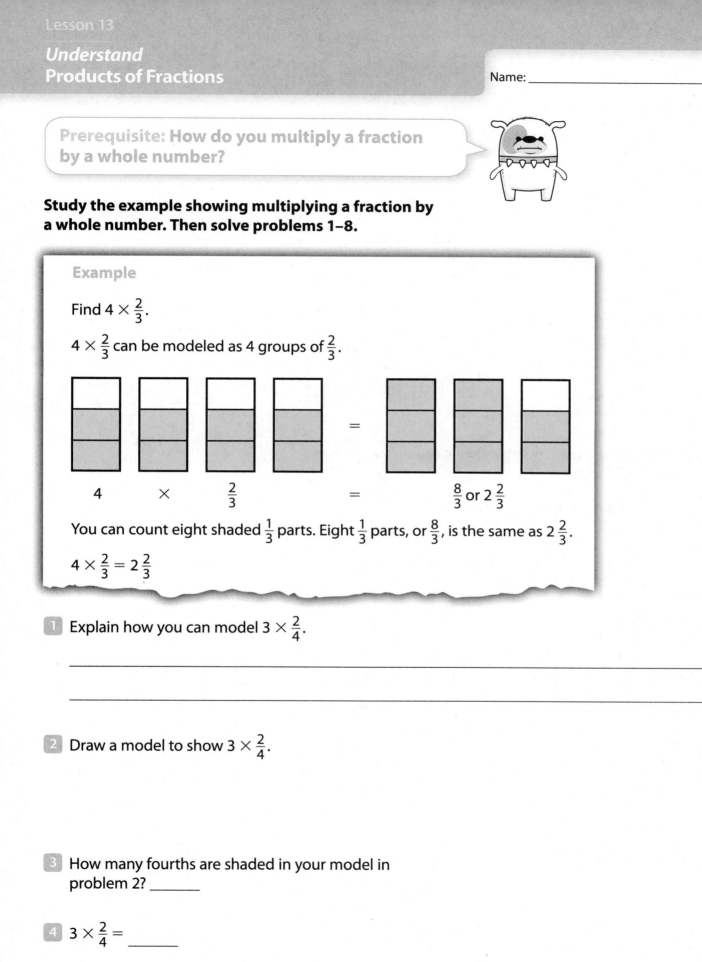

Example

Find $4 \times \frac{2}{3}$.

$4 \times \frac{2}{3}$ can be modeled as 4 groups of $\frac{2}{3}$.

$$4 \quad \times \quad \frac{2}{3} \quad = \quad \frac{8}{3} \text{ or } 2\frac{2}{3}$$

You can count eight shaded $\frac{1}{3}$ parts. Eight $\frac{1}{3}$ parts, or $\frac{8}{3}$, is the same as $2\frac{2}{3}$.

$4 \times \frac{2}{3} = 2\frac{2}{3}$

1 Explain how you can model $3 \times \frac{2}{4}$.

_____

_____

2 Draw a model to show $3 \times \frac{2}{4}$.

3 How many fourths are shaded in your model in problem 2? _____

4 $3 \times \frac{2}{4} =$ _____

©Curriculum Associates, LLC   Copying is not permitted.

Solve.

5 What might a model for $3 \times \frac{3}{5}$ look like? How many fifths would be shaded in all?

_____

_____

_____

_____

6 Fill in the blanks to write a multiplication problem for the model shown to the right.

$\boxed{} \times \frac{1}{5} = \boxed{}$

7 You can also use a number line to multiply a fraction by a whole number.

Label the number line below and use it to show $3 \times \frac{3}{5}$.

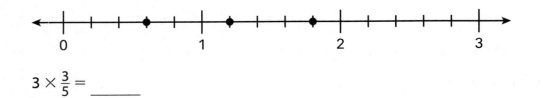

$3 \times \frac{3}{5} =$ _____

8 Tristan jogs a route that is $\frac{7}{10}$ mile. If he wants to jog between 2 and 3 miles, how many times should he plan to run the route? Circle the letter for all that apply.

A 2 times

B 3 times

C 4 times

D 5 times

   ©Curriculum Associates, LLC   Copying is not permitted.

Name: _____

Multiply a Fraction by a Fraction

Study the example showing multiplying a fraction by a fraction. Then solve problems 1–6.

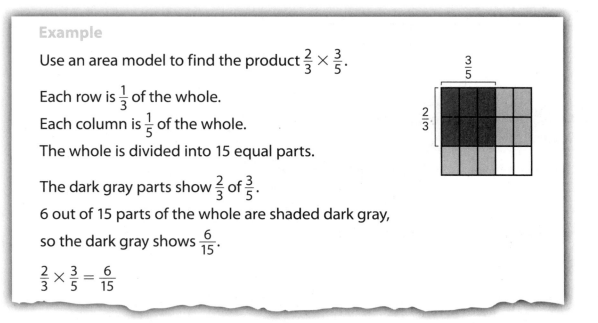

Example

Use an area model to find the product $\frac{2}{3} \times \frac{3}{5}$.

Each row is $\frac{1}{3}$ of the whole.

Each column is $\frac{1}{5}$ of the whole.

The whole is divided into 15 equal parts.

The dark gray parts show $\frac{2}{3}$ of $\frac{3}{5}$.

6 out of 15 parts of the whole are shaded dark gray,

so the dark gray shows $\frac{6}{15}$.

$$\frac{2}{3} \times \frac{3}{5} = \frac{6}{15}$$

1 Why are fifteenths shown in the example model?

_____

_____

2 Use the area model in the example to write the product.

$\frac{1}{3} \times \frac{3}{5} =$ _____

$\frac{2}{3} \times \frac{4}{5} =$ _____

$\frac{3}{3} \times \frac{2}{5} =$ _____

3 Choose *Yes* or *No* to tell whether the denominator of each product is twelfths.

a. $\frac{1}{2} \times \frac{1}{6}$ ☐ Yes ☐ No

b. $\frac{3}{4} \times \frac{2}{5}$ ☐ Yes ☐ No

c. $\frac{1}{4} \times \frac{2}{3}$ ☐ Yes ☐ No

d. $\frac{5}{6} \times \frac{2}{2}$ ☐ Yes ☐ No

> *The denominator of the product is the same as the product of the denominators of the factors.*

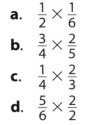

©Curriculum Associates, LLC   Copying is not permitted.

Solve.

4 The number line shows $\frac{1}{2} \times \frac{3}{4}$.

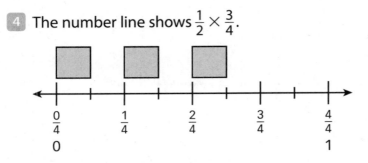

a. Each fourth on the number line is divided into how many equal parts? _____

b. Each of these parts is what fraction of the whole?

_____

c. How many eighths of the whole are shaded?

_____

d. $\frac{1}{2} \times \frac{3}{4} =$ _____

5 Use the area model. Write the product.

a. $\frac{1}{3} \times \frac{1}{3} =$ _____

b. $\frac{1}{3} \times \frac{2}{3} =$ _____

c. $\frac{2}{3} \times \frac{2}{3} =$ _____

d. $\frac{3}{3} \times \frac{2}{3} =$ _____

e. $\frac{3}{3} \times \frac{3}{3} =$ _____

6 Choose whether the statement is *True* or *False* for the product of $\frac{2}{4} \times \frac{3}{5}$.

a. The denominator is 20. ☐ True ☐ False

b. The denominator is 9. ☐ True ☐ False

c. The product is less than either factor. ☐ True ☐ False

d. The product is greater than either factor. ☐ True ☐ False

  ©Curriculum Associates, LLC Copying is not permitted.

Name: _____

Reason and Write

Study the example. Underline two parts that you think make it a particularly good answer and a helpful example.

Example

Draw a model to represent $\frac{2}{3} \times \frac{4}{5}$. Find the product and then explain how your model shows the product of $\frac{2}{3} \times \frac{4}{5}$.

Show your work. Use models, words, and numbers to explain your answer.

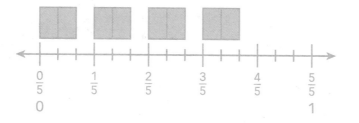

Where does the example . . .
- draw a model?
- find the product?
- use words to explain?

I drew a number line from 0 — 1 divided into fifths, to

show $\frac{4}{5}$. I am multiplying $\frac{4}{5}$ by $\frac{2}{3}$ so I divide each fifth

into thirds. That makes 15 equal parts in the whole.

Each equal part is 1 fifteenth of the whole.

To show $\frac{2}{3} \times \frac{4}{5}$, in each fifth, I shade $\frac{2}{3}$ of the parts.

Four of the fifths are $\frac{2}{3}$ shaded. That means there are

2 fifteenths shaded in each section. That is 2 × 4, or

8 fifteenths shaded in all. So, $\frac{2}{3} \times \frac{4}{5} = \frac{8}{15}$.

©Curriculum Associates, LLC   Copying is not permitted.

Solve the problem. Use what you learned from the model.

Draw a model to represent $\frac{3}{4} \times \frac{3}{5}$. Find the product and then explain how your model shows the product of $\frac{3}{4} \times \frac{3}{5}$.

Show your work. Use models, words, and numbers to explain your answer.

Did you . . .
• draw a model?
• find the product?
• use words to explain?

©Curriculum Associates, LLC   Copying is not permitted.

Dear Family,

This week your child is learning to multiply fractions using an area model.

He or she might see a problem like this:

Mark has a square placemat that measures 1 foot on each side. He divides it in half vertically and in fourths horizontally. He wants to decorate each part with a different pattern. What is the area of each part of the placemat?

To understand the problem, your child could draw and label a picture.

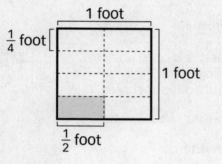

The dashed lines show 8 equal parts. Each part is $\frac{1}{2}$ foot wide and $\frac{1}{4}$ foot long. Each part is $\frac{1}{8}$ of the whole. Multiply to find the area of each part. The area of each part of the placemat is $\frac{1}{8}$ square foot.

$$\frac{1}{2} \text{ foot} \times \frac{1}{4} \text{ foot} = \frac{1}{8} \text{ square foot}$$

Invite your child to share what he or she knows about multiplying fractions with area models by doing the following activity together.

NEXT

Materials: a bowl and the ingredients shown in the recipe

- Look at the recipe for snack mix below.

- Rewrite the recipe so that it will make one-fourth as much by multiplying the amount of each ingredient by $\frac{1}{4}$. This will make a small amount.

- Make the recipe and enjoy!

Recipe for Snack Mix

Ingredients:

$\frac{2}{4}$ cup pretzels

$\frac{3}{4}$ cup nuts of your choice

$\frac{1}{2}$ cup raisins

$\frac{2}{3}$ cup dried fruit

$\frac{1}{3}$ cup chocolate chips (optional)

Directions:

Mix all ingredients in a bowl.

 ©Curriculum Associates, LLC Copying is not permitted.

Multiply Fractions Using an Area Model

Name: _____

Study the example problem showing a model of multiplying a fraction by a fraction. Then solve problems 1–7.

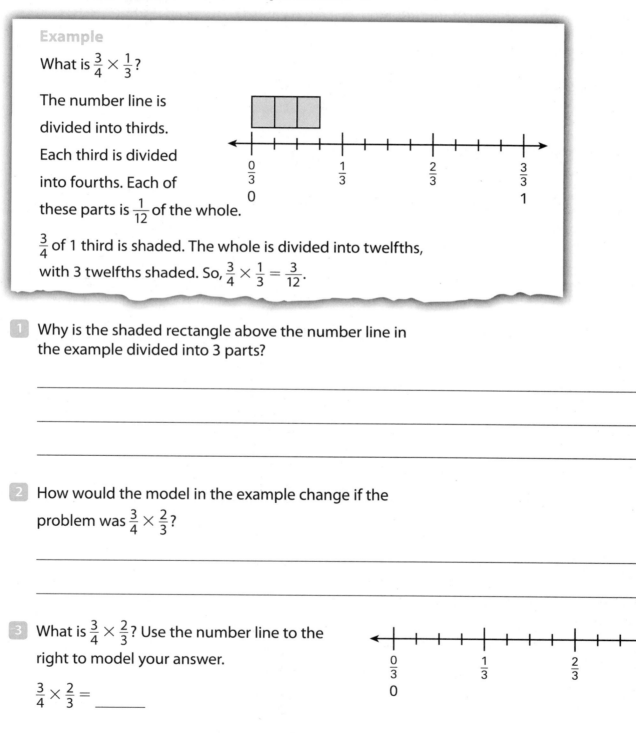

Example

What is $\frac{3}{4} \times \frac{1}{3}$?

The number line is divided into thirds. Each third is divided into fourths. Each of these parts is $\frac{1}{12}$ of the whole.

$\frac{3}{4}$ of 1 third is shaded. The whole is divided into twelfths, with 3 twelfths shaded. So, $\frac{3}{4} \times \frac{1}{3} = \frac{3}{12}$.

1 Why is the shaded rectangle above the number line in the example divided into 3 parts?

_____

_____

_____

2 How would the model in the example change if the problem was $\frac{3}{4} \times \frac{2}{3}$?

_____

_____

3 What is $\frac{3}{4} \times \frac{2}{3}$? Use the number line to the right to model your answer.

$\frac{3}{4} \times \frac{2}{3} =$ _____

Solve.

4 Look at the model and answer the following questions.

Each column is what fraction of the whole? _____

Each row is what fraction of the whole? _____

How many parts are in the whole? _____

The dark gray parts show $\frac{3}{4}$ of $\frac{1}{3}$. What fraction of the whole is $\frac{3}{4} \times \frac{1}{3}$? _____

What is the product of $\frac{3}{4} \times \frac{1}{3}$? _____

$$\frac{1}{3}$$

$$\frac{3}{4}$$

5 Shade and label the model to show $\frac{3}{4} \times \frac{2}{3}$. Complete the equation.

$$\frac{3}{4} \times \frac{2}{3} = \frac{\boxed{}}{\boxed{}}$$

6 $\frac{6}{12}$ is equal to $\frac{1}{2}$. How does the model you shaded in problem 6 show that?

_____

_____

_____

_____

_____

7 Write a fraction from the box to complete the expression. Then complete the model to show the problem.

$$\frac{\boxed{}}{\boxed{}} \times \frac{1}{5}$$

$$\frac{1}{5}$$

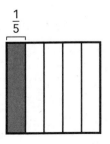

©Curriculum Associates, LLC   Copying is not permitted.

Name: _____

Multiply Unit Fractions to Find Areas

Study the example problem showing multiplying unit fractions to find area. Then solve problems 1–5.

Example

Cardboard that measures 1 meter on each side is cut into cards that are $\frac{1}{10}$-meter wide and $\frac{1}{2}$-meter long. What is the area of each card?

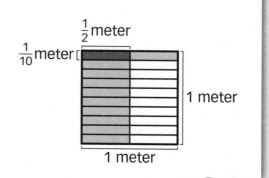

You can model the problem with a picture:

You can model the problem with an equation.

$$\text{area} = \frac{1}{2} \times \frac{1}{10} = \frac{1 \times 1}{2 \times 10} = \frac{1}{20} \text{ square meter}$$

1 Suppose the length of each card in the example problem is shortened to $\frac{1}{4}$ meter. Will the area of each card now be greater or less than $\frac{1}{20}$ square meter? Explain.

_____

_____

_____

_____

_____

2 Which expression represents the area of a card described in problem 1?

A $\frac{1}{2} \times \frac{1}{4}$ **C** $\frac{1}{4} \times \frac{1}{10}$

B $\frac{1}{2} \times \frac{1}{10}$ **D** $\frac{1}{4} \times \frac{1}{20}$

©Curriculum Associates, LLC   Copying is not permitted.

Solve.

3 What is the area of a card that is $\frac{1}{10}$-meter wide and $\frac{1}{4}$-meter long?

Show your work.

Solution: _____

4 Mr. Von's 5th-grade class is going on a field trip. Each student is given a name card to wear that is $\frac{1}{4}$-foot wide and $\frac{1}{3}$-foot long.

Shade the model to find the area of each name card. Complete the equation.

$\frac{1}{4}$-foot $\times$ $\frac{1}{3}$-foot $= \dfrac{\boxed{}}{\boxed{}}$ square foot

$\frac{1}{3}$ foot

$\frac{1}{4}$ foot

1 foot

1 foot

5 Signs for science project displays are cut from pieces of poster board that measure 1 yard on each side. Each sign is $\frac{1}{3}$-yard long and $\frac{1}{9}$-yard wide. How many signs can be cut from 1 piece of poster board? What is the area of each sign?

Show your work.

How can you draw an area model to solve this problem?

Solution: _____

©Curriculum Associates, LLC   Copying is not permitted.

Name: _____

Multiply Fractions Greater than One

Study the example problem showing multiplying fractions greater than 1. Then solve problems 1–6.

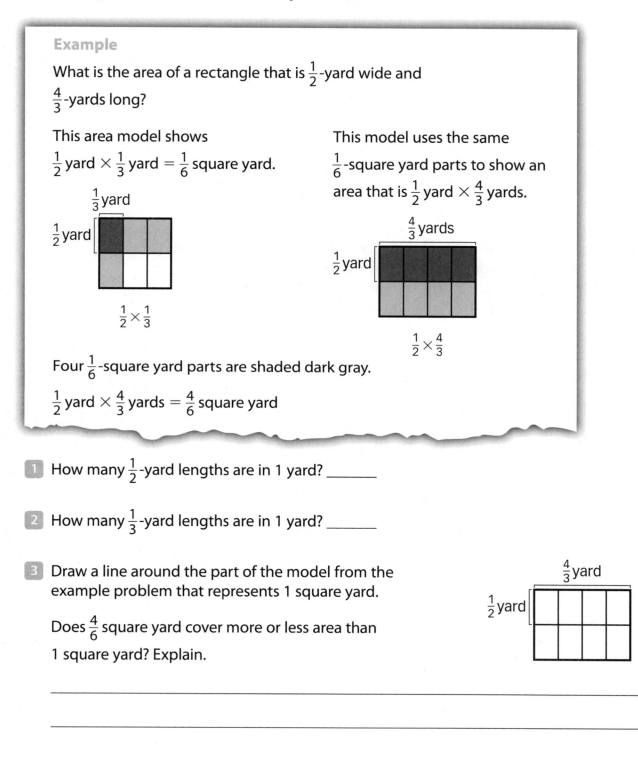

Example

What is the area of a rectangle that is $\frac{1}{2}$-yard wide and $\frac{4}{3}$-yards long?

This area model shows $\frac{1}{2}$ yard $\times \frac{1}{3}$ yard $= \frac{1}{6}$ square yard.

$\frac{1}{3}$ yard

$\frac{1}{2}$ yard

$\frac{1}{2} \times \frac{1}{3}$

This model uses the same $\frac{1}{6}$-square yard parts to show an area that is $\frac{1}{2}$ yard $\times \frac{4}{3}$ yards.

$\frac{4}{3}$ yards

$\frac{1}{2}$ yard

$\frac{1}{2} \times \frac{4}{3}$

Four $\frac{1}{6}$-square yard parts are shaded dark gray.

$\frac{1}{2}$ yard $\times \frac{4}{3}$ yards $= \frac{4}{6}$ square yard

1 How many $\frac{1}{2}$-yard lengths are in 1 yard? _____

2 How many $\frac{1}{3}$-yard lengths are in 1 yard? _____

3 Draw a line around the part of the model from the example problem that represents 1 square yard.

Does $\frac{4}{6}$ square yard cover more or less area than 1 square yard? Explain.

$\frac{4}{3}$ yard

$\frac{1}{2}$ yard

_____

_____

_____

Lesson 14 Multiply Fractions Using an Area Model   **141**

Solve.

4 Danah has a strawberry patch in her garden. Its border is $\frac{4}{5}$-meters wide and $\frac{3}{2}$-meters long. What is the area of Danah's strawberry patch?

Show your work.

Solution: _____

5 Danah is planting a second strawberry patch and wants it to have an area of exactly 1 square meter. Which of the following could be the width and length of its borders? Circle the letter for all that apply.

A $\frac{1}{2}$-meter wide and $\frac{3}{2}$-meters long

B $\frac{2}{3}$-meter wide and $\frac{3}{2}$-meters long

C $\frac{4}{5}$-meter wide and $\frac{5}{4}$-meters long

D $\frac{2}{3}$-meter wide and $\frac{6}{4}$-meters long

> If I find the area of each different shape strawberry patch, I can figure out which options have an area of 1 square meter.

6 Look at problem 5. If Danah wants her strawberry patch to be exactly 1 square meter, can the length of her strawberry patch be greater than 1 meter? Explain.

_____

_____

_____

_____

_____

 ©Curriculum Associates, LLC   Copying is not permitted.

Name: _____

Multiply Fractions to Find Area

Solve the problems.

1 Owen has a square sheet of paper that measures 1 foot on each side. He folds the paper vertically and horizontally so that it makes equal sections. The model shows the unfolded paper. Which expression represents the area of 1 section?

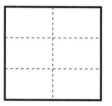

If each side of the paper is 1-foot long, how wide is each section? How long?

A $\frac{1}{3} \times \frac{1}{3}$ square feet

C $\frac{1}{2} \times \frac{1}{3}$ square foot

B $\frac{2}{1} \times \frac{1}{3}$ square foot

D $\frac{3}{1} \times \frac{1}{2}$ square foot

2 What is the area of a rectangle with a length of $\frac{7}{5}$ meter and a width of $\frac{5}{10}$ meter?

A $\frac{35}{50}$ square meter

B $\frac{50}{35}$ square meter

C $\frac{12}{15}$ square meter

D $\frac{12}{10}$ square meters

If I draw a model that is 1 square meter divided into fifths and tenths, what is the area of each small part?

Patsy chose **C** as the correct answer. How did she get that answer?

_____

_____

_____

_____

_____

Lesson 14 Multiply Fractions Using an Area Model   **143**

Solve.

3 Each expression below shows the length and width of a rectangle in yards. Write each expression in the correct box according to the area it represents.

$\dfrac{2}{3} \times \dfrac{3}{5}$ $\qquad$ $\dfrac{2}{3} \times \dfrac{5}{3}$ $\qquad$ $\dfrac{1}{2} \times \dfrac{9}{10}$

$\dfrac{1}{4} \times \dfrac{4}{1}$ $\qquad$ $\dfrac{1}{4} \times \dfrac{5}{3}$ $\qquad$ $\dfrac{4}{3} \times \dfrac{6}{8}$

Area less than 1 square yard	Area equal to 1 square yard	Area greater than 1 square yard

How do the numerator and denominator compare in a fraction less than 1? A fraction equal to 1? A fraction greater than 1?

4 Pick one of the expressions from problem 3. Draw an area model to represent the expression.

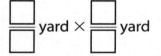 yard × yard

If I choose $\dfrac{1}{4} \times \dfrac{5}{3}$, how many rows should I draw in my area model? How many columns?

5 Write an equation to show the area of the rectangle in problem 4.

I already figured out whether the area is less than, greater than, or equal to 1 square yard in problem 3.

©Curriculum Associates, LLC   Copying is not permitted.

Dear Family,

This week your child is exploring multiplication as scaling.

Scaling is changing the size of a quantity by increasing or decreasing it by a certain amount. You can think of scaling as stretching or shrinking.

You can multiply by a number greater than 1 to *increase* the size of a quantity. Multiply by a number less than 1 to *decrease* the size of a quantity.

Look at the size of the rectangle at the right. It has an area of 6 square units.
$1 \times 6 = 6$ square units

If you multiply by 2, you double the size of the rectangle.
$2 \times 6 = 12$ square units

This rectangle is twice as big as the first rectangle.

If you multiply by $\frac{1}{2}$, you shrink the rectangle to half its original size.
$\frac{1}{2} \times 6 = \frac{6}{2} = 3$

The shaded rectangle is half as big as the first rectangle.

Your child is learning to generalize about multiplication and scaling. Multiplying by a number . . .

- greater than 1 increases the quantity.

- less than 1 decreases the quantity.

- equal to 1, such as $\frac{4}{4}$, means that the quantity stays the same.

Invite your child to share what he or she knows about multiplication as scaling by doing the following activity together.

NEXT

©Curriculum Associates, LLC   Copying is not permitted.

Multiplication as Scaling Activity

Use the examples below to talk with your child about multiplication as scaling.

- This is the actual size of a pencil that is 4 centimeters long.

actual size

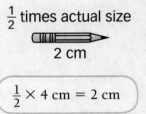

4 cm

- What if the pencil were twice as long? How long would it be? It would be two times the size of the original pencil. It would be longer because multiplying by 2 is multiplying by a number greater than 1.

2×4 cm $= 8$ cm

2 times actual size

8 cm

- What if the pencil were half as long? How long would it be? It would be half the size of the original pencil. It would be shorter because multiplying by $\frac{1}{2}$ is multiplying by a number less than 1.

$\frac{1}{2}$ **times actual size**

2 cm

$\frac{1}{2} \times 4$ cm $= 2$ cm

- Ask your child these questions.

  - What if the pencil were 3 times as long? Would it be shorter or longer than the original pencil? How do you know? (longer, because 3 is greater than 1; 3×4 cm $= 12$ cm)

  - What if the pencil were $\frac{3}{4}$ as long? Would it be shorter or longer? How do you know? $\left(\text{shorter, because } \frac{3}{4} \text{ is less than 1}; \frac{3}{4} \times 4 = 3 \text{ cm}\right)$

  - What if the pencil were $\frac{4}{4}$ as long? How would the length of the pencil compare to the original pencil? $\left(\frac{4}{4} = 1; \text{ multiplying by 1 means the pencil would be the same size.}\right)$

  - What would it mean to multiply the size of the pencil by $\frac{7}{4}$? How would the size of the pencil change? $\left(\text{It would be longer because } \frac{7}{4} \text{ is more than 1}; \frac{7}{4} \times 4 = 7 \text{ cm.}\right)$

 ©Curriculum Associates, LLC   Copying is not permitted.

Understand
Multiplication as Scaling

Name: _____

> Prerequisite: How can you use area models to multiply fractions less than 1 and greater than 1?

Study the example showing one way to multiply by fractions less than 1 and greater than 1. Then solve problems 1–7.

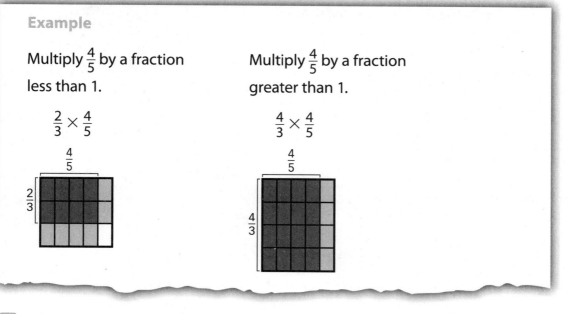

Example

Multiply $\frac{4}{5}$ by a fraction less than 1.

$$\frac{2}{3} \times \frac{4}{5}$$

Multiply $\frac{4}{5}$ by a fraction greater than 1.

$$\frac{4}{3} \times \frac{4}{5}$$

1 Look at the example. Write the products.

$\frac{2}{3} \times \frac{4}{5} =$ _____

$\frac{4}{3} \times \frac{4}{5} =$ _____

2 How are the two models in the example the same? How are they different?

_____

_____

_____

_____

_____

_____

_____

©Curriculum Associates, LLC   Copying is not permitted.

Solve.

3 You can also use area models to show multiplying by a fraction equal to 1.

Use the area model to show $\frac{3}{3} \times \frac{4}{5}$. Then complete the equation.

$$\frac{3}{3} \times \frac{4}{5} = \underline{\hspace{1cm}}$$

4 Which expression is represented by the area model?

A $\frac{3}{4} \times \frac{6}{4}$

B $\frac{1}{4} \times \frac{6}{4}$

C $\frac{3}{4} \times \frac{4}{6}$

D $\frac{1}{4} \times \frac{4}{6}$

5 Use the area model in problem 4 to write the products in the table.

$\frac{1}{4} \times \frac{4}{6} = \underline{\hspace{0.6cm}}$	$\frac{2}{4} \times \frac{4}{6} = \underline{\hspace{0.6cm}}$	$\frac{3}{4} \times \frac{4}{6} = \underline{\hspace{0.6cm}}$	$\frac{4}{4} \times \frac{4}{6} = \underline{\hspace{0.6cm}}$

6 Draw an area model to represent the expression $\frac{5}{4} \times \frac{4}{6}$.

7 Look at the model you drew in problem 6. Complete the equation.

$$\frac{5}{4} \times \frac{4}{6} = \underline{\hspace{1cm}}$$

©Curriculum Associates, LLC   Copying is not permitted.

Name: _____

Compare Factors and Products

Study the example showing how to use a number line to multiply by fractions less than 1 and greater than 1. Then solve problems 1–6.

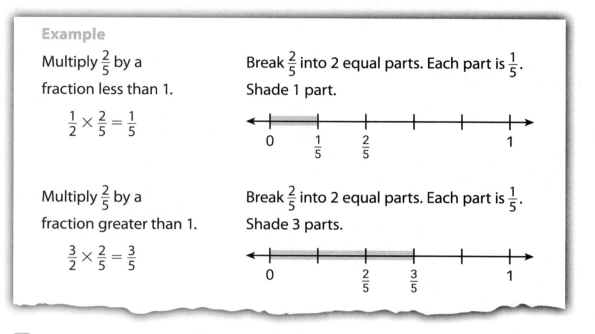

Example

Multiply $\frac{2}{5}$ by a fraction less than 1.

$\frac{1}{2} \times \frac{2}{5} = \frac{1}{5}$

Break $\frac{2}{5}$ into 2 equal parts. Each part is $\frac{1}{5}$. Shade 1 part.

Multiply $\frac{2}{5}$ by a fraction greater than 1.

$\frac{3}{2} \times \frac{2}{5} = \frac{3}{5}$

Break $\frac{2}{5}$ into 2 equal parts. Each part is $\frac{1}{5}$. Shade 3 parts.

1   When you multiply a whole number by a fraction less than 1, the product is less than the whole number. Does the example showing $\frac{1}{2} \times \frac{2}{5}$ support a similar rule when multiplying a fraction by a fraction less than 1? Explain.

_____

_____

2   When you multiply a whole number by a fraction greater than 1, the product is greater than the whole number. Does the example showing $\frac{3}{2} \times \frac{2}{5}$ support a similar rule when multiplying a fraction by a fraction greater than 1? Explain.

_____

_____

    Lesson 15 Understand Multiplication as Scaling   **149**

Solve.

3 Shade the number line to show $\frac{3}{5} \times \frac{5}{8}$.

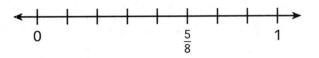

0                      $\frac{5}{8}$ 1

4 Complete the area model to show $\frac{3}{5} \times \frac{5}{8}$.

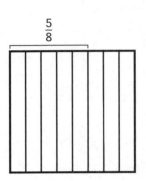

$\frac{5}{8}$

5 Is the product of $\frac{3}{5} \times \frac{5}{8}$ greater or less than $\frac{5}{8}$? Is it easier to compare the product to $\frac{5}{8}$ using the number line or area model? Explain.

_____

_____

_____

_____

_____

6 Fill in the blanks. Use the words in the box.

always	sometimes	never

a. When you multiply a given fraction by a factor greater than 1, the product will _____ be less than the given fraction.

b. When you multiply a given fraction by a factor less than 1, the product will _____ be less than the given fraction.

c. When you multiply a given fraction by a factor greater than 1, the product will _____ be less than 1.

©Curriculum Associates, LLC   Copying is not permitted.

Name: _____

Reason and Write

Study the example. Underline two parts that you think make it a particularly good answer and a helpful example.

Example

Choose a fraction from the box to make the statement true.

The product of _____ $\times \frac{4}{5}$ is greater than $\frac{4}{5}$.

$\frac{1}{4}$	$\frac{6}{4}$
$\frac{3}{4}$	
$\frac{5}{4}$	$\frac{2}{4}$

Then draw a model to show the product. Explain why you chose the fraction you did and how the model you drew supports the statement.

Show your work. Use models, words, and numbers to explain your answer.

I chose $\frac{6}{4}$ because it is greater than 1. I know that the product of a fraction and a number greater than 1 is greater than the fraction.

I drew an area model that shows that the product of $\frac{6}{4} \times \frac{4}{5}$ is $\frac{24}{20}$. $\frac{24}{20}$ is greater than 1. $\frac{4}{5}$ is less than 1, so $\frac{24}{20}$ is greater than $\frac{4}{5}$. This supports the statement that the product of $\frac{6}{4}$ and $\frac{4}{5}$ is greater than $\frac{4}{5}$.

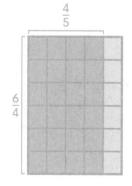

Where does the example . . .

• use words to explain which fraction was chosen?

• use a model to show the product?

• use numbers and words to explain how the model supports the statement?

Solve the problem. Use what you learned from the example.

Choose a fraction from the box to make the statement true.

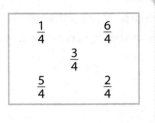

The product of _____ × $\frac{4}{5}$ is less than $\frac{4}{5}$.

Then draw a model to show the product. Explain why you chose the fraction you did and how the model you drew supports the statement.

Show your work. Use models, words, and numbers to explain your answer.

Did you . . .

• use words to explain which fraction was chosen?

• use a model to show the product?

• use numbers and words to explain how the model supports the statement?

©Curriculum Associates, LLC   Copying is not permitted.

Dear Family,

This week your child is learning about multiplying fractions in word problems.

He or she might see a problem like this:

> Michael found $\frac{3}{4}$ of a pizza in the refrigerator. He ate $\frac{2}{3}$ of it. How much of the original whole pizza did Michael eat?

One way to understand this problem is to draw a picture. Your child could draw $\frac{3}{4}$ of a pizza.

To show the part of the pizza that Michael ate, your child could shade 2 of the 3 pieces to show $\frac{2}{3}$.

The shaded parts show how much of the original whole pizza Michael ate. Michael ate $\frac{2}{4}$, or $\frac{1}{2}$, of the original whole pizza.

Another way your child could solve the problem is to write a multiplication equation.

$\frac{2}{3}$ of $\frac{3}{4}$ means $\frac{2}{3} \times \frac{3}{4}$.

$\frac{6}{12}$ is equivalent to $\frac{2}{4}$, or $\frac{1}{2}$.

$$\frac{2}{3} \times \frac{3}{4} = \frac{2 \times 3}{3 \times 4} = \frac{6}{12}$$

The answer is the same using both ways to solve the problem. Michael ate $\frac{1}{2}$ of the original whole pizza.

Invite your child to share what he or she knows about multiplying fractions and word problems by doing the following activity together.

NEXT ⟹

Multiplying Fractions in Word Problems Activity

Together with your child, make up and solve real-world problems about multiplying fractions or use the problems below.

- Here are some example problems:

Pete found $\frac{5}{6}$ of a party sandwich left in the refrigerator. He took $\frac{1}{2}$ of the $\frac{5}{6}$ of the sandwich to his neighbor. How much of the original sandwich did Pete take to his neighbor?

Shawn had $\frac{3}{5}$ of a gallon of paint left in the can. He used $\frac{2}{3}$ of it to paint a cabinet. How much of the gallon of paint did he use?

Renee made some money babysitting. She saved $\frac{3}{4}$ of the money. She spent $\frac{2}{5}$ of the money she saved to buy a shirt. What fraction of the money did Renee spend on the shirt?

©Curriculum Associates, LLC Copying is not permitted.

Multiply Fractions in Word Problems

Name: _____

Prerequisite: Multiply Fractions with Models

Study the example problem showing three ways to model multiplying fractions. Then solve problems 1–6.

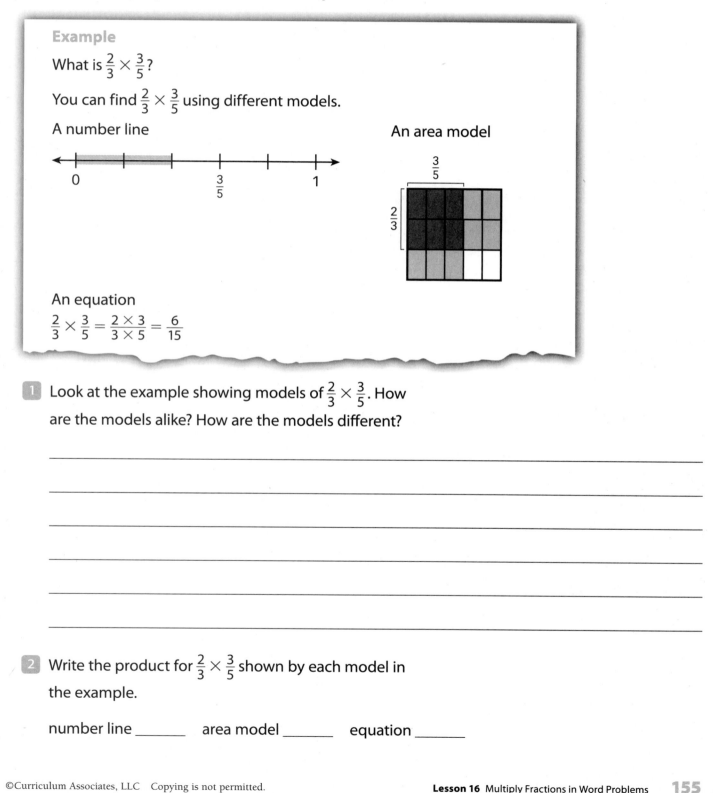

Example

What is $\frac{2}{3} \times \frac{3}{5}$?

You can find $\frac{2}{3} \times \frac{3}{5}$ using different models.

A number line

An area model

An equation

$$\frac{2}{3} \times \frac{3}{5} = \frac{2 \times 3}{3 \times 5} = \frac{6}{15}$$

1 Look at the example showing models of $\frac{2}{3} \times \frac{3}{5}$. How are the models alike? How are the models different?

_____

_____

_____

_____

_____

_____

2 Write the product for $\frac{2}{3} \times \frac{3}{5}$ shown by each model in the example.

number line _____   area model _____   equation _____

©Curriculum Associates, LLC   Copying is not permitted.

Solve.

3 Write the missing numbers that show that $\frac{2}{5}$ and $\frac{6}{15}$ are equivalent fractions.

$$\frac{2 \times \boxed{}}{5 \times \boxed{}} = \frac{6}{15}$$

4 Explain how the numbers you wrote in problem 3 show that $\frac{2}{5}$ and $\frac{6}{15}$ are equivalent.

_____

_____

_____

_____

_____

_____

5 What is $\frac{2}{3} \times \frac{3}{8}$?
   Show your work.

   Solution: _____

6 Check your answer to problem 5 by modeling $\frac{2}{3} \times \frac{3}{8}$ a different way.
   Show your work.

   Solution: _____

  ©Curriculum Associates, LLC   Copying is not permitted.

Name: _____

Solve Word Problems with Fractions

Study the example problem showing one way to solve a word problem with fractions. Then solve problems 1–5.

Example

Vicky's favorite beach towel is green and white and has a fish design. The green part covers $\frac{5}{8}$ of the towel. A fish design is drawn on $\frac{3}{5}$ of that. What part of the towel has a fish design on it?

You can draw a picture.

Show a towel with $\frac{5}{8}$ shaded green.   Draw fish on $\frac{3}{5}$ of the green part.

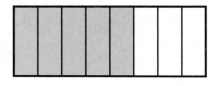   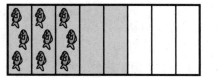

3 of the 8 parts of the towel have fish drawn on them, so $\frac{3}{8}$ of the towel has a fish design on it.

---

1 You can also write an equation to solve the example problem. Write the numbers to complete the equation showing what part of the towel has the fish design.

$\frac{3}{5}$ of $\frac{5}{8}$ means $\frac{3}{5} \times \frac{5}{8}$.

$$\frac{3}{5} \times \frac{\boxed{}}{\boxed{}} = \frac{\boxed{} \times 5}{\boxed{} \times 8} = \frac{\boxed{}}{\boxed{}}$$

2 Is your answer to problem 1 the same as the answer, $\frac{3}{8}$, shown in the example problem? Explain.

_____

_____

_____

Solve.

3 Suppose the green part of Vicky's towel covers $\frac{4}{5}$ of the towel and the fish design is drawn on $\frac{3}{4}$ of that. Draw a picture to find the part of the towel that has the fish design on it. Then write the answer.

Solution: _____

4 Write an equation to show the answer to problem 3.

Solution: _____

5 At noon Ada and Kent had $\frac{3}{8}$ gallon of lemonade left at their lemonade stand. The next customer bought $\frac{1}{3}$ of the remaining lemonade. How much lemonade did the customer buy?

Show your work.

Solution: _____

 ©Curriculum Associates, LLC   Copying is not permitted.

Name: _____

Multiply Mixed Numbers in Word Problems

Study the example problem showing one way to solve a word problem with a mixed number. Then solve problems 1–4.

Example

Mr. Urrego is painting his deck to get it ready for the summer. He's painted an area that is $3\frac{1}{5}$-meters long and $\frac{2}{3}$-meter wide. How many square meters of deck are painted?

You can use an area model.

The larger sections of the area model are $\frac{1}{3} \times 1 = \frac{1}{3}$ square meter.

The smaller sections of the area model are $\frac{1}{3} \times \frac{1}{5} = \frac{1}{15}$ square meter.

$3\frac{1}{5}$ meters

$\frac{2}{3}$ meter

1 meter

The model shows the number of square meters painted is:

$\frac{2}{3} + \frac{2}{3} + \frac{2}{3} + \frac{2}{15} = \frac{6}{3} + \frac{2}{15} = 2 + \frac{2}{15} = 2\frac{2}{15}$

1 Write the missing numbers to complete the multiplication equation showing how much of the deck is painted.

Multiply the length and width of the painted area:

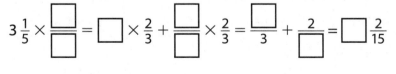

$3\frac{1}{5} \times \dfrac{\square}{\square} = \square \times \frac{2}{3} + \dfrac{\square}{\square} \times \frac{2}{3} = \dfrac{\square}{3} + \dfrac{2}{\square} = \square\frac{2}{15}$

_____ square meters

2 Look at the worked-out solutions in the example and problem 1. Which method do you prefer to solve the problem? Explain why.

_____

_____

_____

©Curriculum Associates, LLC   Copying is not permitted.

Solve.

3 To multiply a mixed number you can also write it first as a fraction and then multiply. Write the missing numbers to show this way of multiplying to find how much of the deck is painted.

Here's the equation you've already used to solve the problem.

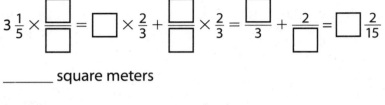

_____ square meters

Now here is a new way to multiply.

Write $3\frac{1}{5}$ as a fraction.   Multiply using $\frac{16}{5}$ as a factor.

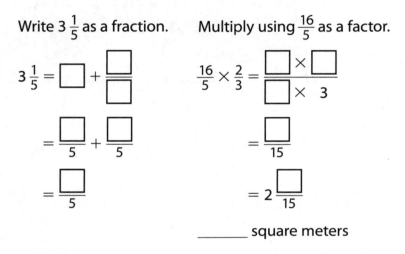

_____ square meters

4 The multipurpose room at the Cortez School is being set up for the annual book sale. Graphic novels will be displayed in an area $1\frac{1}{4}$-yards long and $\frac{3}{4}$-yard wide. Will the graphic novels be displayed in an area greater than or less than 1 square yard?

Show your work.

Solution: _____

Name: _____

Multiply Fractions in Word Problems

Solve the problems.

1. Tell whether each equation showing a mixed number written as a fraction is *True* or *False*

   a. $1\frac{3}{4} = \frac{7}{4}$ ☐ True ☐ False

   b. $4\frac{2}{5} = \frac{22}{5}$ ☐ True ☐ False

   c. $3\frac{2}{3} = \frac{11}{2}$ ☐ True ☐ False

   d. $2\frac{7}{10} = \frac{27}{10}$ ☐ True ☐ False

   How do you know what the denominator is when you write a mixed number as a fraction?

2. Camilla's class played soccer for $\frac{2}{3}$ hour. She played for $\frac{3}{5}$ of the game. How much time did Camilla play?

   A $\frac{5}{15}$ hour   **C** $\frac{5}{8}$ hour

   B $\frac{6}{15}$ hour   **D** $\frac{6}{8}$ hour

   Will chose **A** as the correct answer. How did he get that answer?

   _____

   _____

   _____

   _____

   What equation can I write to solve this problem?

3. How many minutes are in $\frac{2}{3}$ hour? How many minutes are in $\frac{3}{5}$ of that time?

   How many minutes are in an hour?

   Solution: _____

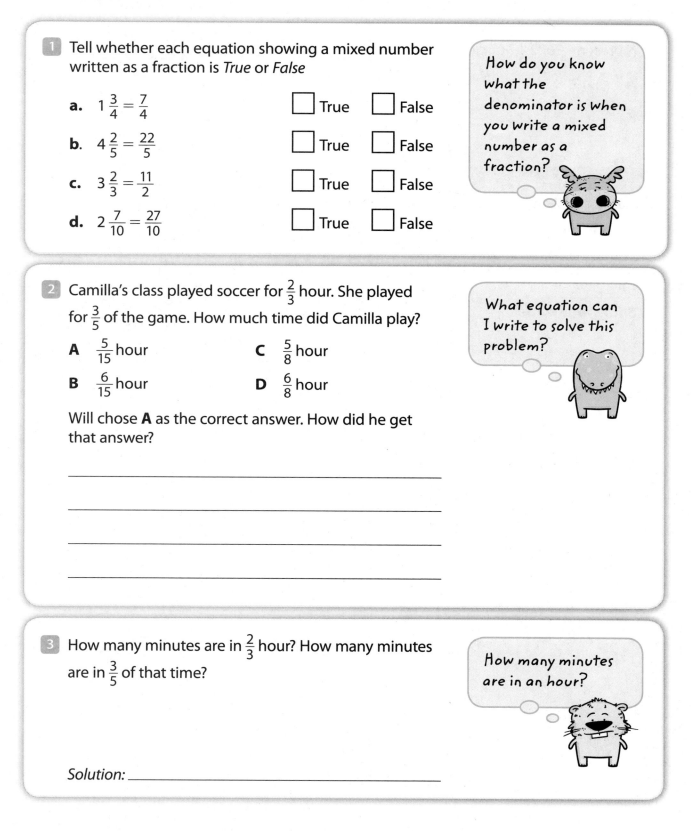

©Curriculum Associates, LLC   Copying is not permitted.

Solve.

4 Caleb has $2\frac{1}{5}$ yards of rope. He uses $\frac{3}{4}$ of the rope to make a dog leash. Which expression can be used to represent $\frac{3}{4}$ of $2\frac{1}{5}$? Circle the letter for all that apply.

A $\frac{3}{4} \times 2 \times \frac{1}{5}$ **C** $\frac{3}{4} \times 2 + \frac{3}{4} \times \frac{1}{5}$

B $\frac{3}{4} \times \frac{11}{5}$ **D** $\frac{3}{4} \times \frac{3}{4} + \frac{1}{5}$

What are other ways to write the mixed number $2\frac{1}{5}$?

5 Dante and 2 classmates are making a poster to advertise a Bike-to-School Day event. It is $1\frac{1}{2}$-yards long and $\frac{3}{4}$-yard wide. How large a writing area does that give them?

Show your work.

What model can I use to help understand this problem?

Solution: _____

6 Manny hiked $6\frac{2}{5}$ miles along a mountain trail. He stopped to climb a lookout tower $\frac{1}{4}$ of the way along his hike. How many miles did Manny hike before he stopped to climb the lookout tower?

Show your work.

Did Manny hike more or less than 1 mile before stopping to climb the tower?

Solution: _____

©Curriculum Associates, LLC   Copying is not permitted.

Dear Family,

This week your child is exploring division with unit fractions.

A unit fraction is a fraction that has 1 as the numerator. $\frac{1}{6}$ and $\frac{1}{4}$ are examples of unit fractions. To learn about division with unit fractions, your child might see a problem like this:

A butcher wants to divide $\frac{1}{4}$ of a pound of meat into 3 equal packages. How much meat does he put in each package?

The division problem is $\frac{1}{4} \div 3$. It can be helpful to use an area model to understand the problem.

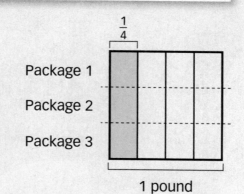

Package 1
Package 2
Package 3

$\frac{1}{4}$

1 pound

This model shows that $\frac{1}{4} \div 3 = \frac{1}{12}$. Each package will have 1 out of 12 equal parts of a whole pound.

Another way to say this is that each package will have $\frac{1}{3}$ of the $\frac{1}{4}$ pound of meat. An equation that shows this is $\frac{1}{3} \times \frac{1}{4} = \frac{1}{12}$.

So $\frac{1}{4} \div 3 = \frac{1}{12}$ and $\frac{1}{3} \times \frac{1}{4} = \frac{1}{12}$. Your child is learning that division and multiplication with fractions are related, just like division and multiplication with whole numbers are related.

Invite your child to share what he or she knows about division with unit fractions by doing the following activity together.

NEXT

Division with Unit Fractions Activity

Work together with your child to solve real-life problems involving division with unit fractions.

- Together with your child, use the picture to solve the problem below.

> Suppose we want to give each person in our family half of a sandwich. The sandwiches are shown below. How many people can we feed with these 4 sandwiches? $\left(4 \div \frac{1}{2} = 8\right)$ Do we have enough for our family or do we have too many?

- Look for similar situations in everyday life that involve dividing with a unit fraction.

- Examples:

    If you divide 2 hours of piano practice into sessions of $\frac{1}{2}$ hour each, how many sessions do you have to practice?
    $\left(2 \div \frac{1}{2} = 4\right)$

    One lap around the track is $\frac{1}{4}$ mile. How many laps do you need to do to run 3 miles? $\left(3 \div \frac{1}{4} = 12 \text{ laps}\right)$

©Curriculum Associates, LLC   Copying is not permitted.

Name: _____

Prerequisite: How do you find a fraction of a fraction?

Study the example problem showing two ways to find a fraction of a fraction. Then solve problems 1–5.

Example

The Padis family had $\frac{1}{2}$ pan of lasagna left from dinner. They ate $\frac{2}{3}$ of the leftovers the next day for lunch. What fraction of the whole pan of lasagna did they eat for lunch?

You need to find $\frac{2}{3}$ of $\frac{1}{2}$. $\frac{2}{3}$ of $\frac{1}{2}$ means $\frac{2}{3} \times \frac{1}{2}$.

You can draw a picture.

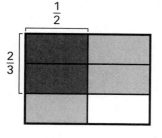

You can write an equation.

$$\frac{2}{3} \times \frac{1}{2} = \frac{2 \times 1}{3 \times 2}$$
$$= \frac{2}{6}$$

Both the picture and equation show that the Padis family ate $\frac{2}{6}$ of the whole pan of lasagna for lunch.

1 Look at the example problem. Felix says if $\frac{2}{3}$ pan of lasagna had been left over from dinner and the Padis family ate $\frac{1}{2}$ of that for lunch, the answer would not change, they would still eat $\frac{2}{6}$ of the whole pan of lasagna for lunch. Is he right? Explain.

_____

_____

_____

©Curriculum Associates, LLC   Copying is not permitted.

Solve.

2 Look at the area model. Which of the following products is represented by the model? Circle the letter for all that apply.

 A $\frac{1}{2} \times \frac{3}{4}$ **C** $\frac{1}{2}$ of $\frac{3}{4}$

 B $\frac{1}{2} \times \frac{1}{3}$ **D** $\frac{2}{4} \times \frac{2}{4}$

3 What is $\frac{1}{2}$ of $\frac{3}{4}$? _____

4 Miguel's physical education class lasts for $\frac{3}{4}$ of an hour. Today they spent $\frac{3}{4}$ of that time playing dodge ball. What fraction of an hour did he spend playing dodge ball?

Show your work.

Solution: _____

5 Maggie and her friend visit a beach that has a shoreline $2\frac{2}{5}$ kilometers long. They walk along $\frac{2}{3}$ of it. How many kilometers of the beach shoreline do they walk?

Show your work.

Solution: _____

 ©Curriculum Associates, LLC   Copying is not permitted.

Name: _____

Use Unit Fractions in Division

Study the example problem showing dividing a whole number by a unit fraction. Then solve problems 1–6.

> ### Example
>
> Teams of students in Mr. Reed's classroom are presenting Social Studies projects. Each team has $\frac{1}{5}$ hour for their presentation. How many projects are presented in 2 hours?
>
> The 2 large rectangles represent the 2 hours.
>
> Each presentation is $\frac{1}{5}$ hour so each rectangle is divided into 5 equal sections.
>
>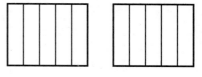
>
> From the model you can write the division equation: $\quad 2 \div \frac{1}{5} = 10$
>
> You can also write the multiplication equation: $\quad 2 \times 5 = 10$
>
> Both equations show 10 projects are presented in 2 hours.

1　Explain how the model in the example problem shows $2 \div \frac{1}{5} = 10$.

_____

_____

2　Explain how the model in the example problem shows $2 \times 5 = 10$.

_____

_____

3　Suppose Mr. Reed's class has 3 hours for presentations. How many projects can be presented? Show your solution by writing both a division equation and a multiplication equation.

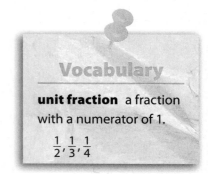

Vocabulary

unit fraction a fraction with a numerator of 1.

$\frac{1}{2}, \frac{1}{3}, \frac{1}{4}$

_____

_____

©Curriculum Associates, LLC   Copying is not permitted.

Solve.

4　Mr. Reed put 3 students on each team. The teams divide the $\frac{1}{5}$ hour presentation time so that each student talks an equal amount of time. Complete the steps to find what fraction of the presentation time each student talks.

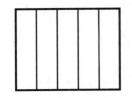

a.　Use the rectangle at the right. Shade $\frac{1}{5}$ of the rectangle to show $\frac{1}{5}$ hour, the time of one presentation.

b.　Divide the rectangle into 3 equal parts to represent the 3 students.

c.　Shade $\frac{1}{3}$ of the rectangle to represent 1 student.

d.　What is the fraction of the presentation time each student talks? _____

e.　$\frac{1}{5} \div 3 =$ _____

5　Look at the model in problem 4. Write the multiplication equation you can also use to find $\frac{1}{3}$ of $\frac{1}{5}$.

_____

6　Use the number line to find $3 \div \frac{1}{3}$. Then write the related multiplication equation that also solves the problem.

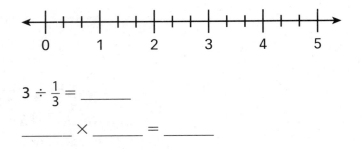

$3 \div \frac{1}{3} =$ _____

_____ × _____ = _____

©Curriculum Associates, LLC　Copying is not permitted.

Name: _____

Reason and Write

Study the example. Underline two parts that you think make it a particularly good answer and a helpful example.

Example

Draw a model to represent $\frac{1}{4} \div 3$. Write a multiplication equation that could also describe the model. Explain how you drew the model and how it represents both the multiplication and division equation.

Show your work. Use models, words, and numbers to explain your answer.

Possible answer shown.

$\frac{1}{4} \div 3 = \frac{1}{12}$

$\frac{1}{4} \times \frac{1}{3} = \frac{1}{12}$

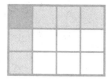

I drew an area model to show $\frac{1}{4} \div 3$. I split a rectangle into 4 equal columns, to show fourths. I shaded one of the columns to show $\frac{1}{4}$. To divide $\frac{1}{4}$ by 3, I divided the model into three equal rows and shaded the top one to show dividing by 3. By making 4 columns and 3 rows, I split the area model into 12 equal parts. The dark green area is 1 of the 12 parts, so it shows $\frac{1}{12}$.

The area model also shows the multiplication equation $\frac{1}{4} \times \frac{1}{3}$. The model is divided into 4 columns with 1 column shaded, representing $\frac{1}{4}$. The model has 3 rows with 1 row shaded, representing $\frac{1}{3}$. The dark green section where they overlap is the product of $\frac{1}{4}$ and $\frac{1}{3}$ and is 1 out of 12 equal parts, or $\frac{1}{12}$.

Where does the example . . .

- *show a model?*
- *use a multiplication equation?*
- *use words to explain?*
- *use numbers to explain?*

Lesson 17 Understand Division with Unit Fractions **169**

Solve the problem. Use what you learned from the example.

Draw a model to represent $6 \div \frac{1}{3}$. Write a multiplication equation that could also describe the model. Explain how you drew the model and how it represents both the multiplication and division equation.

Show your work. Use models, words, and numbers to explain your answer.

Did you . . .

• show a model?

• use a multiplication equation?

• use words to explain?

• use numbers to explain?

©Curriculum Associates, LLC   Copying is not permitted.

Dear Family,

This week your child is learning about dividing unit fractions in word problems.

He or she might see a word problem like this:

> Molly used $\frac{1}{5}$ of a square meter of fabric to decorate 3 flags. She used an equal amount of fabric for each flag. How much fabric did she use for each flag?

The division problem to solve is $\frac{1}{5} \div 3$.
One way to understand this problem is to use a model.

The rectangle to the right represents the whole square meter of fabric. The shaded part of the rectangle shows the $\frac{1}{5}$ of a square meter that Molly used.

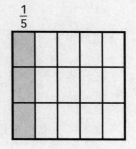

You can divide the shaded rectangle into 3 equal parts to represent the amount of fabric used for the 3 flags.

The part shaded dark green shows the amount used for one flag. 1 out of 15 parts of the whole square meter is used for 1 flag. $\frac{1}{15}$ of a square meter is used for each flag.

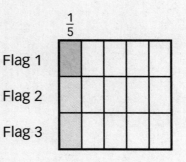

Your child can also write a division equation to solve the problem:
$\frac{1}{5} \div 3 = \frac{1}{15}$.

Invite your child to share what he or she knows about dividing unit fractions in word problems by doing the following activity together.

NEXT

Lesson 18 Divide Unit Fractions in Word Problems

Materials: a yard stick, tape measure, or ruler

- Together with your child, solve the problem below about dividing with a unit fraction.

> How many square tiles are needed to make a border along a wall? Each tile measures $\frac{1}{3}$ foot on each side, and the wall is 6 feet long. Calculate the answer using the division problem $6 \div \frac{1}{3}$.

- Now suppose you are going to use the tiles to make a border along a wall in your own house. First, measure to find the length of the wall in feet. Round to the nearest foot. Then divide that number by $\frac{1}{3}$ to find the number of tiles you need.

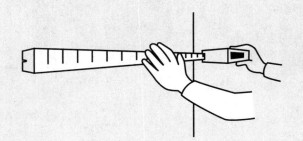

©Curriculum Associates, LLC   Copying is not permitted.

Divide Unit Fractions in Word Problems

Name: _____

Prerequisite: Divide with Unit Fractions

Study the example showing a word problem about dividing unit fractions by a whole number. Then solve problems 1–5.

Example

Eva and her two brothers, Bo and Sam, have $\frac{1}{2}$ hour to play on the computer and want to share the time equally. What fraction of an hour will they each have on the computer?

Eva, Bo, and Sam will each get $\frac{1}{3}$ of the $\frac{1}{2}$ hour.

You can represent this with a division expression or a multiplication expression:

$$\frac{1}{2} \div 3 \qquad \frac{1}{3} \times \frac{1}{2}$$

You can solve by drawing a picture, or by multiplying fractions:

$$\frac{1}{3} \times \frac{1}{2} = \frac{1}{6}$$

Eva, Bo, and Sam will each have $\frac{1}{6}$ hour on the computer.

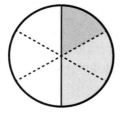

The circle represents 1 hour. The green shading is the $\frac{1}{2}$ hour they have to play. And the dark shading is the $\frac{1}{3}$ of $\frac{1}{2}$ hour for each child.

1 You divide to find either the number of groups or the quantity in each group. Which of those are you trying to find in the example problem? Explain.

_____

_____

_____

_____

2 Suppose only Eva and Bo share the $\frac{1}{2}$-hour computer time. Write the multiplication equation that you can use to solve $\frac{1}{2}$ of $\frac{1}{2}$. _____

Solve.

3 Fifth-grade students are selling popcorn at a school festival. Pairs of students work in $\frac{1}{3}$-hour shifts. Complete the steps to find how many shifts there are in 3 hours.

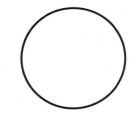

a. To solve $3 \div \frac{1}{3}$ you need to find the number of thirds in 3 hours. The circle represents 1 hour. Divide it to show the number of thirds in 1 hour.

b. How many thirds are in 3 hours? _____

c. Complete the division and multiplication equations for this problem.

$3 \times 3 =$ _____ $3 \div \frac{1}{3} =$ _____

d. How many $\frac{1}{3}$-hour shifts are in 3 hours?

_____

4 In problem 3 did you divide to find the number of groups or the quantity in each group? Explain.

_____

_____

_____

5 Each lap around the track at Emma's high school is $\frac{1}{4}$ mile. How many laps will Emma need to jog if she wants to jog 3 miles?

Show how you can use multiplication to find $3 \div \frac{1}{4}$.

Solution: _____

©Curriculum Associates, LLC   Copying is not permitted.

Name: _____

Divide a Fraction by a Whole Number

Study the example problem showing one way to solve a word problem involving dividing a fraction by a whole number. Then solve problems 1–5.

Example

Felicia makes $\frac{1}{2}$ gallon of fruit punch. She pours an equal amount into 8 glasses. What fraction of a gallon of fruit punch is in each glass?

Find $\frac{1}{2} \div 8$.

The model shows a rectangle divided into halves, then divided into 8 equal parts. There are a total of 16 parts, and one part is the amount of fruit punch in 1 glass.

$\frac{1}{2} \div 8 = \frac{1}{16}$.

The amount in 1 glass is $\frac{1}{16}$ gallon.

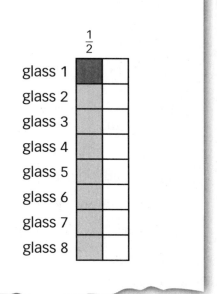

1 **What multiplication equation could you write to solve the example problem?**

_____

2 **Suppose Felicia had made $\frac{1}{4}$ gallon of punch and poured an equal amount into 8 glasses. Would the amount in each glass be more or less than $\frac{1}{16}$ gallon? Explain how the model in the example problem would change to show this.**

_____

_____

_____

_____

Solve.

3 Donal buys a $\frac{1}{4}$-pound package of cheese. There are 8 slices of cheese in the package. Each slice has the same weight. What fraction of a pound is each slice?

Show your work.

Solution: _____

4 Student volunteers are getting ready to hand out programs at a talent show. Leah and Tomas are each given $\frac{1}{2}$ of a stack of programs to hand out. Leah divides her $\frac{1}{2}$ equally among herself and 2 friends. What fraction of the original stack of programs do Leah and her 2 friends each have?

Show your work.

Solution: _____

5 Look at problem 4. If Tomas divides his stack of programs between himself and his 3 friends, what fraction of the original stack will each of his friends have?

Show your work.

Solution: _____

©Curriculum Associates, LLC   Copying is not permitted.

Name: _____

Divide a Whole Number by a Fraction

Study the example showing one way to solve a word problem involving dividing a whole number by a fraction. Then solve problems 1–6.

Example

Darius walks dogs at an animal shelter. He walks each dog for $\frac{1}{5}$ hour. How many dog walks can he do in 2 hours?

Find $2 \div \frac{1}{5}$.

The number line shows two hours. Each hour is divided into fifths.

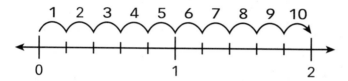

There are 10 fifths in 2.

$2 \div \frac{1}{5} = 10$.   Darius can do 10 dog walks in 2 hours.

---

1 What multiplication equation could you write to solve the example problem?

_____

2 Use the information from the example problem. In one month Darius spends 10 hours walking dogs. How many dog walks does he do in one month?

_____

3 Explain how you got your answer to problem 2.

_____

_____

_____

_____

Solve.

4 Mrs. Wing is preparing to tape up posters made by her students on the wall. She cuts tape into $\frac{1}{4}$-foot pieces. How many $\frac{1}{4}$-foot pieces can she cut from 5 feet of tape?

Show your work.

Solution: _____

5 Taylor is helping decorate tables with flowers for a graduation celebration. She has 7 dozen tulips. She will put $\frac{1}{2}$ dozen tulips in each vase. How many vases does she need?

Show your work.

Solution: _____

6 Look at how you solved problem 5. Show how to solve problem 5 a different way.

Show your work.

Solution: _____

©Curriculum Associates, LLC   Copying is not permitted.

Name: _____

Divide Unit Fractions in Word Problems

Solve the problems.

1 Ms. Kaimal prints out address labels on 3 sheets of paper. Each sheet is entirely covered in labels. Each label takes up $\frac{1}{12}$ of a sheet. How many labels did she print?

How can I draw a model to help understand the problem?

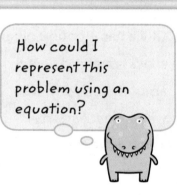

A 36 labels   **C** 15 labels

B 24 labels   **D** 12 labels

2 Derek has $\frac{1}{4}$ gallon of white paint. He pours an equal amount into 3 containers so he and his friends can paint different sections of a fence at the same time. What fraction of a gallon of paint is in each container?

How could I represent this problem using an equation?

A $\frac{3}{4}$ gallon   **C** $\frac{1}{12}$ gallon

B $\frac{1}{9}$ gallon   **D** $\frac{1}{16}$ gallon

Wendy chose **A** as the correct answer. How did she get that answer?

_____

_____

_____

_____

Solve.

3 Jameson is following a 3-kilometer exercise route. After every $\frac{1}{5}$ kilometer there is a sign describing an exercise to do, including at the end of the route. Which expression can be used to find the number of exercise signs along the route? Circle the letter for all that apply.

How is this problem like other problems that I've seen?

A $3 \div \frac{1}{5}$

C 3×5

B $\frac{1}{5} \div 3$

D 1×3

4 Olivia has $\frac{1}{2}$ pound of raisins. She plans to eat them for snacks over the next 6 days. If she eats the same amount each day, what fraction of a pound of raisins will she eat each day?

Show your work.

How can you use multiplication to solve this problem?

Solution: _____

5 Complete each sentence by writing either *greater than* or *less than* in the blank.

Think of an example problem with a fraction and whole number to help you answer this question.

a. When you divide a unit fraction by a whole number, the quotient is _____ the unit fraction.

b. When you divide a whole number by a unit fraction, the quotient is _____ the whole number.

©Curriculum Associates, LLC Copying is not permitted.

Unit 2 Game

Name: _____

Fraction Sums and Differences

What you need: Recording Sheet,
1 number cube (1–6)

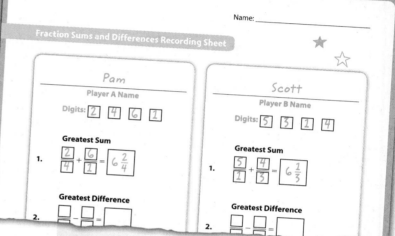

Directions

- Both players roll the number cube four times and record the four numbers at the top of the Recording Sheet. Players use these same numbers for Rounds 1 through 4.

- In each round the players use these four digits to create two fractions.

- In Round 1, the player with the *greatest sum* wins the round. Use the digits to make two fractions, and add them. Record the addition and sum on the Recording Sheet.

- In Round 2, the player with the *greatest difference* wins the round. Make two fractions, and subtract one from the other. Record the difference.

- In Round 3, the player who makes the *least sum* wins.

- In Round 4, the player who makes the *least difference* wins.

- In Round 5, the players decide together whether to add or subtract and whether to try for the greatest or least result. After deciding, players both roll 4 new numbers to use in the final round.

The greater the fractions, the greater the sum. But what does it mean to have the greatest difference?

Name: _____

Fraction Sums and Differences Recording Sheet

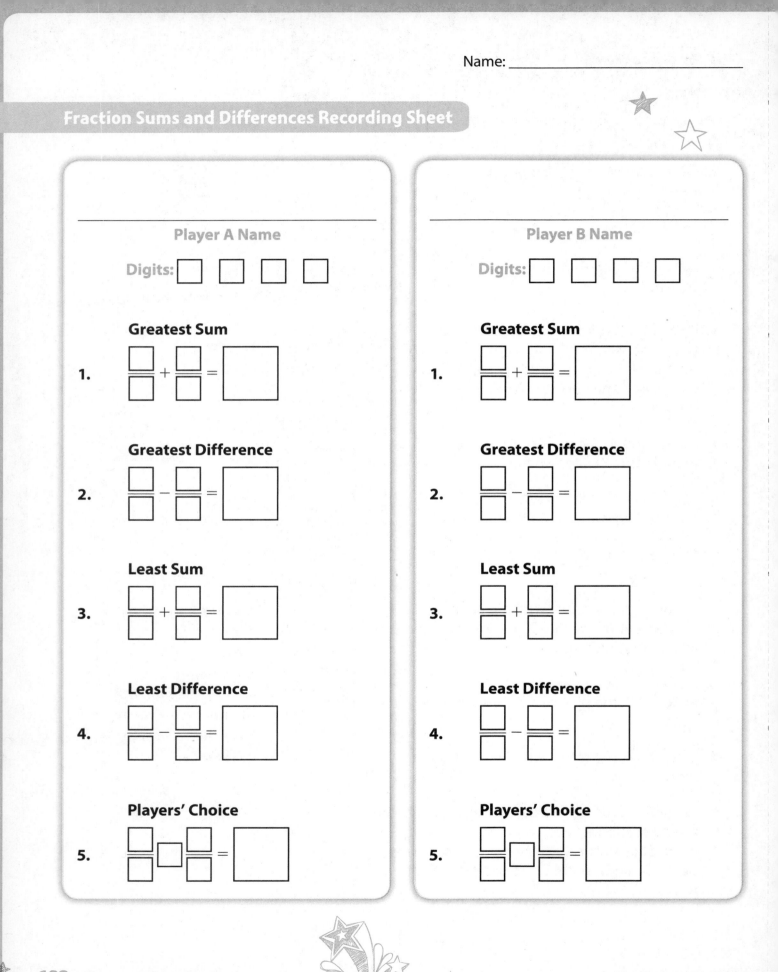

_____
Player A Name

Digits: ☐ ☐ ☐ ☐

Greatest Sum

1. ☐/☐ + ☐/☐ = ☐

Greatest Difference

2. ☐/☐ − ☐/☐ = ☐

Least Sum

3. ☐/☐ + ☐/☐ = ☐

Least Difference

4. ☐/☐ − ☐/☐ = ☐

Players' Choice

5. ☐/☐ ☐ ☐/☐ = ☐

_____
Player B Name

Digits: ☐ ☐ ☐ ☐

Greatest Sum

1. ☐/☐ + ☐/☐ = ☐

Greatest Difference

2. ☐/☐ − ☐/☐ = ☐

Least Sum

3. ☐/☐ + ☐/☐ = ☐

Least Difference

4. ☐/☐ − ☐/☐ = ☐

Players' Choice

5. ☐/☐ ☐ ☐/☐ = ☐

©Curriculum Associates, LLC

Name: _____

Number and Operations—Fractions

In this unit you learned to:	Lesson
add and subtract fractions with unlike denominators, for example: $\frac{3}{5} + \frac{1}{4} = \frac{17}{20}$.	10, 11
estimate sums or differences of fractions, for example: $2\frac{3}{8} + 5\frac{1}{2}$ is a little less than 8.	11
multiply fractions, for example: $\frac{2}{3} \times \frac{5}{6} = \frac{10}{18}$ or $\frac{5}{9}$.	12, 13, 14, 15, 16
divide unit fractions, for example: $4 \div \frac{1}{7} = 28$.	17, 18

Use these skills to solve problems 1–7.

1 Roma makes 44 ounces of salsa. She pours an equal amount into 5 containers. How much salsa does she pour in each container? Write a division expression to represent the problem and solve.

_____

_____

_____

2 Which of the following does the dark gray area of the area model represent? Circle the letter of all that apply.

A $\frac{1}{2} \times \frac{1}{4}$

B $\frac{1}{8} \times \frac{1}{2}$

C $\frac{1}{4} \div 2$

D $\frac{1}{8} \div \frac{1}{2}$

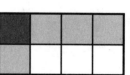

3 Write one fraction from the box to make each sentence true.

a. The product _____ $\times \frac{3}{8}$ is greater than $\frac{3}{8}$.

b. The product _____ $\times \frac{3}{8}$ is less than $\frac{3}{8}$.

c. The product _____ $\times \frac{3}{8}$ is equal to $\frac{3}{8}$.

$\frac{2}{3}$	$\frac{5}{2}$
	$\frac{3}{5}$
$\frac{5}{4}$	$\frac{4}{4}$

Solve.

4 Nance is riding her bike to a friend's house $4\frac{1}{2}$ miles away. She's ridden $2\frac{3}{5}$ miles. How much farther does she need to ride? Estimate, and then compute. Explain how you know your answer is reasonable.

Show your work.

Solutions: _____

_____

5 Nick's grandfather grows tomatoes in a section of his yard that is $\frac{4}{5}$-meter long and $\frac{2}{3}$-meter wide. What is the area of the tomato section?

_____

6 Ron is slicing 5 pizzas. Each slice is $\frac{1}{8}$ of the pizza. How many pizza slices will there be in all?

A 5 slices

B 8 slices

C 13 slices

D 40 slices

7 Natan's family spent $2\frac{1}{4}$ hours visiting a national monument near their home. They watched a video in the visitor's center for $\frac{1}{3}$ of that time. How much time did they spend watching the video?

Show your work.

Solutions: _____

©Curriculum Associates, LLC   Copying is not permitted.

Name: _____

Answer the questions and show all your work on separate paper.

It's snack time and you are going to make some snack mix for you and your friends. You have two snack mix recipes. You will make at least one batch of each recipe.

For **Recipe 1**, each batch needs: $\frac{1}{3}$ cup almonds, $\frac{1}{4}$ cup raisins, and $\frac{1}{2}$ cup sunflower seeds.

For **Recipe 2**, each batch needs: $\frac{1}{4}$ cup almonds, $\frac{1}{8}$ cup chocolate chips, and $\frac{1}{6}$ cup sunflower seeds.

Here's what you have in the kitchen: 5 cups of almonds, 2 cups of raisins, 3 cups of sunflower seeds, and 1 cup of chocolate chips.

- How many batches of each recipe will you make? Explain your decisions. Use visual models and/or write equations. Show how much of each ingredient you will use to make the number of batches of snack mix that you choose.

- How many cups of snack mix will you have in all when you are finished?

Reflect on Mathematical Practices

1 **Model** What visual models did you use, and why? How did each model help you understand and solve the problem?

2 **Reason Mathematically** Both recipes use sunflower seeds, but they use different amounts. How did you make sure that you had enough sunflower seeds for all your batches of snack mix?

©Curriculum Associates, LLC   Copying is not permitted.

Checklist

Did you . . .

- ☐ show all the ingredients you need?

- ☐ use a visual model?

- ☐ check your answer for accuracy?

Word Bank Here are some words that you might use in your answer.

divide	quotient	multiply
product	total	fraction
third	half	fourth
sixth	eighth	cups

Models Here are some models that you might use to find the solution.

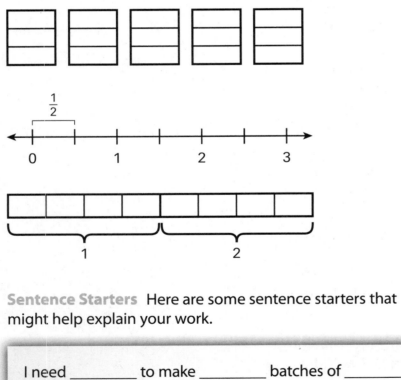

Sentence Starters Here are some sentence starters that might help explain your work.

I need _____ to make _____ batches of _____

5 cups of almonds can make _____

3 cups of sunflower seeds can make _____

©Curriculum Associates, LLC   Copying is not permitted.

Unit 2 Vocabulary

Name: _____

My Examples

fraction

a number that compares a part, the numerator, to a whole, the denominator

numerator

the top number in a fraction that tells the number of equal parts described by the fraction

denominator

the bottom number in a fraction that tells the total number of equal parts in a whole

common denominator

a denominator shared by two or more fractions, which can be found by finding the least common multiple of the denominators

©Curriculum Associates, LLC   Copying is not permitted.

equivalent fractions

two or more fractions that name the same part of a whole

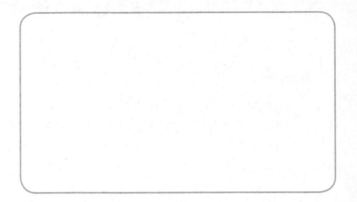

benchmark fraction

a common fraction that you can judge other numbers against $\left(\text{e.g., } \frac{1}{4}, \frac{1}{2}, \frac{3}{4}\right)$

unit fraction

a fraction with a numerator of 1

division

an operation used to find the number in each group or the number of groups in equal-sized groups

©Curriculum Associates, LLC   Copying is not permitted.

divide

to separate into equal groups

quotient

the result of division

remainder

the amount left over that, as a whole number, will not divide equally into groups

multiplication

an operation used to find the total number of items in equal-sized groups

©Curriculum Associates, LLC   Copying is not permitted.

multiply

to find the total number of items in equal-sized groups

product

the result of multiplication

factor

a number that is multiplied by another number

area

the amount of space a two-dimensional figure covers

©Curriculum Associates, LLC   Copying is not permitted.

equation

a mathematical sentence that uses an equal sign (=) to show that two expressions have the same value

My Words

_____

_____

_____

_____

_____

_____

_____

_____

_____

©Curriculum Associates, LLC   Copying is not permitted.

My Words

My Examples

Unit 2 Vocabulary

©Curriculum Associates, LLC   Copying is not permitted.

Dear Family,

This week your child is learning to evaluate and write expressions.

Here are some vocabulary terms your child is becoming familiar with:

> **expression** a group of numbers and symbols that shows a mathematical relationship
> **evaluate** to find the value of an expression

Your child might see an expression like this:
$$0.5 \times (24 + 8)$$

To evaluate the expression, you first do the operation inside the parentheses. So, first add $24 + 8$. Then multiply that sum by 0.5.
$$0.5 \times (24 + 8)$$
$$0.5 \times (32)$$
$$16$$
The value of the expression is 16.

The same expression can also be stated in words. You can say "half of the sum of 24 and 8."

0.5	×	(24 + 8)
↑	↑	↑
half	of	the sum of 24 and 8

Your child might also see a written phrase that describes an expression. He or she can write the expression using numbers and symbols:

"15 minus the sum of 6 and 7" $15 - (6 + 7)$

Because you first need to add $6 + 7$, you put parentheses around that part of the expression. To evaluate the expression, add $6 + 7$ and subtract the sum from 15: $15 - 13 = 2$.

Invite your child to share what he or she knows about evaluating and writing expressions by doing the following activity together.

Evaluating and Writing Expressions Activity

With your child, play a game called "Evaluate That Expression!"

- One person uses some of the math words in the box below to describe an expression in words and phrases.

sum	one less than	quotient
plus	product	difference
times	minus	divided by
triple	double	half

- The other person writes the expression using numbers and symbols. Remember to use parentheses if they are needed!
- Evaluate the expressions together. Take turns.
- Examples:
  - The sum of 8 and one less than 8. [8 + (8 − 1)]
  - Triple the difference of 5 and 2. [3 × (5 − 2)]

12 divided by the difference of 8 and 6

12 ÷ (8 − 6)

That's 12 divided by 2, so the value of the expression is 6.

©Curriculum Associates, LLC   Copying is not permitted.

Evaluate and Write Expressions

Name: _____

Prerequisite: Solve Multiplication Word Problems

Study the example problem showing multiplication as a way to compare two numbers. Then solve problems 1–5.

Example

Isak has 7 baseball cards. He has 3 times as many basketball cards as baseball cards. How many basketball cards does he have?

You can use a bar model to help you understand the relationship between the numbers.

You can describe the relationship two ways.

Use words: What is 3 times as many as 7?

Use an equation: $? = 3 \times 7$

Solve: $21 = 3 \times 7$ Isak has 21 basketball cards.

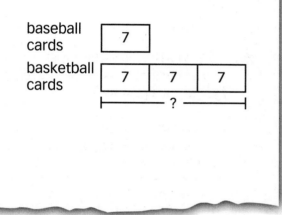

1. Draw and label a bar model to show the number that is 7 times as many as 3. Then complete the equation.

   _____ $= 7 \times 3$

2. How does 21 compare to 7? How does 21 compare to 3? Write the numbers to describe the relationships.

   21 is _____ times as many as 7.

   21 is _____ times as many as 3.

©Curriculum Associates, LLC   Copying is not permitted.

Solve.

3 Lauren babysat over the summer. In June she had
$20 dollars. At the end of August she had 12 times that
amount. How much money did Lauren have at the
end of August?

Show your work.

Solution: _____

4 Kyle swam 4 laps in the pool on Monday. He swam
6 times as many laps on Tuesday. Choose *True* or *False*
for each statement.

a. The expression 6 × 4 represents the number of
    laps Kyle swam on Tuesday.   ☐ True   ☐ False

b. The words *6 times as many as 4* represents the
    number of laps Kyle swam on Tuesday.   ☐ True   ☐ False

c. The number of laps Kyle swam on Tuesday can be   ☐ True   ☐ False
    found by solving the equation ? = 6 × 4.

d. Kyle swam 10 laps on Tuesday.   ☐ True   ☐ False

5 Mrs. Altman's class recycled 72 water bottles in March.
The number of juice cans they recycled was $\frac{1}{4}$ times as
many. What is the total number of water bottles and
juice cans they recycled in March?

Show your work.

Solution: _____

   ©Curriculum Associates, LLC   Copying is not permitted.

Name: _____

Evaluate Expressions

Study the example problem showing two ways to think about an expression that has parentheses. Then solve problems 1–6.

Example

Ms. Nakos works 4 hours on Mondays and 8 hours on Tuesdays in the school library. During one week in May she worked $\frac{1}{4}$ of her regular hours. Evaluate the expression $\frac{1}{4} \times (4 + 8)$ to find the number of hours she worked that week.

To understand the problem you can:

Use a picture.

Monday Hours + Tuesday Hours

$\frac{1}{4}$ of (4 + 8)

M	T T
M	T T
M	T T
M	T T

Use words.

$\frac{1}{4}$ $\times$ (4 + 8)

↑   ↑   ↑

One fourth   of   the sum of the number of Monday and Tuesday hours

$$\frac{1}{4} \times (4 + 8) = \frac{1}{4} \times 12 = \frac{12}{4} = 3$$

Ms. Nakos worked 3 hours that week.

1 Look at the expression in the example. There are parentheses around 4 + 8 to show it is to be evaluated first. Are the parentheses necessary? Explain.

_____

_____

_____

2 The expression $\frac{1}{2} \times (4 + 8)$ represents the number of hours Ms. Nakos works the last week of school. Evaluate the expression to find the number of hours she works that week.

_____

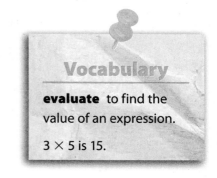

Vocabulary

evaluate to find the value of an expression.

3×5 is 15.

©Curriculum Associates, LLC   Copying is not permitted.

Solve.

3 Each day, Theo walks his dog 15 minutes in the morning and 25 minutes in the afternoon. Evaluate the expression $7 \times (15 + 25)$ to find how many minutes Theo walks his dog each week.

Show your work.

Solution: _____

4 Lin, Mac, and Starr spend $6 on supplies to set up a lemonade stand. They sell $21 worth of lemonade. They are going to share the money equally. Evaluate the expression $(21 - 6) \div 3$ to find how much money each one will make.

Show your work.

Solution: _____

5 Which of the following shows another way to write the expression $(21 - 6) \div 3$?

A $\frac{21 - 6}{3}$ C $\frac{21}{3} - 6$

B $\frac{3}{21 - 6}$ D $21 - \frac{6}{3}$

6 Describe what happens if you divide a difference by 3.

_____

_____

_____

©Curriculum Associates, LLC   Copying is not permitted.

Name: _____

Write Expressions

Study the example showing how to write a numerical expression. Then solve problems 1–8.

Example

Write a numerical expression to show the following phrase:

   12 plus the quotient of 8 and 4

Think about what the words mean:

12 plus	the quotient of	8 and 4
↑	↑	↑
Plus means add.	The quotient is the result of division.	The numbers in the division operation.

Since you add 12 *to the quotient* of 8 and 4, you need to first divide 8 by 4. Use parentheses to show that you do the division first.

The numerical expression is $12 + (8 \div 4)$.

---

1 Draw a picture to show what the word phrase in the example means.

   12   plus   the quotient of 8 and 4

2 Suppose you wrote a numerical expression for the phrase "20 minus the product of 5 and 2." To evaluate the expression, should you subtract or multiply first? Explain.

_____

_____

_____

Solve.

3   Write a numerical expression to represent "20 minus the product of 5 and 2." Then evaluate your expression.

_____

4   Which expression represents the phrase "16 divided by the product of 4 and 4." Circle the letter for all that apply.

A $16 \div 4 \times 4$

C $\dfrac{16}{4 \times 4}$

B $16 \div (4 \times 4)$

D $\dfrac{4 \times 4}{16}$

5   Write a numerical expression to represent "6 times the difference of 9 and 3". Then evaluate your expression.

_____

6   Write a word phrase for the expression $10 + (6 - 4)$.

_____

_____

7   Shana is doing a craft project using yarn and craft sticks. She has 5 green yarn pieces and 7 blue yarn pieces. She has 3 times as many craft sticks as yarn pieces.

Which expression can you use to find the number of craft sticks Shana has?

A $5 + (7 \times 3)$

B $(5 + 7) \times 3$

C $(5 + 7) + 3$

D $5 \times (7 \times 3)$

8   Look at your answer to problem 7. Evaluate the expression to find the number of craft sticks Shana has.

_____

Vocabulary

evaluate to find the value of an expression.

3×5 is 15.

©Curriculum Associates, LLC   Copying is not permitted.

Name: _____

Write and Evaluate Expressions

Solve the problems.

1 Look at the expression below. Tell whether each statement about its value is *True* or *False*.

$$\frac{1}{2} \times (137 + 87)$$

What are the expressions you are comparing in this problem? How are they different?

a. It is greater than the value of $\frac{1}{4} \times (137 + 87)$.   ☐ True   ☐ False

b. It is less than the value of $137 + 87$.   ☐ True   ☐ False

c. It is greater than the value of $137 + 87$.   ☐ True   ☐ False

d. It is less than the value of $\frac{1}{8} \times (137 + 87)$.   ☐ True   ☐ False

2 Which expression represents "14 minus the difference of 7 and 2?"

How many steps are described in the word phrase? What is the operation for each step?

A $14 - 7 - 2$ **C** $14 - (7 + 2)$

B $14 - (7 - 2)$ **D** $14 - 7 + 2$

Devon chose **C** as the correct answer. How did he get that answer?

_____

_____

_____

_____

_____

_____

_____

Solve.

3 Which expression is *not* 2 times the value of the expression 473 + 165?

How do you represent "2 times" in an expression?

A 2 + (473 + 165)

B 2 × (473 + 165)

C (473 + 165) × 2

D (2 × 473) + (2 × 165)

4 Complete each expression to make its value equal to 9.

I can try substituting different numbers and evaluating the expression.

a. $\left(24 - \boxed{}\right) \div 2$

b. $29 - \left(\boxed{} \times 5\right)$

c. $\boxed{} \div (2 \times 3)$

5 Abbey's cat weighs 18 pounds. Her dog weighs 2 pounds more than half her cat's weight. Write and evaluate an expression to show how much Abbey's dog weighs.

Which animal weighs more, the dog or the cat?

Show your work.

Solution: _____

©Curriculum Associates, LLC Copying is not permitted.

Dear Family,

This week your child is learning to analyze patterns and relationships.

Your child is learning ways to describe how two number patterns are related. He or she might see a problem like this:

> At the school fair, a box of raisins costs $2 and a box of nuts costs $4. How do the costs of boxes of raisins compare to the costs of the same number of boxes of nuts for 0, 1, 2, 3, or 4 boxes?

A picture shows the number patterns for the raisins and the nuts:

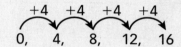

+2 +2 +2 +2
0,   2,   4,   6,   8

+4   +4   +4   +4
0,   4,   8,   12, 16

You can use a table to see how the number patterns are related.

Look for a pattern. The second number in each ordered pair is twice the first number. For example, in the ordered pair (4, 8), $8 = 2 \times 4$.

Raisins (x)	Nuts (y)	Ordered Pairs (x, y)
0	0	(0, 0)
2	4	(2, 4)
4	8	(4, 8)
6	12	(6, 12)
8	16	(8, 16)

Another way to see how the number patterns are related is to plot the ordered pairs on a graph, or coordinate plane.

The graph at the right shows a point for each ordered pair in the table. From point to point, the pattern is: move 2 to the right, move up 4.

Invite your child to share what he or she knows about analyzing number patterns and relationships by doing the following activity together.

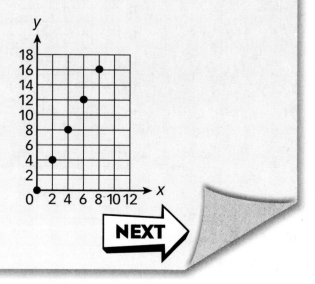

NEXT

Work with your child to show how the costs of two items are related.

- Together with your child, find the cost of your child's two favorite snacks. Round each to the nearest dollar. (Example: A box of crackers costs $2, and a carton of ice cream costs $5.)

- In the table write the cost of 0, 1, 2, 3, 4, and 5 of each snack.

Snack 1: _____ (x)	Snack 2: _____ (y)	Ordered Pairs (x, y)

- Together, plot the ordered pairs on the graph below and describe the relationship between the costs of the snacks.

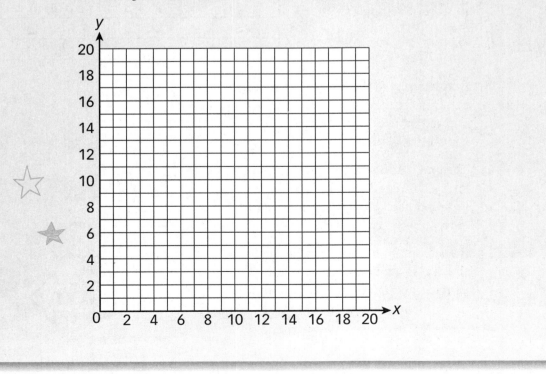

©Curriculum Associates, LLC   Copying is not permitted.

Analyze Patterns and Relationships

Name: _____

Study the example of using a number line to describe and extend a number pattern. Then solve problems 1–6.

Example

Elaine wrote the pattern below.

3, 6, 9, 12, 15

What is the rule for the pattern? What would be the next number in the pattern?

A number line can help you find a pattern.

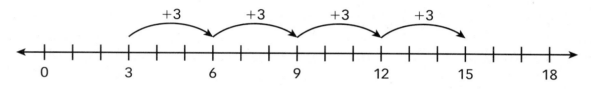

The rule for the pattern is "add 3." The next number would be 15 + 3, or 18.

---

1 Harry looks at the example and says you multiply 3 by 2 to get 6, so the rule is "multiply by 2." Can you use this rule to describe the pattern in the example problem? Explain.

_____

_____

_____

2 What other pattern(s) do you see in the set of numbers in the example?

_____

_____

_____

©Curriculum Associates, LLC   Copying is not permitted.

Solve.

3 Use the same rule as in the example, "add 3," but start at 1. Write the next 3 numbers in the pattern. Use the number line to show the pattern.

1, _____, _____, _____

```
◄──┼──┼──┼──┼──┼──┼──┼──┼──┼──┼──┼──┼──┼──┼──┼──┼──┼──┼──┼──┼──►
   0     2     4     6     8    10    12    14    16    18    20
```

4 Tell whether each statement is *True* or *False* for the following pattern.

1, 5, 9, 13, 17, 21

a. The rule is "multiply by 5."   ☐ True   ☐ False

b. The rule is "add 4."   ☐ True   ☐ False

c. If the pattern continues, the next number will be an even number.   ☐ True   ☐ False

d. If the pattern continues, the next number will be an odd number.   ☐ True   ☐ False

5 The rule for a pattern is "multiply by 10." Write the next 3 numbers in the pattern.

7, _____, _____, _____

6 Look at the pattern below.

45, 39, 33, 27, 21, 15

a. What is the rule for the pattern?

_____

b. If the pattern continues, what would be the next number?

_____

©Curriculum Associates, LLC   Copying is not permitted.

Name: _____

Compare Two Numerical Patterns

Study the example problem showing one way to identify relationships between two numerical patterns. Then solve problems 1–6.

Example

The school store sells laces and decals in the school colors. Laces cost $1, and decals cost $5. Write ordered pairs to compare the cost of laces to decals for selling 0, 1, 2, 3, 4, and 5 of each item.

Use a table to show the two numerical patterns. Then write the corresponding terms as ordered pairs.

The cost of laces pattern follows the rule "add 1."
  0, 1, 2, 3, 4, 5

The cost of decals pattern follows the rule "add 5."
  0, 5, 10, 15, 20, 25

Cost of Laces (Add 1)	Cost of Decals (Add 5)	Ordered Pairs
0	0	(0, 0)
1	5	(1, 5)
2	10	(2, 10)
3	15	(3, 15)
4	20	(4, 20)
5	25	(5, 25)

1 Look at the example. What is the cost for 6 decals? Explain how you got your answer.

_____

_____

_____

2 Look at the example. How are the terms in the cost of decals pattern related to the corresponding terms in the cost of laces pattern?

_____

_____

_____

_____

Solve.

3 Suppose school bookmarks cost $3 each. Complete the table to show how the terms in this pattern compare to the corresponding terms in the pattern for the cost of laces.

Cost of Laces	Cost of Bookmarks	Ordered Pairs
0	0	(0, 0)
1	3	(1, 3)
2	☐	(☐, ☐)
3	☐	(☐, ☐)
4	☐	(☐, ☐)
5	☐	(☐, ☐)

4 Look at problem 3. How do the corresponding terms of the two patterns compare?

_____

_____

_____

5 Look at problem 3. What is the rule for finding the cost of bookmarks?

_____

6 Look at problem 3. If the table was continued, which ordered pair could be in it? Circle the letter for all that apply.

A (8, 21)   **C** (12, 36)

B (10, 30)   **D** (15, 60)

Vocabulary

corresponding terms the numbers that are in the same place in two or more related patterns.

ordered pair a pair of numbers that locate a point on a coordinate plane.

©Curriculum Associates, LLC   Copying is not permitted.

Name: _____

Graph Ordered Pairs

Study the example comparing two patterns on a graph.
Then solve problems 1–8.

Example

Luke compared a numeric pattern with the rule "add 2" to a pattern with the rule "add 6."

He started at 0 and wrote the first three numbers of each pattern.
add 2: 0, 2, 4
add 6: 0, 6, 12

He wrote three ordered pairs:
(0, 0)   (2, 6)   (4, 12)

Then he plotted the ordered pairs on a graph.

The first number in each ordered pair shows the location on the *x*-axis.

The second number in each ordered pair shows the location on the *y*-axis.

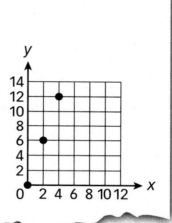

1 Look at the ordered pairs in the example. Describe the relationship between corresponding terms of the two patterns.

_____

_____

_____

2 Suppose you connect the points on the graph in the example, what would the graph look like?

_____

_____

_____

Solve.

At a bake sale, cookies are sold in packages of 4 and fruit bars are sold in packages of 2.

3 Complete the table comparing the number of cookies and fruit bars sold for 0, 1, 2, and 3 packages.

Number of Cookies (x)	Number of Fruit Bars (y)	Ordered Pairs (x, y)
0	0	(0, 0)
4	2	(4, 2)
☐	☐	(☐, ☐)
☐	☐	(☐, ☐)

4 What is the rule for the number of cookies pattern?

_____

5 What is the rule for the number of fruit bars pattern?

_____

6 Plot the ordered pairs on the coordinate plane to the right.

7 What directions would you give someone to get from one point to the next on the graph?

_____

_____

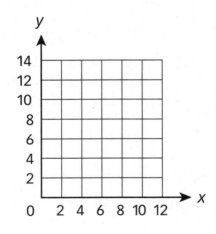

8 How do your directions relate to the rules for the patterns?

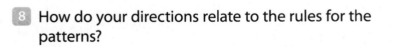

_____

_____

_____

_____

Lesson 20 Analyze Patterns and Relationships   ©Curriculum Associates, LLC   Copying is not permitted.

Name: _____

Analyze Patterns and Relationships

Solve the problems.

1 How do the corresponding terms compare in a pattern that has the rule "add 3" and a pattern that has the rule "add 9"? Start each pattern at 0.

Show your work.

How do I generate the patterns?

Solution: _____

_____

_____

2 Peg is counting nickels and dimes and comparing the values for 0, 1, 2, and 3 coins in a table. What ordered pair will Peg write next? Circle the letter of the correct answer.

How many coins does the next row of the table represent?

Value of Nickels (x)	Value of Dimes (y)	Ordered Pairs (x, y)
0	0	(0, 0)
5	10	(5, 10)
10	20	(10, 20)

A (20, 40) **C** (15, 40)

B (20, 30) **D** (15, 30)

Leroy chose **A** as the correct answer. How did he get that answer?

_____

_____

_____

©Curriculum Associates, LLC   Copying is not permitted.

Solve.

3 Complete the table for the rules "add 6" and "add 2."

Add 6	Add 2	Ordered Pairs (x, y)
0	0	(0, 0)
6	2	(6, 2)
☐	☐	(☐, ☐)
☐	☐	(☐, ☐)

How do you know which number to write first in an ordered pair?

4 Plot the ordered pairs from problem 3 on the coordinate plane below.

How do the corresponding terms in the patterns compare?

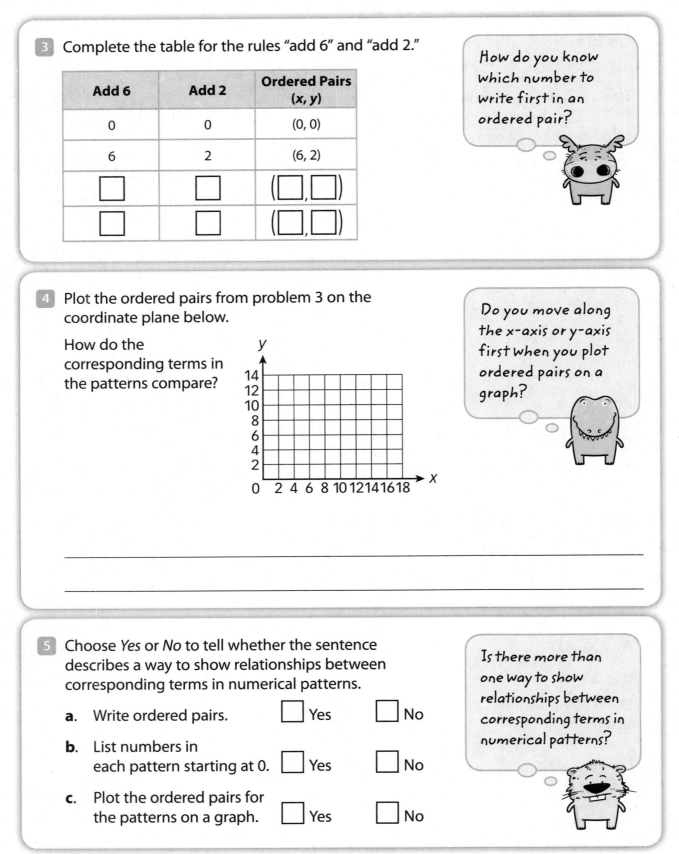

Do you move along the x-axis or y-axis first when you plot ordered pairs on a graph?

_____

_____

5 Choose *Yes* or *No* to tell whether the sentence describes a way to show relationships between corresponding terms in numerical patterns.

a. Write ordered pairs. ☐ Yes ☐ No

b. List numbers in each pattern starting at 0. ☐ Yes ☐ No

c. Plot the ordered pairs for the patterns on a graph. ☐ Yes ☐ No

Is there more than one way to show relationships between corresponding terms in numerical patterns?

©Curriculum Associates, LLC   Copying is not permitted.

Name: _____

Most Valuable Expressions

What you need: Recording Sheet, 3 sets of Digit Decimal, and Fraction Cards

Directions

● Mix the cards. Deal 3 cards to each player.

● Players use the numbers on their cards to write an expression on the Recording Sheet. Players can use any operation (+, −, ×, ÷) and parentheses to form their expression.

● For the first 4 rounds, the player whose expression has the greater value gets 1 point. If the expressions are equal, both players get 1 point.

● For the last 4 rounds, the player whose expression has the lesser value gets 1 point.

● After each round, players set aside their cards and choose three new cards each.

● The player with the most points after 8 rounds wins.

Name: _____

Most Valuable Expression Recording Sheet

_____ Charlize _____
Player A Name

1. $(2 \times 9) \div \frac{1}{10}$ = 180

2. _____ = _____

_____ Tina _____
Player B Name

1. $(4 \times 3) \div 0.25$ = 48

2. _____ = _____

I think I know how I would use 0 to get a small number. I wonder how I would use 0 if I were trying to make a large number?

©Curriculum Associates, LLC   Copying is not permitted.

Most Valuable Expression Recording Sheet

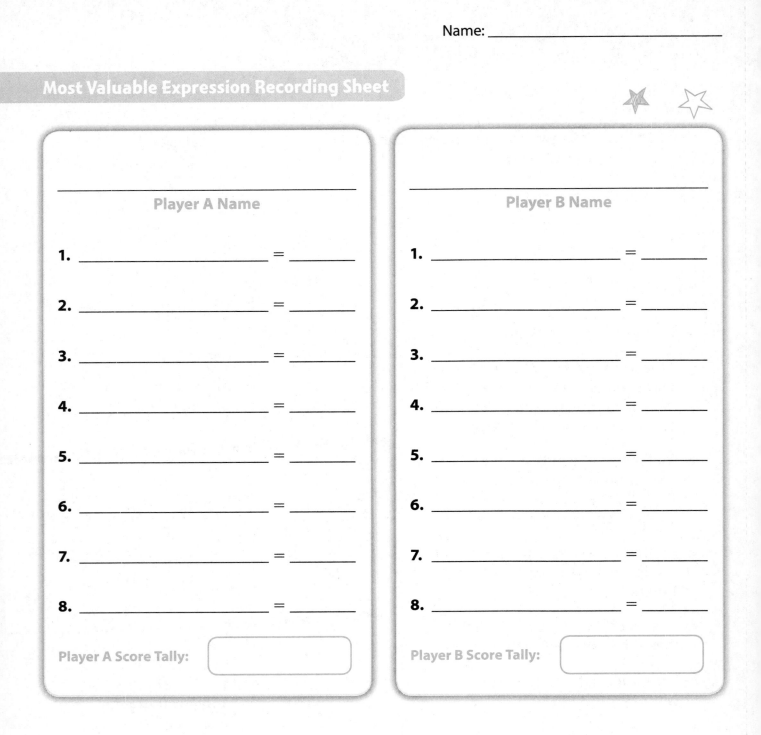

_____
Player A Name

1. _____ = _____

2. _____ = _____

3. _____ = _____

4. _____ = _____

5. _____ = _____

6. _____ = _____

7. _____ = _____

8. _____ = _____

Player A Score Tally: [_____]

_____
Player B Name

1. _____ = _____

2. _____ = _____

3. _____ = _____

4. _____ = _____

5. _____ = _____

6. _____ = _____

7. _____ = _____

8. _____ = _____

Player B Score Tally: [_____]

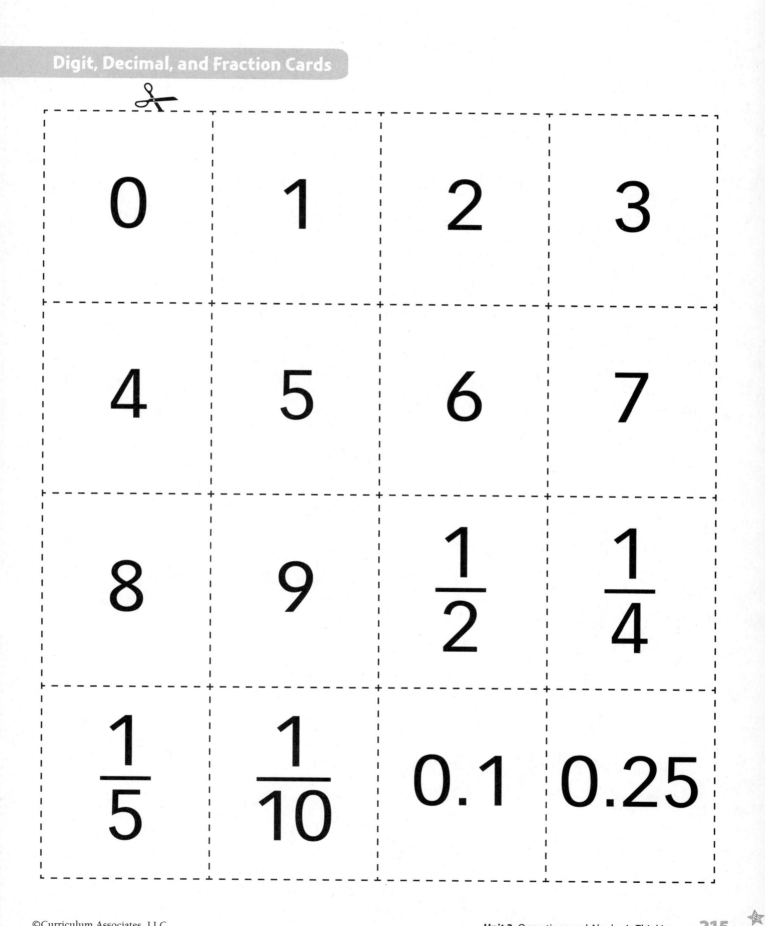

0	1	2	3
4	5	6	7
8	9	$\frac{1}{2}$	$\frac{1}{4}$
$\frac{1}{5}$	$\frac{1}{10}$	0.1	0.25

©Curriculum Associates, LLC

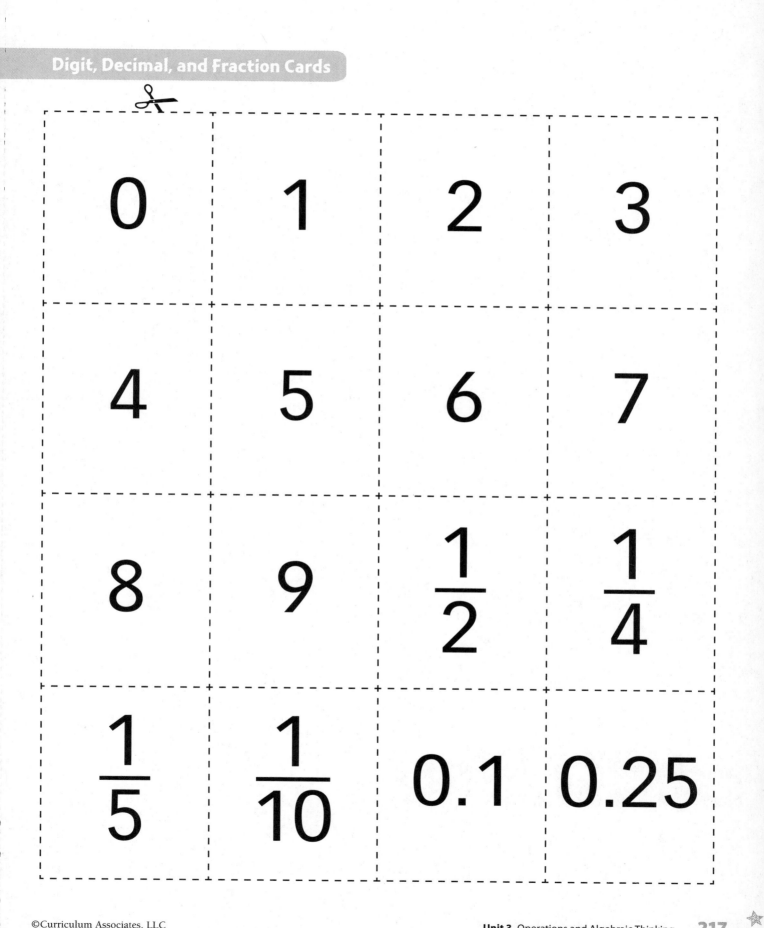

0	1	2	3
4	5	6	7
8	9	$\frac{1}{2}$	$\frac{1}{4}$
$\frac{1}{5}$	$\frac{1}{10}$	0.1	0.25

©Curriculum Associates, LLC

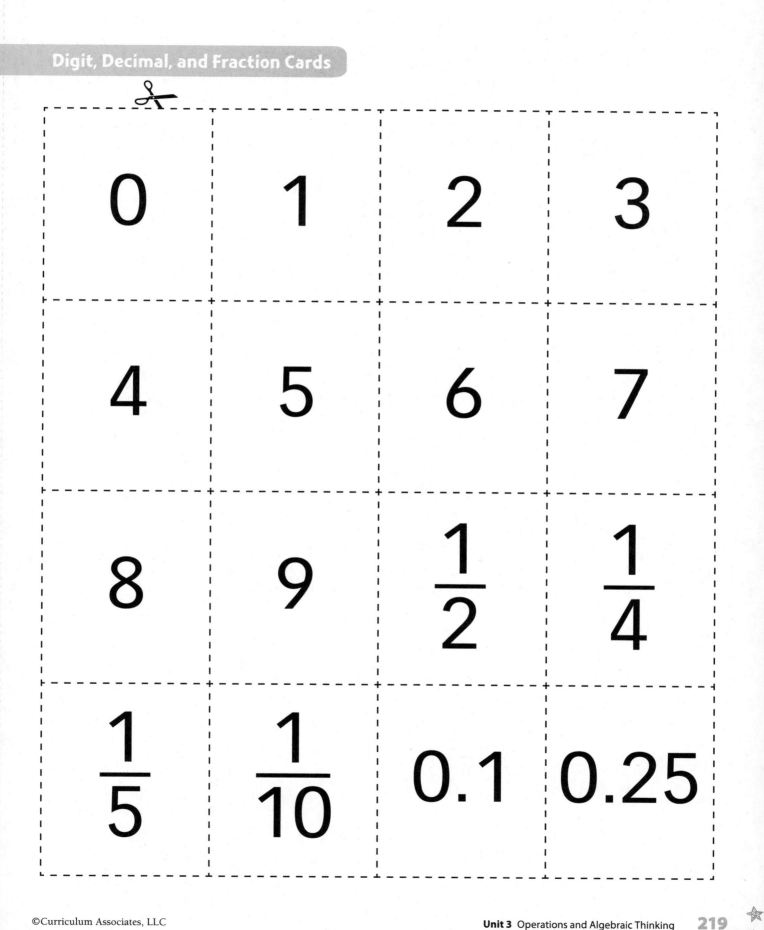

Name: _____

Operations and Algebraic Thinking

In this unit you learned to:	Lesson
evaluate expressions, for example: 48 ÷ (6 + 10) = 3.	19
write expressions, for example: "subtract 5 from 12, then multiply by 4" can be written as (12 − 5) × 4.	19

find the relationship between two sequences, for example:
   sequence 1: 0, 2, 4, 6, 8, . . .
   sequence 2: 0, 8, 16, 24, 32, . . .
Each term in sequence 2 is 4 times the corresponding term in sequence 1.
	20

create ordered pairs for two sequences and graph the relationship on the coordinate plane, for example: ordered pairs for sequence 1 and 2 above are (0, 0), (2, 8), (4, 16), (6, 24), (8, 32).	20

Use these skills to solve problems 1–5.

1 Replace ▢ with a number from the box to write the expression described.

| 6 | 10 | 8 |
| 14 | 9 | 7 |

$$12 \times (▢ - 5)$$

a. The expression with the greatest value.

$$12 \times (\boxed{} - 5)$$

b. The expression with the least value.

$$12 \times (\boxed{} - 5)$$

2 Write numerical expressions for "the quotient of 18 and 6, plus 3" and "18 divided by the sum of 6 and 3." Compare the expressions using <, >, or =.

_____ ◯ _____

Solve.

3 Begin at 0 and use the rules "add 3" and "add 1" to complete the table. Then plot the ordered pairs on the graph.

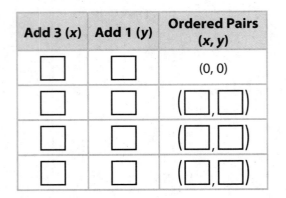

Add 3 (x)	Add 1 (y)	Ordered Pairs (x, y)
☐	☐	(0, 0)
☐	☐	(☐, ☐)
☐	☐	(☐, ☐)
☐	☐	(☐, ☐)

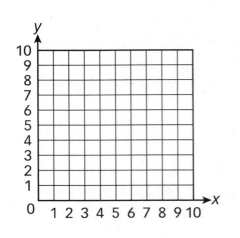

4 Look at the ordered pairs in problem 3. How do the values of the *x*-coordinates compare to the values of the *y*-coordinates?

A They are 3 times as great.

B They are $\frac{1}{3}$ as great.

C They are 4 times as great.

D They are $\frac{1}{4}$ as great.

5 If you were to connect the points on the graph in problem 3, what would the graph look like?

_____

_____

_____

_____

_____

©Curriculum Associates, LLC Copying is not permitted.

Name: _____

Answer the questions and show all your work on separate paper.

You are decorating the school cafeteria for a party. The tables will have flower vases on them.

You can spend between $15 and $25 per table on flowers. Roses cost $10 for a bunch of 3 flowers. Tulips cost $5 for a bunch of 3 flowers. Daisies cost $2 each.

Choose two types of flowers. Decide how many of each type to put in the vase for each table. Show how you are staying within the budget.

Make a table to show how many of each type of flower you will need for 0, 1, 2, 3, 4, 5, and 6 tables. Describe the rule for finding the number of the first type of flower and for finding the number of the second type of flower.

Write the corresponding numbers of flowers as ordered pairs. Plot the ordered pairs on a graph.

The planning committee decides to have 9 tables at the party. How many of each kind of flower will you need? Explain how you used the rules or the graph to find out.

Reflect on Mathematical Practices

1 **Make Sense of Problems** Explain how you decided which flowers to use and how many of each type.

2 **Use Repeated Reasoning** How did you find the rule for each type of flower? How is the rule related to the way to move from one point to the next on the graph?

Checklist

Did you . . .

☐ make a table?

☐ label your graph?

☐ check to see if your answers make sense and fit the situation?

Word Bank Here are some words that you might use in your answer.

ordered pair	add	multiply
rule	graph	coordinates
corresponding terms	as many as	

Models Here are some models that you might use to find the solution.

+? +? +? +?
0, 3, 6, 9, 12

Flower *x*	Flower *y*	Ordered Pairs (*x, y*)

Sentence Starters Here are some sentence starters that might help explain your work.

To find the number of _____

The rule for _____

Each table needs _____

 ©Curriculum Associates, LLC   Copying is not permitted.

Unit 3 Vocabulary

Name: _____

My Examples

evaluate

to find the value of an expression

expression

a group of numbers and symbols that
shows a mathematical relationship

parentheses

the grouping symbol ( ); they group part
of an expression

corresponding terms

the numbers that are in the same place in
two or more related patterns

coordinate plane

a two-dimensional space formed by two perpendicular number lines called axes

ordered pair

a pair of numbers, or coordinates, (*x*, *y*) describing the location of a point on a coordinate plane

My Words

_____

_____

_____

_____

_____

_____

_____

_____

©Curriculum Associates, LLC   Copying is not permitted.

Dear Family,

This week your child is learning to convert from one measurement unit to another.

Your child is learning to convert:

- from one unit of length to another, using kilometers, meters, and centimeters.

- from one unit of weight to another, using pounds and ounces.

- from one unit of capacity to another, using gallons, quarts, and cups.

You can describe the same measurement using different units. For example, 1 kilometer describes the same distance as 1,000 meters. The length is the same. The units used to measure the length are different, so the number of units in the measurement is different, too.

Kilometers are a larger unit of measurement than meters. Since there are 1,000 meters in each kilometer, you can multiply the length, or distance, in kilometers by 1,000 to convert the measurement to meters.

> 4.5 kilometers = ? meters
> $4.5 \times 1,000 = 4,500$
> 4.5 kilometers = 4,500 meters

Meters are a smaller unit of measurement than kilometers. Since 1 kilometer is equivalent to 1,000 meters, you can divide the length, or distance, in meters by 1,000 to convert the measurement to kilometers.

> 6,700 meters = ? kilometers
> $6,700 \div 1,000 = 6.7$
> 6,700 meters = 6.7 kilometers

Your child is becoming familiar with the relative sizes of units: which units are larger and which units are smaller. And as your child practices converting units, he or she is also applying multiplication and division skills.

Invite your child to share what he or she knows about converting measurement units by doing the following activity together.

NEXT

Convert Measurement Units Activity

Materials: ruler or measuring tape, sheet of paper

Play a game with your child to convert measurements in real-life situations.

- Choose a place to mark a starting line. It can be inside your home or outside. Make sure there's enough open space if you choose to play inside.

- Make a paper ball by crumpling a sheet of paper.

- Have your child stand at the starting line and toss the paper ball.

- Together, measure the length of the toss to the nearest foot. Then convert the length of the toss from feet to inches. [1 foot = 12 inches.] So multiply the number of feet by 12 to find the number of inches.

- Take turns tossing the ball, measuring, and converting measurements.

Look out for other real-life opportunities to practice converting measurements with your child. You might convert measurements when you use a recipe, do a craft project together, make a home repair, or plan a trip.

©Curriculum Associates, LLC   Copying is not permitted.

Convert Measurement Units

Name: _____

Study the example problem showing how to convert between meters and centimeters. Then solve problems 1–11.

Example

How many centimeters are in 4 meters?

1 meter equals 100 centimeters.

```
0 cm   10    20    30    40    50    60    70    80    90    100
                                                         1 m
```

You can multiply by 100 to find how many centimeters are in 4 meters.

$4 \times 100 = 400$

There are 400 centimeters in 4 meters.

---

1 Which is the smaller unit, meter or centimeter?

_____

2 How can you find how many centimeters are in 5 meters?

_____

_____

3 How many centimeters are in 5 meters? _____

4 Complete the table.

meters (m)	1	2	3	4	5	6	7	8
centimeters (cm)	100	200	300	400				

5 Write an expression that shows how to convert any number of meters to centimeters. Use *m* to stand for the number of meters. _____

6 Use the expression you wrote in problem 5 to find the number of centimeters in 9 meters.

_____

Solve.

7 Fill in the table to show how many milliliters are in the number of liters shown.

liters (L)	1	2	3	4	5	6	7	8
milliliters (mL)	1,000	2,000	3,000	4,000				

8 Write an equation to describe the relationship between each pair of numbers in the table.

_____

9 Use the equation you wrote in problem 8. How many milliliters are in 9 liters?

_____

10 Jack's bicycle has a mass of 9 kilograms. What is the mass of Jack's bicycle in grams?

Show your work.

> 1 kilogram = 1,000 grams

Solution: _____

11 Look at problem 10. Jack's little sister has a tricycle that has a mass of 7 kilograms. How much greater is the mass of Jack's bicycle, in grams, than his sister's tricycle?

Show your work.

Solution: _____

©Curriculum Associates, LLC   Copying is not permitted.

Name: _____

Convert Measurement Units Using Multiplication

Study the example problem showing how to convert between meters and millimeters. Then solve problems 1–10.

Example

How many millimeters are in 2.52 meters?

The table below shows the relationship between meters and millimeters.

meters (m)	1	2	3	4	5
millimeters (mm)	1,000	2,000	3,000	4,000	5,000

The number of millimeters is always 1,000 times the number of meters.

To find the number of millimeters in 2.52 meters, multiply 2.52 by 1,000.

$2.52 \times 1,000 = 2,520$ millimeters

1 Which is the larger unit, meters or millimeters? _____

2 How can you find how many millimeters are in 4.06 meters?

_____

_____

3 How many millimeters are in 4.06 meters? _____

4 Fill in the missing information in the table.

meters (m)	0.34	1	1.5	2	2.09	3	3.77	4
millimeters (mm)	☐	1,000	☐	2,000	☐	3,000	☐	4,000

5 What operation do you use to convert from a larger measurement unit to a smaller measurement unit? Explain why.

_____

_____

Solve.

6   The pattern in the table shows that the number of
centimeters is always 100 times the number of meters.
Fill in the missing number of centimeters.

meters (m)	1	1.5	2	2.07	3	3.26	4
centimeters (cm)	100	150	200				

7   In football, the goal posts in the end zone are
7.11 meters apart. How many centimeters are in
7.11 meters?

Show your work.

Solution: _____

8   There are 4 cups in 1 quart. If you want to convert
quarts to cups, should you multiply or divide by 4?
Explain.

_____

_____

9   Look at problem 8. How many cups are in 5.5 quarts?

Show your work.

Solution: _____

10   16 ounces is equivalent to 1 pound. A lion cub born at
the zoo weighs $2\frac{1}{2}$ pounds. How many ounces does
the lion cub weigh?

Show your work.

Solution: _____

   ©Curriculum Associates, LLC   Copying is not permitted.

Name: _____

Convert Measurement Units Using Division

Study the example problem showing how to convert between ounces and pounds. Then solve problems 1–8.

Example

How many pounds are equivalent to 56 ounces?

The table below shows the relationship between pounds and ounces.

pounds (lb)	1	2	3	4
ounces (oz)	16	32	48	64

The pattern in the table shows that there are 16 ounces in every pound.

To find the number of pounds equivalent to 56 ounces, divide by 16.

$56 \div 16 = 3\frac{1}{2}$

$3\frac{1}{2}$ pounds is equivalent to 56 ounces.

---

1 Which is the smaller unit, pounds or ounces? _____

2 What operation do you use to convert from a smaller measurement to a larger measurement unit? _____

3 Look at the example problem. Explain how you can use multiplication to check the answer.

_____

_____

_____

4 Use the relationship between pounds and ounces shown in the example to complete the table below.

pounds (lb)		1		2	
ounces (oz)	8	16	20	32	40

©Curriculum Associates, LLC   Copying is not permitted.

Solve.

5 One yard is equivalent to 3 feet. How many yards are equivalent to 38 feet?

Show your work.

Solution: _____

6 1 quart is equivalent to 4 cups. How many quarts are equivalent to 60 cups?

Show your work.

Solution: _____

7 When converting between two measurement units, how can you tell which operation to use?

_____

_____

_____

_____

_____

8 1 gallon is equivalent to 4 quarts, and 1 quart is equivalent to 4 cups. How many gallons are equivalent to 24 cups?

Show your work.

Solution: _____

  ©Curriculum Associates, LLC   Copying is not permitted.

Convert Measurement Units

Solve the problems.

1 Jillian has a rope that is 50 inches long. Write the length of her rope in feet and inches. Explain how you converted the units of measurement.

Show your work.

1 foot is equivalent to 12 inches.

Solution: _____

_____

_____

_____

_____

2 1 kilogram is equivalent to 1,000 grams. How many grams are in 3.5 kilograms? Circle the letter of the correct answer.

Which unit is smaller and which is larger? Which operation do you use to convert?

A 0.35 gram   **C** 3,500 grams

B 3.5 grams   **D** 35,000 grams

Rodney chose **D** as the correct answer. How did he get that answer?

_____

_____

_____

_____

Solve.

3　1 gallon is equivalent to 8 pints. Fill in the table with the missing number of gallons or pints.

gallons	1	2	☐	4	☐
pints	8	16	24	☐	40

Which measurement unit is smaller? Which is larger?

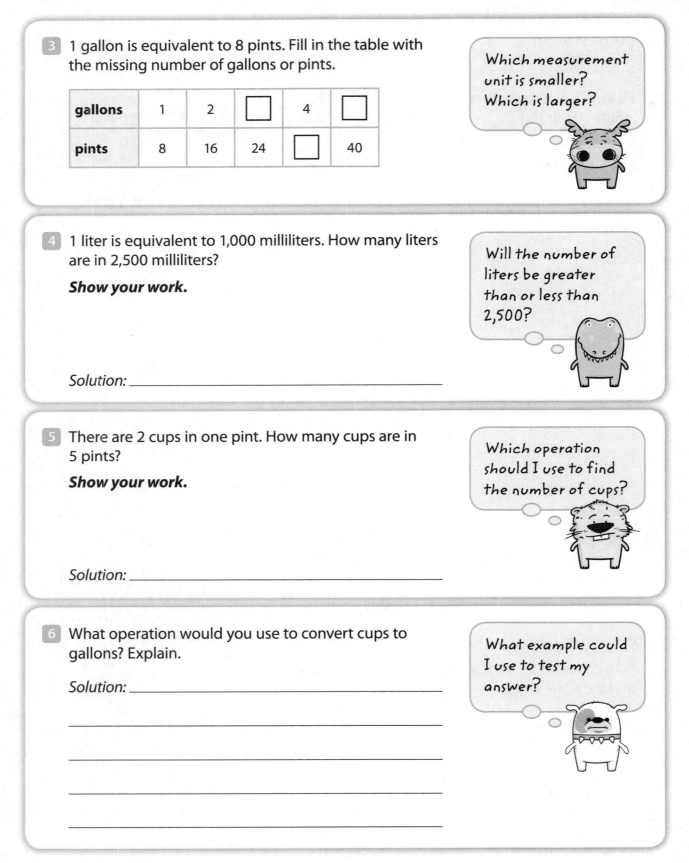

4　1 liter is equivalent to 1,000 milliliters. How many liters are in 2,500 milliliters?

Show your work.

Will the number of liters be greater than or less than 2,500?

Solution: _____

5　There are 2 cups in one pint. How many cups are in 5 pints?

Show your work.

Which operation should I use to find the number of cups?

Solution: _____

6　What operation would you use to convert cups to gallons? Explain.

Solution: _____

What example could I use to test my answer?

_____

_____

_____

©Curriculum Associates, LLC　Copying is not permitted.

Dear Family,

This week your child is learning how to solve word problems that involve converting units of measurement.

Your child might see a problem like this:

> Laura is making punch for a party. The recipe calls for $3\frac{1}{2}$ cups of lemonade per batch. Laura wants to make 10 batches of punch. How many gallons of lemonade will she need to buy?

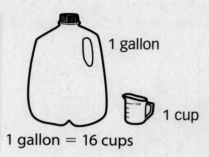

1 gallon

1 cup

1 gallon = 16 cups

The picture shows how cups and gallons are related. You can see that gallons are larger units of measurement than cups.

The first step in solving the problem is to find how many cups are needed to make 10 batches of lemonade. Then you can convert cups to gallons.

- Multiply the number of cups needed for one batch by 10.

  35 cups are needed for 10 batches.

$$10 \times 3\frac{1}{2} = 10 \times \left(3 + \frac{1}{2}\right)$$
$$= 10 \times 3 + 10 \times \frac{1}{2}$$
$$= 30 + 5$$
$$= 35 \text{ cups}$$

- Convert 35 cups to gallons. Gallons are larger than cups, so you need fewer of them. So, divide by 16.

  $35 \div 16 = 2$ gallons with 3 cups left over

The 3 cups left over means that Laura will need to buy another gallon of lemonade in addition to the 2 gallons. She will need to buy 3 gallons of lemonade in all in order to have enough to make 10 batches of punch.

Invite your child to share what he or she knows about solving word problems that involve converting units of measurement by doing the following activity together.

NEXT

Work with your child to make up and solve real-life problems involving converting units of measurement.

- Use the examples below or use your own ideas. To convert units, you can use the equivalent units of measurement that are shown at the bottom of the page.

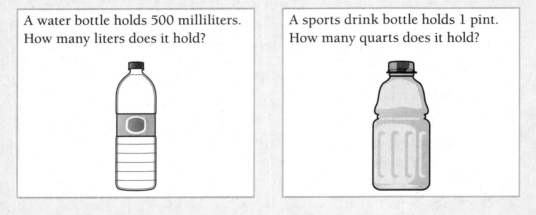

A water bottle holds 500 milliliters. How many liters does it hold?

A sports drink bottle holds 1 pint. How many quarts does it hold?

- Work together to create and solve problems about real-life situations.

- Example: Sally is bringing sports drink to a team party. The coach asks her to bring $2\frac{1}{2}$ gallons of sports drink. How many of the sports drink bottles shown above will Sally need to bring? (1 gallon = 8 pints; $2\frac{1}{2} \times 8 = 20$ pints; Sally needs to bring 20 bottles.)

Be on the lookout for real-life situations when you can convert measurements with your child.

1 kilometer = 1,000 meters
1 meter = 100 centimeters
1 centimeter = 10 millimeters

1 liter = 1,000 milliliters

1 gallon = 16 cups	1 gallon = 4 quarts
1 quart = 4 cups	1 gallon = 8 pints
1 pint = 2 cups	1 quart = 2 pints

1 mile = 1,760 yards
1 yard = 3 feet
1 foot = 12 inches

©Curriculum Associates, LLC   Copying is not permitted.

Solve Word Problems Involving Conversions

Name: _____

Prerequisite: Convert Measurement Units

Study the example problem showing how to convert between feet and yards. Then solve problems 1–13.

Example

How many feet are in $7\frac{1}{3}$ yards?

1 yard is equivalent to 3 feet.

1 yard (yd)

3 feet (ft)

To find how many feet are in $7\frac{1}{3}$ yards, multiply the number of yards by 3.

$7 \times 3 = 21$ $\frac{1}{3} \times 3 = 1$ $21 + 1 = 22$

There are 22 feet in $7\frac{1}{3}$ yards.

---

1. Which is the smaller unit of measurement, foot or yard? _____

2. How many feet are in 5 yards? Explain how you calculated your answer.

   _____

   _____

3. Complete the table.

yards (yd)	1	2	3	4	5	6	7	8
feet (ft)	3	6	9	12	☐	☐	☐	☐

4. How many yards are equivalent to 30 feet? Explain how you calculated your answer.

   _____

   _____

Lesson 22 Solve Word Problems Involving Conversions   **239**

Solve.

5 Which is the larger unit of measurement, meter or centimeter? _____

1 meter = 100 centimeters.

6 Look at problem 5. How did you know which unit of measurement was larger?

_____

_____

_____

7 How many centimeters are in *x* meters?

_____

8 Use your expression from problem 7. How many centimeters are in 2.7 meters?

_____

9 Write an expression to show how many meters are equivalent to *x* centimeters. _____

10 Use your expression from problem 9. How many meters are equivalent to 400 centimeters?

_____

11 Complete the table.

centimeters (cm)	100	150	200	270			400	480
meters (m)	1	1.5			3	3.2		

12 How many meters are equivalent to 175 centimeters?

_____

13 How many centimeters are in 2.37 meters?

_____

    ©Curriculum Associates, LLC   Copying is not permitted.

Name: _____

Convert Units Using Equations

Study the example problem showing how to solve a word problem by converting units. Then solve problems 1–5.

Example

Michael is planning a party for 30 people. He plans that each guest will drink 1 cup of juice. He has $2\frac{1}{2}$ gallons of juice. Does he have enough juice for the party?

Michael multiplies $2\frac{1}{2}$ by 16 to find the number of cups of juice he has.

$$2\frac{1}{2} \times 16 = \left(2 + \frac{1}{2}\right) \times 16$$
$$= 2 \times 16 + \frac{1}{2} \times 16$$
$$= 32 + 8$$
$$= 40 \qquad \text{There are 40 cups of juice.}$$

$40 > 30$, so Michael has enough juice for the party.

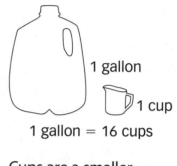

1 gallon

1 cup

1 gallon = 16 cups

Cups are a smaller measurement unit than gallons, so to convert, use multiplication.

1 Juanita has $1\frac{1}{2}$ gallons of milk. How many cups of milk does she have? Explain how you know.

_____

_____

_____

2 Benjamin has 3 gallons of punch. He adds another $\frac{1}{2}$ gallon of juice to the punch. How many gallons of punch does he have now? How many cups? Explain your reasoning.

_____

_____

_____

Lesson 22 Solve Word Problems Involving Conversions   **241**

Solve.

Units of Capacity
1 quart = 4 cups

3 Ms. Monet, the art teacher at Giverny School, has 3 quarts of liquid glue and 24 empty glue bottles that each hold 1 cup. Does she have enough glue to fill all of the bottles? Explain.

_____

_____

_____

_____

4 Ms. Monet gave 1 cup of red paint to each of her 20 students. How many quarts of red paint did she give out?

Show your work.

Solution: _____

5 Ms. Monet is combining 15 cups of green paint with 15 cups of white paint. She is pouring the paint mixture into empty quart bottles. How many quart bottles does she need? Explain.

Show your work.

Solution: _____

_____

_____

_____

©Curriculum Associates, LLC   Copying is not permitted.

Name: _____

Solve Word Problems Involving Conversions

Study the example problem showing how to compare measurements in different units. Then solve problems 1–7.

Example

Ryan and Layla measured the length of their hermit crabs. Ryan measured his crab to be 34 millimeters. Layla measured her crab to be 2.8 centimeters. Who has the longer crab?

34 millimeters

2.8 centimeters

It is easier to compare measurements in the same units. You can compare in millimeters or centimeters.

$$1 \text{ cm} = 10 \text{ mm}$$

To compare the crabs in millimeters, you have to convert the measurement of Layla's crab into millimeters. To convert from centimeters to millimeters, use multiplication because centimeters are the larger measurement unit.

2.8 cm × 10 = 28 mm   Layla's crab is 28 mm long.
34 mm > 28 mm
Ryan has the longer crab.

1　Which is the smaller unit of measurement, centimeter or millimeter? _____

2　In the example problem, multiplication was used to convert centimeters to millimeters. What operation would you use to convert millimeters to centimeters?

_____

3　Look at the example problem. Ryan and Layla's friend Jan also has a hermit crab. Jan measures her hermit crab to be 3.3 cm long.

a. Who has the longer crab, Jan or Layla? _____

b. Who has the longer crab, Jan or Ryan? _____

Show your work.

Solve.

4 Geno has two hamsters, Zippy and Popcorn. Zippy is
94 millimeters long, and Popcorn is 8.7 centimeters
long. How much longer is Zippy in millimeters? Explain.

Show your work.

Solution: _____

_____

_____

_____

5 Carissa's gerbil has a tail that is the same length as its
body length. Its tail is 102 millimeters. How long is her
gerbil in centimeters?

Show your work.

> The length of
> Carissa's gerbil is the
> length of its body
> plus the length of
> its tail.

Solution: _____

6 Diego's parakeet is 13 centimeters, 4 millimeters tall.
How tall is his parakeet in millimeters?

Show your work.

Solution: _____

7 Amelia takes her two cats, Sparkle and Twinkle, to the
vet. The vet says that Sparkle is 464 mm long and
Twinkle is 46 cm long. Which of Amelia's cats is longer?
Explain.

_____

_____

_____

    ©Curriculum Associates, LLC   Copying is not permitted.

Name: _____

Solve Word Problems Involving Conversions

Solve the problems.

1 Audrey's dog is 40 inches tall. How tall is her dog in feet and inches?

| 1 foot = 12 inches |

Show your work.

What operation do I use to convert inches to feet?

Solution: _____

2 Denver is called the "Mile High City" because the city's official elevation is 1 mile, or 5,280 feet, above sea level. What is Denver's elevation in yards? Circle the letter of the correct answer.

| 1 yard = 3 feet |

Are there more feet or yards in one mile?

A 15,840 yards   **C** 1,760 yards

B 5,277 yards   **D** 440 yards

Katherine chose **A** as the correct answer. How did she get that answer?

_____

_____

_____

_____

_____

_____

_____

Lesson 22 Solve Word Problems Involving Conversions   **245**

Solve.

3 Jake and Nico both measured their thumbs. Jake's thumb is 55 millimeters long. Nico's thumb is 5.7 centimeters long. Who has the longer thumb? Explain how you know.

_____

_____

_____

_____

_____

> There are 10 millimeters in 1 centimeter.

4 Toby's house is 25 feet high. How high is Toby's house in yards and feet?

Show your work.

Solution: _____

> There are 3 feet in 1 yard.

5 Mica is making a paste mixture for an art project. He mixes 8 cups of water with glue. If he wants to make a double batch, how many quarts of water does he need? How much water is that in gallons?

Show your work.

Solution: _____

_____

> I know there are 4 cups in 1 quart, and there are 4 quarts in 1 gallon.

©Curriculum Associates, LLC   Copying is not permitted.

Dear Family,

This week your child is learning about line plots and about how to interpret data on line plots.

A **line plot** is a graph that uses Xs above a number line to show data. A line plot is useful for showing how data are grouped.

The line plot below shows the weights of tomatoes. Each tomato is represented by an X on the line plot. Xs that are one above another represent tomatoes that have the same weight. Weights are labeled beneath the number line.

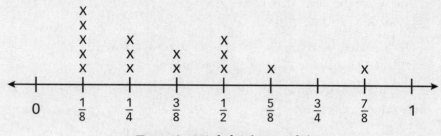

Tomato Weight (pounds)

The line plot shows how the data are grouped. You can describe the data by looking at the line plot. Most pieces of data on this line plot are grouped between $\frac{1}{8}$ and $\frac{1}{2}$.

You can also do mathematical operations on the data to describe the data. For example, you can find the difference between the heaviest and lightest tomatoes. The weights vary from $\frac{1}{8}$ pound to $\frac{7}{8}$ pound. The difference is $\frac{6}{8}$, or $\frac{3}{4}$, pound.

$$\frac{7}{8} - \frac{1}{8} = \frac{6}{8} \text{ pound}$$

Using line plots can help your child ask and answer complex questions about data.

Invite your child to share what he or she knows about making line plots and interpreting data by doing the following activity together.

NEXT

Line Plot Activity

Materials: centimeter ruler

Work with your child to make a line plot of the lengths of book covers.

- Gather several books. Measure the length of the cover of each book. Measure to the nearest centimeter. Use your own centimeter ruler or cut out and use the centimeter ruler below.

- Make a list of the lengths and use the data to make a line plot.

  - Use the number line below. Title the line plot "Lengths of Book Covers" and write the label "Cover Lengths" beneath the number line.

  - Decide what labels to use based on the measurements you collect. Then mark Xs to show the data.

- Describe the data shown on the line plot. Talk about whether the data values are grouped.

- Do mathematical operations on the data to describe the data.

  - Example: The difference between the length of the longest book cover and the length of the shortest book cover is _____ centimeters.

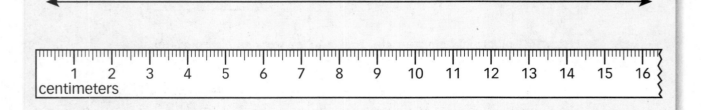

©Curriculum Associates, LLC   Copying is not permitted.

Make Line Plots and Interpret Data

Name: _____

Study the example problem showing how to solve a problem by reading a line plot. Then solve problems 1–7.

Example

Mason sold pumpkin seeds at the farmer's market on Saturday. The line plot shows the different weights of bags that he sold. What is the total weight of pumpkin seeds sold on Saturday?

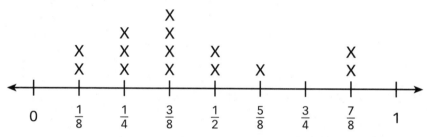

Pumpkin Seed Weight (in pounds)

Each X stands for 1 bag of pumpkin seeds sold. Add the weight of each bag.

$$\frac{1}{8} + \frac{1}{8} + \frac{1}{4} + \frac{1}{4} + \frac{1}{4} + \frac{3}{8} + \frac{3}{8} + \frac{3}{8} + \frac{3}{8} + \frac{1}{2} + \frac{1}{2} + \frac{5}{8} + \frac{7}{8} + \frac{7}{8} = 5\frac{7}{8}$$

$5\frac{7}{8}$ pounds of pumpkin seeds were sold on Saturday.

1　What are the weights of the lightest and heaviest pumpkin seed bags sold? What is the difference between these weights?

lightest _____

heaviest _____

difference _____

2　What is the total weight of the $\frac{1}{2}$-pound bags of pumpkin seeds sold? _____

3　Suppose 3 bags of $\frac{3}{4}$-pound seeds and 2 bags of 1-pound seeds were also sold. Add this data to the line plot in the example.

Vocabulary

line plot a graph that uses Xs above a number line to show data; useful for showing how data is grouped.

Solve.

Rodrigo recorded the weight of each acorn squash he sold at the farmer's market. The weights are shown below.

$2\frac{1}{4}$	$2\frac{3}{8}$	$2\frac{3}{4}$	$2\frac{1}{4}$	$2\frac{3}{4}$	$2\frac{5}{8}$	$2\frac{1}{2}$	$2\frac{1}{4}$	$2\frac{3}{4}$	$2\frac{1}{8}$
$2\frac{1}{2}$	$2\frac{7}{8}$	$2\frac{1}{8}$	$2\frac{1}{2}$	$2\frac{1}{4}$	$2\frac{3}{4}$	$2\frac{1}{8}$	$2\frac{5}{8}$	$2\frac{3}{8}$	$2\frac{1}{4}$

4 Use the data in the table to complete the line plot.

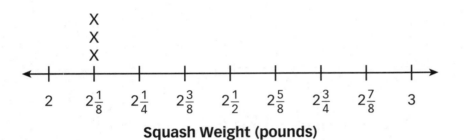

Squash Weight (pounds)

5 What is the difference between the weights of the heaviest and lightest squash sold?

_____

6 Which weight includes the greatest number of squashes? Explain how you know.

_____

_____

7 What is the total weight of all the squashes that weigh less than $2\frac{1}{2}$ pounds?
Show your work.

Solution: _____

©Curriculum Associates, LLC   Copying is not permitted.

Name: _____

Make a Line Plot

Study the example problem showing how to make a line plot. Then solve problems 1–4.

Example

Rosa's grandfather gave her a box of old foreign coins. She measured the diameter of each coin. Then she made a table that showed the diameters and how many coins she had of each diameter. How can Rosa show this data in a line plot?

Make one X to stand for each coin in the table. The line plot below shows the number of coins with a $\frac{3}{8}$-inch diameter.

Diameter (in inches)	Number of Coins
$\frac{3}{8}$	3
$\frac{5}{8}$	8
$\frac{3}{4}$	11
$\frac{7}{8}$	5

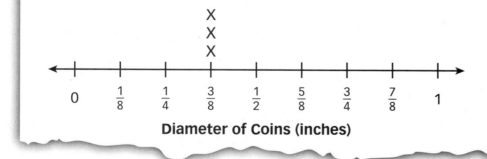

Diameter of Coins (inches)

1 Plot the rest of the data from the table in the example on the line plot.

2 Describe how the data in the line plot are clustered.

_____

_____

_____

Lesson 23 Make Line Plots and Interpret Data   **251**

Solve.

Gabe has a collection of stamps. He recorded the heights of the stamps along with the number of stamps at each height.

Height (in inches)	Number of Stamps
$\frac{1}{2}$	2
1	5
$1\frac{1}{2}$	9
2	6
$2\frac{1}{2}$	3
3	1

3 Make a line plot to show the data in the table.

4 Below are widths in inches of some of Gabe's stamps. Make a line plot to show this data. Then write a statement to describe the distribution of the data.

$\frac{3}{4}$, 1, $1\frac{1}{2}$, $1\frac{1}{4}$, $1\frac{1}{2}$, 1, $1\frac{3}{4}$, $1\frac{3}{4}$, $1\frac{1}{2}$, $\frac{1}{2}$

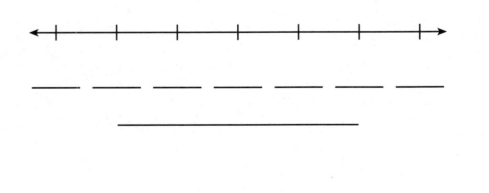

Vocabulary

distribution how spread out or how clustered pieces of data are.

©Curriculum Associates, LLC   Copying is not permitted.

Name: _____

Solve Problems Using Data in a Line Plot

Study the example showing how to solve a problem using data in a line plot. Then solve problems 1–7.

Example

Miguel has strips of colored tape that he uses to decorate his model planes. The line plot shows how many strips he has in several different lengths.

If Miguel places all of the $\frac{1}{4}$-inch strips in a row, how long is the line that he makes?

There are six $\frac{1}{4}$-inch strips, and $6 \times \frac{1}{4} = \frac{6}{4}$, or $1\frac{1}{2}$. The line would be $1\frac{1}{2}$ inches long.

```
                          X           X
                      X   X           X
              X       X   X           X
              X       X   X   X       X
              X       X   X   X       X
              X       X   X   X       X
              X       X   X   X       X
              X       X   X   X       X
    ←——+———+———+———+———+———+———+———+———+———→
       0   1   1   3   1   5   3   7   1
           8   4   8   2   8   4   8
```

Tape Strip Lengths (inches)

---

1 How long a line can you make using all the $\frac{3}{8}$-inch strips?

Show your work.

Solution: _____

2 How long a line can you make using all the $\frac{5}{8}$-inch strips?

_____

3 Miguel wants to make a 5-inch line. Can he do this using the $\frac{1}{2}$-inch strips that he has? Explain.

_____

_____

_____

Use the data in the line plot to solve.

4 If Miguel uses 2 of each length strip to make a line, how long would it be?

Show your work.

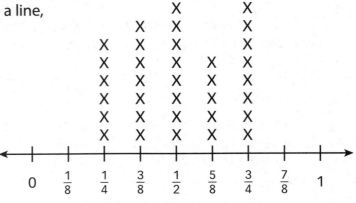

Tape Strip Lengths (inches)

Solution: _____

5 How many times longer are the longest strips than the shortest strips? Explain.

_____

_____

_____

6 Can Miguel use $\frac{3}{4}$-inch strips to make a line that is

exactly 5 inches long? Explain.

_____

_____

_____

7 How could Miguel use strips of different lengths to make a 4-inch line?

_____

_____

_____

©Curriculum Associates, LLC   Copying is not permitted.

Name: _____

Make Line Plots and Interpret Data

Solve the problems.

Kelly works at a grocery store. One day, she recorded the weight of each melon before she put it in a bin. The line plot shows the data.

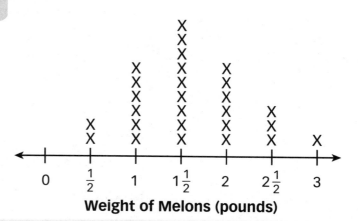

Weight of Melons (pounds)

1 Look at the data in the line plot. Which statement about the data is true?

A There are 3 melons at the heaviest weight.

B The heaviest melon is $2\frac{1}{2}$ times the weight of the lightest melon.

C All of the melons weigh between 1 and 3 pounds.

D The weight of the greatest number of melons is $1\frac{1}{2}$ pounds.

Shrina chose **B** as the correct answer. How did she get that answer?

_____

_____

_____

> Be sure to check each statement against the data in the line plot.

2 Describe the distribution of the data in the line plot.

_____

_____

_____

_____

_____

> Do the weights in the line plot have about the same number of Xs or do some have more than others?

Solve.

Dorothy has a basket of apples. She weighs them and makes a table to show how many apples she has of each weight.

Weight (pounds)	Number of Apples
$\frac{1}{4}$	3
$\frac{3}{8}$	6
$\frac{1}{2}$	5
$\frac{5}{8}$	4
$\frac{3}{4}$	2

3 Make a line plot to show the data.

> I would first look at the fractions that I need to show and decide what scale to use.

4 What is the total weight of Dorothy's apples?

Show your work.

> What is the total weight of the apples for each weight?

Solution: _____

5 Dorothy groups apples that have the same weight in a basket. She has five baskets. Do any baskets have the same weight? Explain.

_____

_____

_____

_____

> This means that all the $\frac{1}{4}$-pound apples are in one basket, all the $\frac{3}{8}$-pound apples are in another basket, and so on.

   ©Curriculum Associates, LLC   Copying is not permitted.

Dear Family,

This week your child is exploring volume.

Volume is the amount of space inside a solid figure.
A **cubic unit** is a cube, 1 unit on each edge, used to measure volume.

Your child has already learned to find the area of a figure, like a rectangle, by covering it with unit squares. Area is the number of square units needed to cover a plane figure.

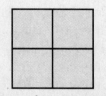

Area = 4 square units

Now your child is learning to find the volume of a solid figure, like a cube, by filling it with unit cubes. Volume is the number of cubic units needed to fill a solid figure. The cube at the right has a volume of 8 cubic units.

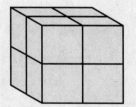

Volume = 8 cubic units

Each unit cube in the solid figures A and B at the right has a measure of 1 cubic unit.

A   B

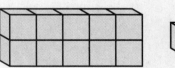

To find which figure has a greater volume, you can count the unit cubes. Figure A has a volume of 10 cubic units. Figure B has a volume of 9 cubic units. Figure A has a greater volume than figure B because 10 > 9.

Invite your child to share what he or she knows about volume by doing the following activity together.

NEXT

Work together with your child to find the volume of solid figures.

- Each solid figure below is made of unit cubes. Each unit cube has a measure of 1 cubic unit.

- Ask your child to explain how to find the volume of each solid figure. Then, write the volume. (Top row: 16 cubic units, 18 cubic units; bottom row: 12 cubic units, 16 cubic units)

- Challenge! Look at all the solid figures below. Which two figures have the same volume? What is the same about the figures? What is different? (The top left and bottom right figures each have a volume of 16 cubic units. They both have 16 unit cubes. The top left figure has 4 layers with 4 cubes in 1 straight row in each layer. The bottom right figure has 2 layers with 8 cubes in 2 rows of 4 in each layer.)

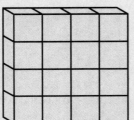

Volume = _____ cubic units

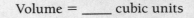

Volume = _____ cubic units

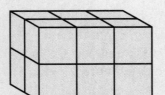

Volume = _____ cubic units

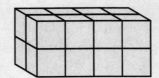

Volume = _____ cubic units

©Curriculum Associates, LLC   Copying is not permitted.

Name: _____

Prerequisite: How do you measure the area of a rectangle?

Study the example problem showing how to find the area of a rectangle. Then solve problems 1–7.

Example

Nan tiled a 5-foot by 8-foot section of her kitchen floor. Each tile covers 1 square foot. What is the area of the floor that she tiled?

Area is the number of square units a figure covers.
The floor has 5 rows of tiles.
There are 8 tiles in each row.

Multiply 5 feet × 8 feet to find the area of the tiled floor.

Area = 5 feet × 8 feet = 40 square feet

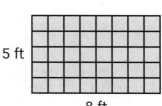

5 ft

8 ft

1 Each square in the rectangle on the right covers 1 square centimeter.

There are _____ rows of squares.

There are _____ squares in each row.

The area of the rectangle is _____ square centimeters.

2 What is the area of the rug at the right?

Show your work.

9 ft

12 ft

Solution: _____

3 The infield of a baseball field is a square with sides that are 90 feet. What is the area of the infield?

_____

©Curriculum Associates, LLC   Copying is not permitted.

Solve.

4 The diagram shows the dimensions of two desks that Hannah is thinking about buying. What is the area of each desktop?

Show your work.

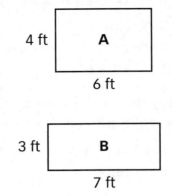

Solution: _____

_____

5 The width of Andy's porch is 5 feet. Its area is 40 square feet. How long is the porch?

Show your work.

Solution: _____

6 Look at problem 5. Andy wants to extend his porch by adding on to the length. This new section will have the same width, but he wants the porch to have a total area of 60 square feet. What should he make the length of the new section?

Show your work.

Solution: _____

7 Jillian wants her rectangular garden to cover an area of 180 square feet. What are the lengths and widths of two possible rectangles she can use? Explain.

_____

_____

_____

_____

 ©Curriculum Associates, LLC   Copying is not permitted.

Name: _____

Find Volume with Unit Cubes

Study the example problem showing how to use unit cubes to find the volume of a rectangular prism. Then solve problems 1–8.

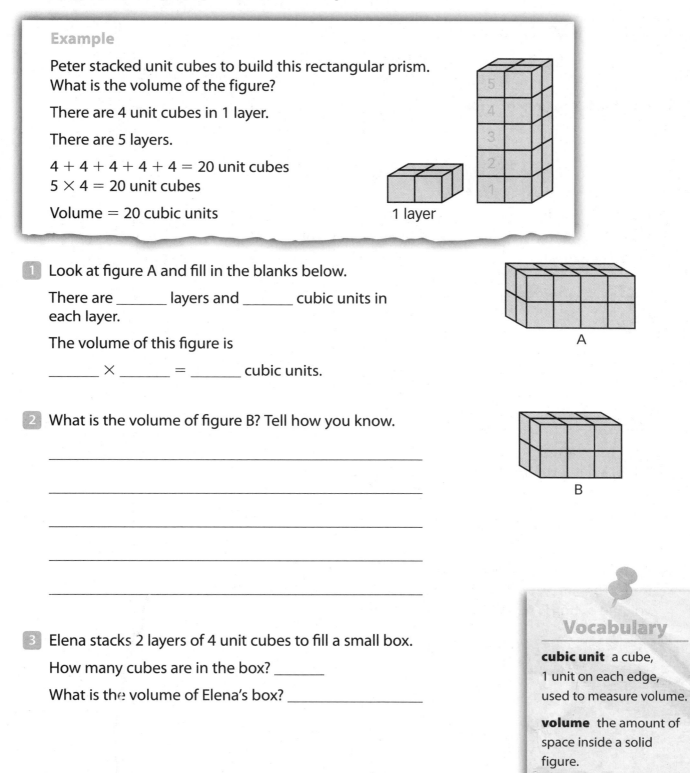

Example

Peter stacked unit cubes to build this rectangular prism. What is the volume of the figure?

There are 4 unit cubes in 1 layer.

There are 5 layers.

$4 + 4 + 4 + 4 + 4 = 20$ unit cubes
$5 \times 4 = 20$ unit cubes

Volume = 20 cubic units

1 layer

1 Look at figure A and fill in the blanks below.

There are _____ layers and _____ cubic units in each layer.

The volume of this figure is

_____ × _____ = _____ cubic units.

A

2 What is the volume of figure B? Tell how you know.

_____

_____

_____

_____

_____

B

3 Elena stacks 2 layers of 4 unit cubes to fill a small box.

How many cubes are in the box? _____

What is the volume of Elena's box? _____

Vocabulary

cubic unit a cube, 1 unit on each edge, used to measure volume.

volume the amount of space inside a solid figure.

©Curriculum Associates, LLC   Copying is not permitted.

Solve.

4 Look at figure C and fill in the blanks below.

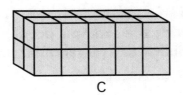

There are _____ layers and _____ cubic units in each layer.

The volume of this block is

_____ × _____ = _____ cubic units.

5 What is the volume of figure D? _____

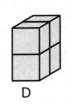

6 How many of figure D does it take to fill figure E? How does the volume of figure D relate to the volume of figure E? Explain.

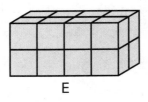

_____

_____

_____

_____

_____

7 A block has a volume of 36 cubic units. It has 9 layers of cubic units. How many cubic units are in each layer?

_____

8 Draw or describe box F that has a volume of 5 cubic units. Then draw or describe a box that has 3 times the volume of box F. What is the volume of the second box?

Solution: _____

_____

©Curriculum Associates, LLC   Copying is not permitted.

Name: _____

Reason and Write

Study the example. Underline two parts that you think make it a particularly good answer and a helpful example.

Example

Niles built this rectangular prism with unit cubes. Then he took apart the prism and built a different prism with the same number of cubes. Draw a picture of the second prism that Niles could have made.

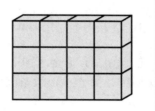

Describe the number of layers and the number of cubes in each layer of both prisms. Write a statement to compare the volume of the prisms.

Show your work. Use pictures, words, or numbers to explain your answer.

The first prism that Niles built has 3 layers and 4 cubes in each layer.

The second prism that Niles built has 2 layers and 6 cubes in each layer.

$3 \times 4 = 12$ and $2 \times 6 = 12$. Both prisms are made of 12 unit cubes, so both have a volume of 12 cubic units.

The volume of both prisms is the same.

Where does the example . . .

• show a drawing?

• describe the number of layers and number of cubes in each layer?

• compare the volume of each prism?

Lesson 24 Understand Volume

Solve the problem. Use what you learned from the example on the previous page.

Example

Leah built this rectangular prism with unit cubes. Then she took apart the prism and built a different prism with the same number of cubes. Draw a picture of the second prism that Leah could have made.

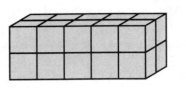

Describe the number of layers and the number of cubes in each layer of both prisms. Write a statement to compare the volume of the prisms.

Show your work. Use pictures, words, or numbers to explain your answer.

Did you. . .
- show a drawing?
- describe the number of layers and number of cubes in each layer?
- compare the volume of each prism?

©Curriculum Associates, LLC   Copying is not permitted.

Dear Family,

This week your child is exploring different ways to find volume.

Suppose you want to find the volume of the rectangular prism at the right. One way to find the volume is to fill it with unit cubes that each have a volume of 1 cubic centimeter.

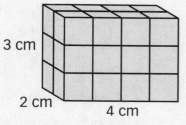

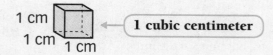

1 cubic centimeter

You can count all the cubes to find the volume. The prism has a volume of 24 cubic centimeters.

Another way to find the volume is to count the cubes in each layer and then add.

There are 8 cubes in each layer and 3 layers in all.
8 + 8 + 8 = 24 cubes

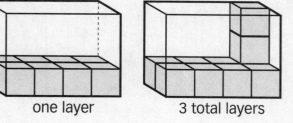

one layer   3 total layers

The volume of the rectangular prism is 24 cubic centimeters. Using either method, the volume is the same.

Your child is also learning that unit cubes can be different sizes. So, it's important to know the size of the cube you're using when you find the volume of a figure.

- A unit cube with side lengths of 1 centimeter has a volume of 1 cubic centimeter.
- A unit cube with side lengths of 1 inch has a volume of 1 cubic inch.
- A unit cube with side lengths of 1 foot has a volume of 1 cubic foot.

Invite your child to share what he or she knows about different ways to find volume by doing the following activity together.

NEXT

Volume with Unit Cubes Activity

Materials: scissors, tape, household containers shaped like rectangular prisms

Work with your child to estimate the volume of household objects that are shaped like rectangular prisms.

- Look around the house for a container that is shaped like a rectangular prism, such as a cracker box, cereal box, or tissue box. Empty the container.

- Cut out the cube pattern below on the solid lines. Fold on the dotted lines and tape into a cube.

- Use the cube to estimate the volume of your container. Remember that you're finding an estimate, not an exact number. You can use an approximate number for the volume.

  - About how many cubes would fit in the bottom of the box?

  - About how many layers of cubes would it take to fill the box?

  - About how many cubes in all would fill the box?

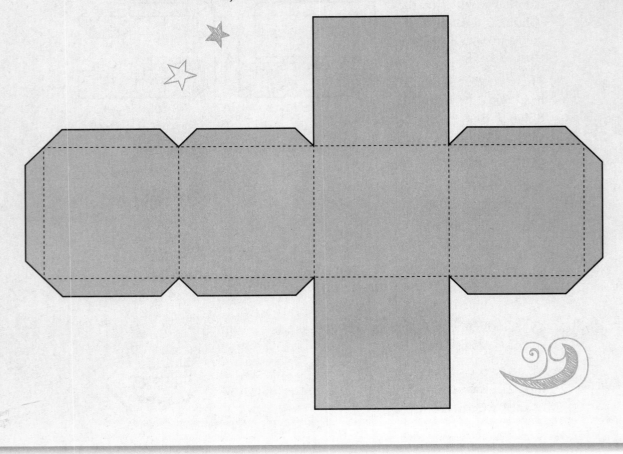

  ©Curriculum Associates, LLC   Copying is not permitted.

Find Volume Using Unit Cubes

Name: _____

Study the example problem showing how to find volume by counting unit cubes. Then solve problems 1–8.

Example

Harry stacked blocks to make a wall. What is the volume of the wall?

The volume of each block is 1 cubic unit.

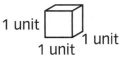

1 unit
1 unit
1 unit

1 cubic unit

Count the blocks in the wall to find the volume.

There are 12 blocks. The volume is 12 cubic units.

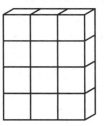

1. The green cubes show 1 layer of figure A.

   Figure A has _____ layers.

   There are _____ cubes in each layer.

   The volume of figure A is _____ cubic units.

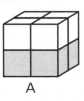

A

2. Fill in the blanks to describe figure B.

   _____ layers

   _____ cubes in each layer

   Volume = _____ cubic units

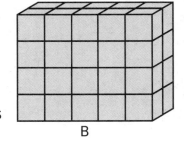

B

3. If you add another layer to figure B, what would the volume be? Explain.

   _____

   _____

   _____

Vocabulary

cubic unit a cube, 1 unit on each edge, used to measure volume.

volume the amount of space inside a solid figure.

Solve.

4 Figure M has _____ layers.

There are _____ cubes in each layer.

The volume of figure M is _____ cubic units.

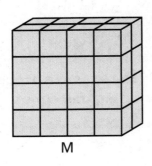

M

5 Figure N is a rectangular prism that has twice the volume of figure M. How many layers and how many cubes in each layer could there be in figure N?

_____

_____

6 What is the volume of figure R? _____

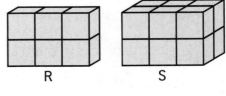

R   S

7 How many of figure R does it take to fill figure S? How does the volume of figure S relate to the volume of figure R? Explain.

_____

_____

_____

8 Show how to find the volume of box T. Then draw or describe a different box that has the same volume as box T.

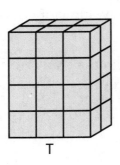

T

©Curriculum Associates, LLC   Copying is not permitted.

Name: _____

Find the Volume of a Rectangular Prism

Study the example problem showing how to use layers to find the volume of a rectangular prism. Then solve problems 1–7.

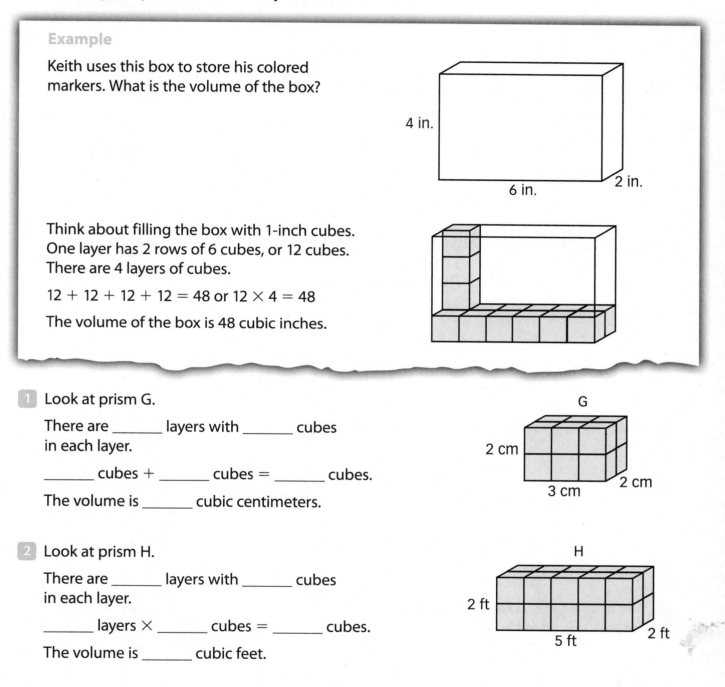

Example

Keith uses this box to store his colored markers. What is the volume of the box?

Think about filling the box with 1-inch cubes. One layer has 2 rows of 6 cubes, or 12 cubes. There are 4 layers of cubes.

12 + 12 + 12 + 12 = 48 or 12 × 4 = 48

The volume of the box is 48 cubic inches.

---

1 Look at prism G.

There are _____ layers with _____ cubes in each layer.

_____ cubes + _____ cubes = _____ cubes.

The volume is _____ cubic centimeters.

2 Look at prism H.

There are _____ layers with _____ cubes in each layer.

_____ layers × _____ cubes = _____ cubes.

The volume is _____ cubic feet.

Solve.

3　What is the volume of this rectangular prism?

Show your work.

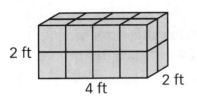
2 ft
4 ft
2 ft

Solution: _____

4　Mia has a box that she filled with the cubes at the right. What is the volume of Mia's box?

Show your work.

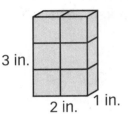
3 in.
2 in.
1 in.

Solution: _____

5　A box is 2 inches long, 1 inch wide, and 6 inches tall. What is the relationship between the volume of this box and the one in problem 4? Tell how you know.

_____

_____

_____

6　Which has a greater volume, box D or box E? Explain.

_____

_____

_____

_____

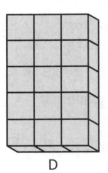
D

7　Add a layer to box D and compare the volumes of the new box D and box E.

_____

_____

_____

_____

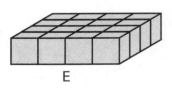
E

©Curriculum Associates, LLC　Copying is not permitted.

Name: _____

Find Volume Using Unit Cubes

Solve the problems.

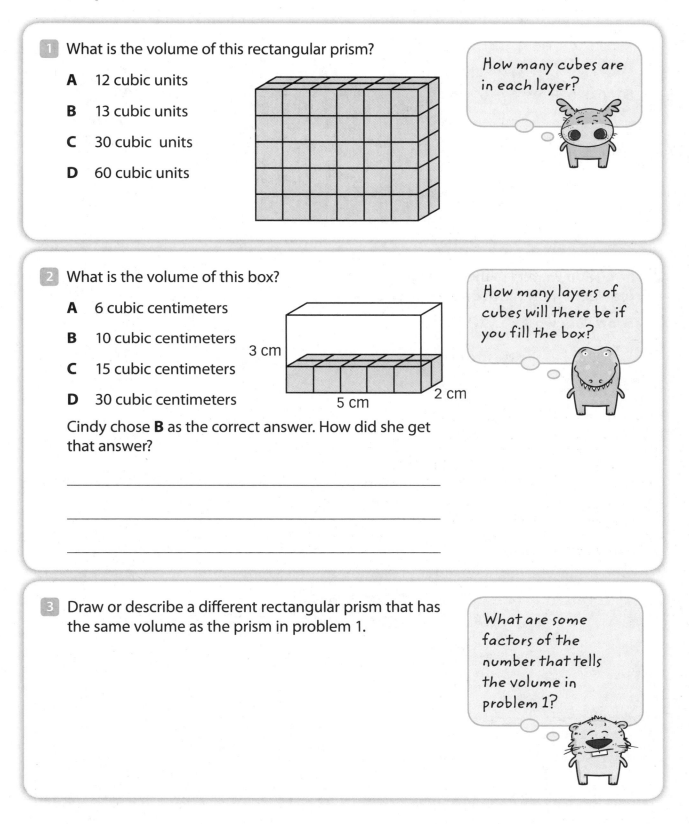

1 What is the volume of this rectangular prism?

A 12 cubic units

B 13 cubic units

C 30 cubic units

D 60 cubic units

How many cubes are in each layer?

2 What is the volume of this box?

A 6 cubic centimeters

B 10 cubic centimeters

C 15 cubic centimeters

D 30 cubic centimeters

3 cm

5 cm

2 cm

How many layers of cubes will there be if you fill the box?

Cindy chose **B** as the correct answer. How did she get that answer?

_____

_____

_____

3 Draw or describe a different rectangular prism that has the same volume as the prism in problem 1.

What are some factors of the number that tells the volume in problem 1?

©Curriculum Associates, LLC   Copying is not permitted.

Solve.

4 Which expressions can be used to find the volume of this rectangular prism? Circle the letter of all that apply.

A 6 + 4 + 1

B 6 + 6 + 6 + 6 + 6 + 6

C 6 × 1

D 6 + 6 + 1

E 6 × 6 × 1

> There is more than one way to find the volume of a rectangular prism.

5 If you add 2 layers to the rectangular prism in problem 4, how much greater is the volume?

Show your work.

> What does the problem ask you to find?

Solution: _____

6 Mr. Carlo is building a storage box in his workshop. The space where he plans to put the box is 5 feet long and 2 feet wide. He wants the volume of the box to be at least 36 cubic feet, but no more than 56 cubic feet. How tall should Mr. Carlo make the box? Explain.

Show your work.

> You can start by finding the number of cubic feet in 1 layer.

? ft

5 ft   2 ft

Solution: _____

_____

_____

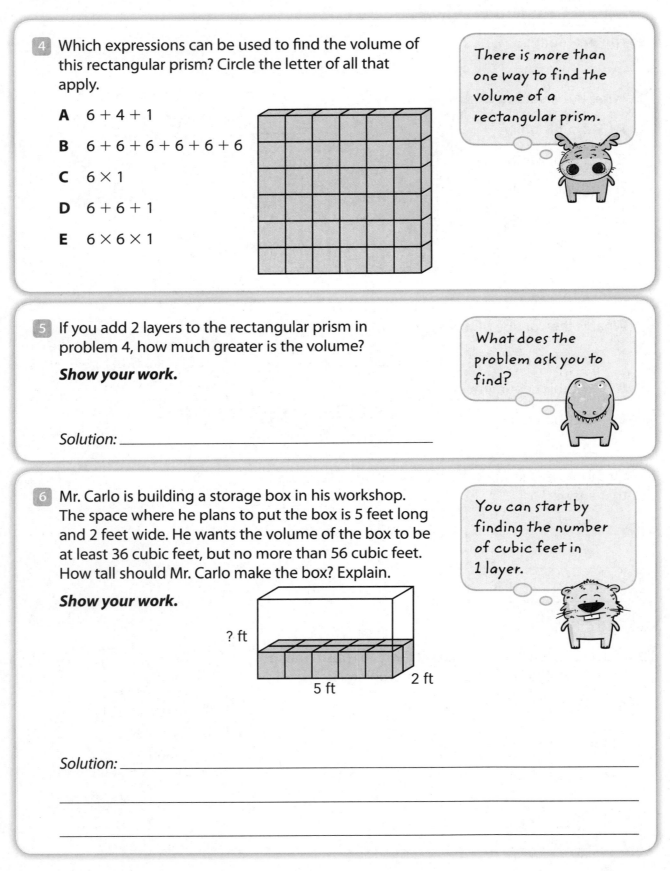

   ©Curriculum Associates, LLC   Copying is not permitted.

Dear Family,

This week your child is learning to find the volume of a solid figure using a formula.

You can use a formula to find the volume of a rectangular prism if you know its length, width, and height. The picture shows a gift bag that is 4 inches long, 2 inches wide, and 3 inches high. The model beside the bag shows the number of 1-inch cubes that would fill the bag.

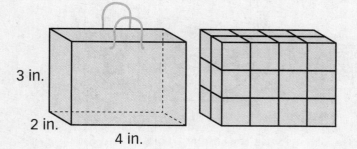

3 in.

2 in.

4 in.

Using the model, you can find the volume of the cube by multiplying the number of cubes in each layer times the number of layers.

The equation to the right shows that multiplying the number of cubes in each layer by the number of layers is the same as multiplying length times width times height. This is the volume formula.

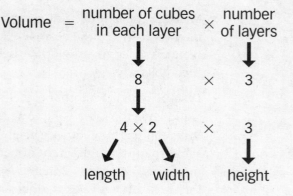

Volume = number of cubes in each layer × number of layers

8 × 3

4 × 2 × 3

length width height

Volume = length × width × height

Volume = 4 inches × 2 inches × 3 inches
= 8 × 3
= 24 cubic inches

The volume of the gift bag is 24 cubic inches.

Invite your child to share what he or she knows about finding volume using a formula by doing the following activity together.

NEXT

©Curriculum Associates, LLC   Copying is not permitted.

Volume Using a Formula Activity

Materials: ruler or tape measure

Play a *Rectangular Prism Scavenger Hunt* game with your child.

- Each person looks around the house for objects that are shaped like rectangular prisms. The goal is to find one that is small and one that is large.

Decide who found the objects with the smallest volume and the largest volume.

- Measure the length, width, and height of each object. Round the measurements to the nearest whole inch or foot. Use the formula (volume = length × width × height) to calculate the volume of each object.

- Discuss whether another object shaped like a rectangular prism could have the same volume as one of your objects, but have a different length, width, or height. (Another object could have the same volume and different dimensions. For example, a box that measures 3 inches × 2 inches × 4 inches has a volume of 24 cubic inches; a different box that measures 6 inches × 2 inches × 2 inches also has a volume of 24 cubic inches.)

 ©Curriculum Associates, LLC   Copying is not permitted.

Find Volume Using Formulas

Name: _____

Study the example problem showing different ways to find the volume of a rectangular prism. Then solve problems 1–5.

Example

A gift box is 3 inches long, 2 inches wide, and 3 inches tall. What is the volume of the box?

You can fill the box with 1-inch cubes.
Count the cubes.
There are 18 cubes.

You can also count the cubes in 1 layer.
There are 6 cubes in 1 layer.
The box has 3 layers.

$6 + 6 + 6 = 18$ or $6 \times 3 = 18$

The volume of the box is 18 cubic inches.

3 in.
3 in.
2 in.

1 layer

3 in.
3 in.
2 in.
3 layers

---

1   The rectangular prism at the right is made of centimeter cubes.

_____ cm
_____ cm
_____ cm

a. Fill in the blanks to show the number of centimeters on each edge.

b. Complete the following sentences.

The bottom layer has _____ cubes.

There are _____ layers.

c. What is the volume of the rectangular prism?

_____

d. Suppose you add another layer to the prism. What would the new volume be?

_____

Vocabulary

volume the amount of space inside a solid figure.

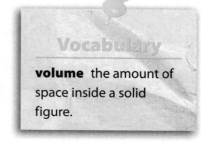

Solve.

2 What is the volume of this rectangular prism?

Show your work.

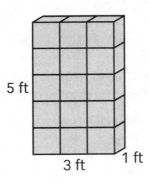

Solution: _____

3 Max fills this box with 1-inch cubes. Tell how many cubes are in 1 layer and how many layers there are. Then find the volume.

_____

_____

_____

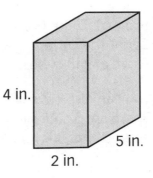

4 A toy box has a volume of 60 cubic feet. The box is 5 feet long and 4 feet wide. What is the height of the toy box?

Show your work.

Solution: _____

5 Jorge has 40 one-inch cubes. What are 2 different ways that he can stack the cubes to make a rectangular prism?

_____

_____

_____

_____

©Curriculum Associates, LLC   Copying is not permitted.

Name: _____

Use a Formula to Find the Volume of a Rectangular Prism

Study the example problem showing how to use formulas to find the volume of a rectangular prism. Then solve problems 1–7.

Example

Gwen puts her leftover food in a rectangular container. The container is 6 inches long, 5 inches wide, and 4 inches tall. What is the volume of the container?

Use the formula *volume = length × width × height.*

volume = 6 × 5 × 4, or 120 cubic inches

Or use the formula *volume = area of the base × height.* The area of the base is the same as the length × width.

6 × 5 = 30 and 30 × 4 = 120 cubic inches

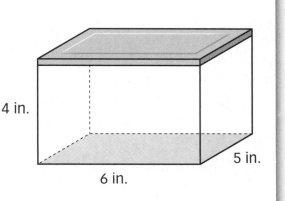

4 in.

5 in.

6 in.

1. Ted's box is 4 inches tall, 3 inches long, and 1 inch wide.

   a. Label the picture of the box with its dimensions.

   b. What is the volume of the box?

   Show your work.

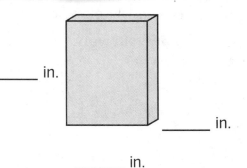

_____ in.

_____ in.

_____ in.

   Solution: _____

2. A rectangular prism has a square base with sides that are 2 feet long. The height of the prism is 5 feet. What is the volume of the prism?

   Show your work.

   Solution: _____

©Curriculum Associates, LLC   Copying is not permitted.

Solve.

3 Greg's shed is 10 feet long, 6 feet wide, and 8 feet tall. What is the volume of the shed?

Show your work.

Solution: _____

4 The base of a rectangular prism has sides that are 2 centimeters and 4 centimeters long. The height of the prism is 3 centimeters. What is the volume of the prism?

Show your work.

Solution: _____

5 What is the volume of a box that is 8 inches long, 2 inches wide, and 6 inches tall?

Show your work.

Solution: _____

6 The base of a rectangular prism is a rectangle with sides that are 7 inches and 5 inches long. Its height is 10 inches. Write two different equations that you can use to find the volume.

_____

7 Jin has two boxes. Box A has dimensions of 6 centimeters, 5 centimeters, and 9 centimeters. Box B has dimensions of 4 centimeters, 10 centimeters, and 7 centimeters. Which box holds more? Explain.

_____

_____

_____

©Curriculum Associates, LLC   Copying is not permitted.

Use the Formula for Volume

Name: _____

Solve the problems.

1 Which of these rectangular prisms have the same volume? Circle the letter for all that apply.

	Length	Width	Height
A	4 ft	2 ft	3 ft
B	5 ft	1 ft	3 ft
C	6 ft	4 ft	1 ft
D	2 ft	8 ft	2 ft
E	6 ft	2 ft	2 ft

Look for equal products.

2 The volume of a rectangular prism is 48 cubic meters. Its height is 2 meters and its length is 3 meters. What is its width?

A 6 meters

B 8 meters

C 16 meters

D 24 meters

This looks like a two-step problem.

Delia chose **A** as the correct answer. How did she get that answer?

_____

_____

_____

_____

3 Tabia stores her hair bands in a cube-shaped container. The cube has a volume of 64 cubic inches. What is the length of the edges of the cube?

Show your work.

All edges of a cube are the same length.

Solution: _____

©Curriculum Associates, LLC   Copying is not permitted.

Solve.

4 A gift shop sells rectangular glass dishes in different
   sizes. Some of the dimensions are given in the table.
   Fill in the missing dimensions.

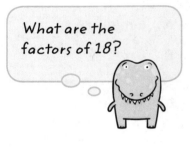

Use the volume
formula and fill in
the numbers that
you know.

Volume in Cubic Inches	Length in Inches	Width in Inches	Height in Inches
18	☐	3	2
24	2	☐	3
30	3	2	☐
40	☐	4	2
48	4	3	☐

5 How can you make three different rectangular prisms
   using 18 one-centimeter cubes? Give the length,
   width, and height of each prism.

What are the
factors of 18?

_____

_____

_____

6 Jamie wants to use this container to make a block of
   ice that has a volume of 600 cubic centimeters. Draw
   a line that shows to what height she should fill the
   container with water.

What dimensions do
you know?

Show your work.

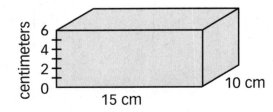

©Curriculum Associates, LLC   Copying is not permitted.

Dear Family,

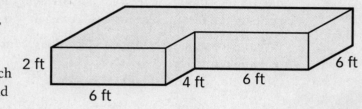

This week your child is learning to find the volume of composite figures.

A **composite figure** is a solid figure made up of, or composed of, other solid figures.

To find the volume of this composite figure, divide the figure into rectangular prisms, find the volume of each rectangular prism, and then add the volumes.

There can be more than one way to break a composite figure into rectangular prisms. The volume of the composite figure remains the same.

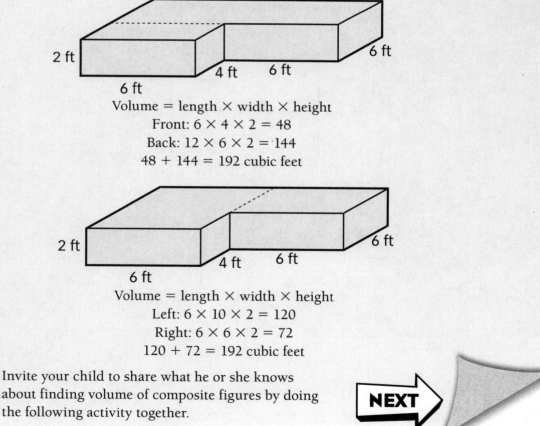

Volume = length × width × height
Front: 6 × 4 × 2 = 48
Back: 12 × 6 × 2 = 144
48 + 144 = 192 cubic feet

Volume = length × width × height
Left: 6 × 10 × 2 = 120
Right: 6 × 6 × 2 = 72
120 + 72 = 192 cubic feet

Invite your child to share what he or she knows about finding volume of composite figures by doing the following activity together.

NEXT ➡

Work with your child to find the volume of the composite figure shown below.

- Talk about different ways to break the composite figure into rectangular prisms.

- Choose two ways to break the figure into rectangular prisms. You might find it useful to draw a picture of the rectangular prisms that make up the composite figure. Label the lengths, widths, and heights of the rectangular prisms. For each way,

  - Use the formula for volume to find the volume of each rectangular prism.
    Volume = length × width × height

  - Add the volumes to find the volume of the composite figure.

- Compare the volumes you found for the composite figure. Are they the same? (Yes.) Suppose there was a third way to break the composite figure into two other rectangular prisms. Would the volume of the composite figure be the same? (Yes.)

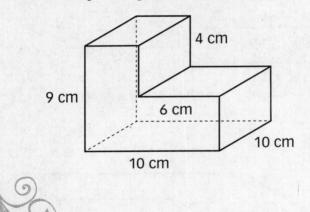

©Curriculum Associates, LLC   Copying is not permitted.

Find Volume of Composite Figures

Name: _____

Study the example problem showing how to use the dimensions of a rectangular prism to find its volume. Then solve problems 1–8.

Example

A puzzle box is 8 inches long, 5 inches wide, and 2 inches tall. What is the volume of the box?

You know the length, width, and height of the box.

Use the formula *volume = length × width × height.*

$8 × 5 × 2 = 80$

The volume of the box is 80 cubic inches.

2 in.

Puzzle Fun

8 in.

5 in.

1. Show how to find the volume of the storage bench to the right.

   _____

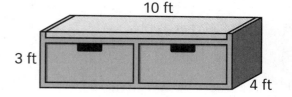

10 ft

3 ft

4 ft

2. What is the volume of a gift box with a length of 12 inches, a width of 5 inches, and a height of 3 inches?

   _____

3. The base of a glass is a square with 6-centimeter sides. The glass is 10 centimeters tall. What is the volume of the glass?

   _____

4. Yvette has a rectangular window box that holds 660 cubic inches of soil. The box is 22 inches long and 5 inches wide. What is the height of the box?

   _____

Vocabulary

volume the amount of space inside a solid figure.

Solve.

5 What is the volume of the rectangular prism to the right?

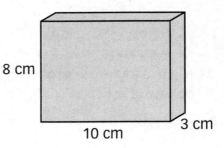

8 cm

10 cm

3 cm

_____

6 Avery is designing a box. He needs the box to have a volume of 72 cubic inches. Give two sets of measurements that he could use as the dimensions of the box.

_____ inches $\times$ _____ inches $\times$ _____ inches

_____ inches $\times$ _____ inches $\times$ _____ inches

7 A rectangular prism has a volume of 240 cubic feet. One of the dimensions is 10 feet. Which could be the other two dimensions of the prism? Circle the letter for all that apply.

A 8 feet, 3 feet

B 24 feet, 10 feet

C 6 feet, 4 feet

D 20 feet, 40 feet

E 2 feet, 12 feet

8 Marina made this raised bed for growing vegetables. She put 100 cubic feet of loam in the bed. She wants to mix in some potting soil and fill it to the top. How much potting soil does Marina need?

Show your work.

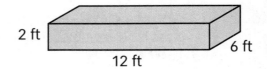

2 ft

12 ft

6 ft

Solution: _____

©Curriculum Associates, LLC   Copying is not permitted.

Name: _____

Break Apart Solid Figures to Find Volume

Study the example problem showing how to break apart a solid figure into rectangular prisms and find its volume. Then solve problems 1–8.

Example

Molly wants to know how much soil she needs to fill her two-tiered planter. What is the volume of the planter?

You can break the figure into two rectangular prisms in different ways. With either way, you then add the volumes of both prisms.

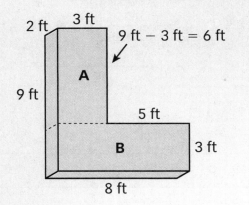

Prism A is 3 ft × 6 ft × 2 ft.
Volume of prism A = 36 cubic feet

Prism B is 8 ft × 3 ft × 2 ft.
Volume of prism B = 48 cubic feet

36 + 48 = 84 cubic feet

Prism A is 3 ft × 9 ft × 2 ft.
Volume of prism A = 54 cubic feet

Prism B is 5 ft × 3 ft × 2 ft.
Volume of prism B = 30 cubic feet

54 + 30 = 84 cubic feet

1 Show how to find the volume of prism D.

_____

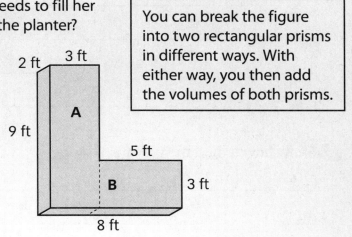

2 Find the volume of prism C.

_____

3 What is the volume of the whole figure?

_____

Lesson 27 Find Volume of Composite Figures   **285**

Solve.

4 Draw lines in figures A and B to separate them into two rectangular prisms. Do each in a different way.

5 Show how to find the volume of shape A.

_____

_____

_____

_____

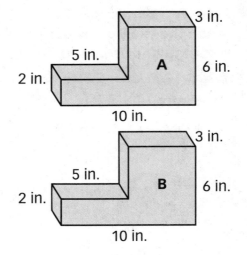

6 Show how to find the volume of shape B.

_____

_____

_____

7 What is the volume of figure X?

Show your work.

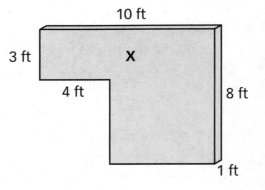

Solution: _____

8 Show how to break figure S into 3 rectangular prisms. Then show how to find the volume.

Show your work.

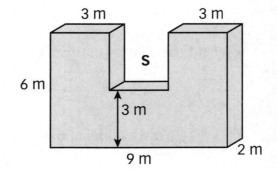

Solution: _____

©Curriculum Associates, LLC   Copying is not permitted.

Name: _____

Find Volume of Composite Figures

Solve the problems.

1 Which expression can you use to find the volume of this figure? Circle the letter for all that apply.

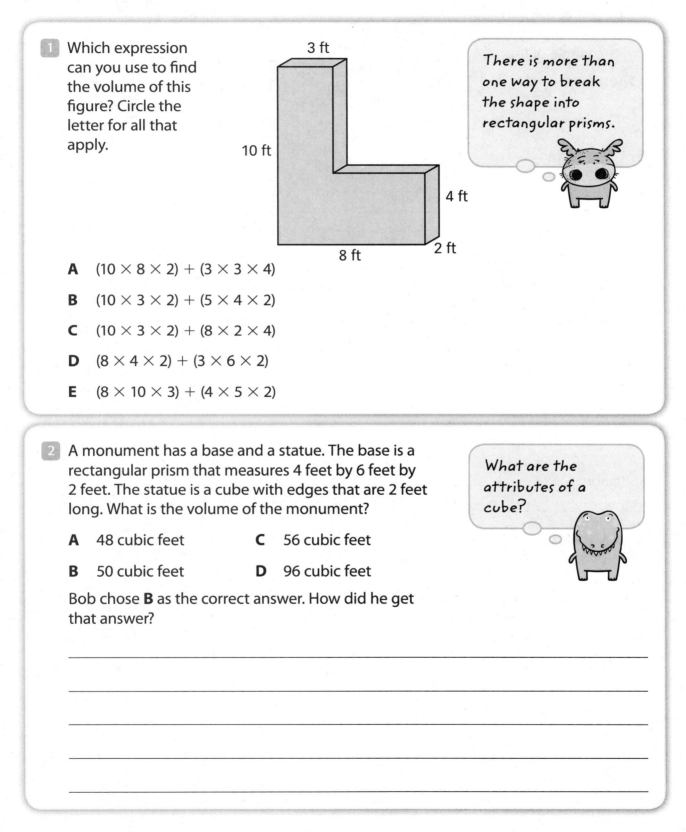

3 ft

10 ft

4 ft

8 ft   2 ft

There is more than one way to break the shape into rectangular prisms.

A $(10 \times 8 \times 2) + (3 \times 3 \times 4)$

B $(10 \times 3 \times 2) + (5 \times 4 \times 2)$

C $(10 \times 3 \times 2) + (8 \times 2 \times 4)$

D $(8 \times 4 \times 2) + (3 \times 6 \times 2)$

E $(8 \times 10 \times 3) + (4 \times 5 \times 2)$

2 A monument has a base and a statue. The base is a rectangular prism that measures 4 feet by 6 feet by 2 feet. The statue is a cube with edges that are 2 feet long. What is the volume of the monument?

What are the attributes of a cube?

A 48 cubic feet   **C** 56 cubic feet

B 50 cubic feet   **D** 96 cubic feet

Bob chose **B** as the correct answer. How did he get that answer?

_____

_____

_____

_____

_____

Solve.

3 Brody makes this wooden platform. Prism B is 10 feet long, 2 feet tall, and 4 feet deep. All dimensions of prism A are half those of prism B. What is the volume of the whole platform?

Show your work.

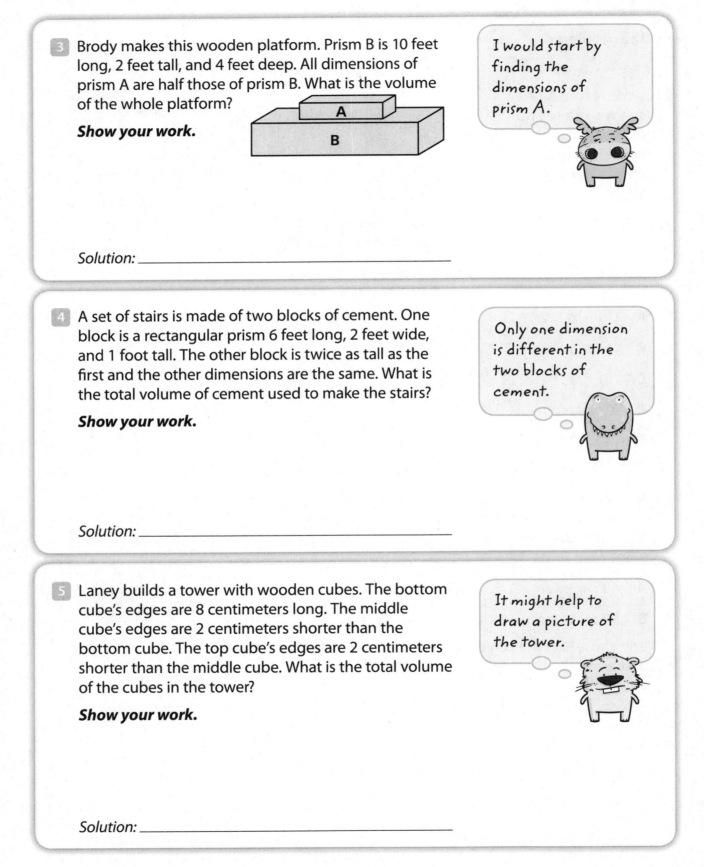

I would start by finding the dimensions of prism A.

Solution: _____

4 A set of stairs is made of two blocks of cement. One block is a rectangular prism 6 feet long, 2 feet wide, and 1 foot tall. The other block is twice as tall as the first and the other dimensions are the same. What is the total volume of cement used to make the stairs?

Show your work.

Only one dimension is different in the two blocks of cement.

Solution: _____

5 Laney builds a tower with wooden cubes. The bottom cube's edges are 8 centimeters long. The middle cube's edges are 2 centimeters shorter than the bottom cube. The top cube's edges are 2 centimeters shorter than the middle cube. What is the total volume of the cubes in the tower?

Show your work.

It might help to draw a picture of the tower.

Solution: _____

©Curriculum Associates, LLC   Copying is not permitted.

Unit 4 Game

Measurement Match

What you need: Recording Sheet, Measurement Cards

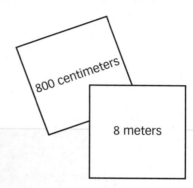

Directions

- Mix the Measurement Cards. Then lay them face down in four rows of six cards each.

- Player A turns over two cards.

- If the measurements are equal, keep the cards and write the measurements on the Recording Sheet.

- If the measurements are not equal, put the cards back, face down.

- Players take turns. When all the cards are matched, the player with the most cards wins.

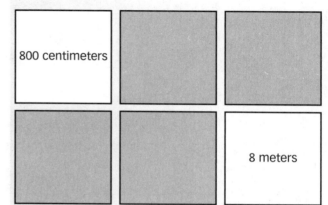

Name: _Dana_

Measurement Match Recording Sheet

1. ___800 centimeters___ = ___8 meters___
2. _____ = _____
3. _____ = _____

A millimeter is just $\frac{1}{1000}$ of a meter. I wonder how many millimeters tall I am?

Measurement Match Recording Sheet

1. _____ = _____

2. _____ = _____

3. _____ = _____

4. _____ = _____

5. _____ = _____

6. _____ = _____

7. _____ = _____

8. _____ = _____

9. _____ = _____

10. _____ = _____

11. _____ = _____

12. _____ = _____

©Curriculum Associates, LLC   Copying is not permitted.

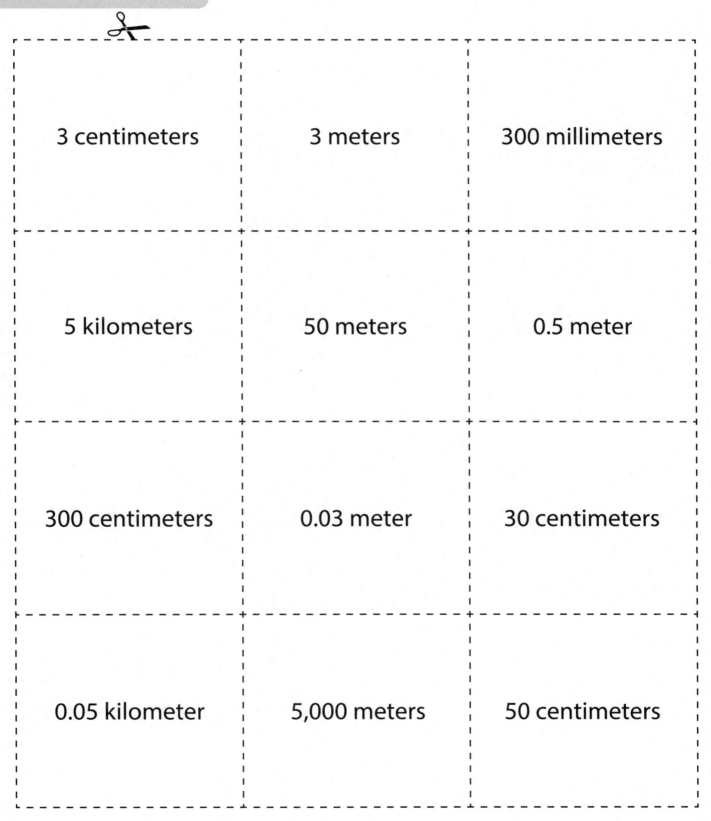

3 centimeters	3 meters	300 millimeters
5 kilometers	50 meters	0.5 meter
300 centimeters	0.03 meter	30 centimeters
0.05 kilometer	5,000 meters	50 centimeters

©Curriculum Associates, LLC

✂

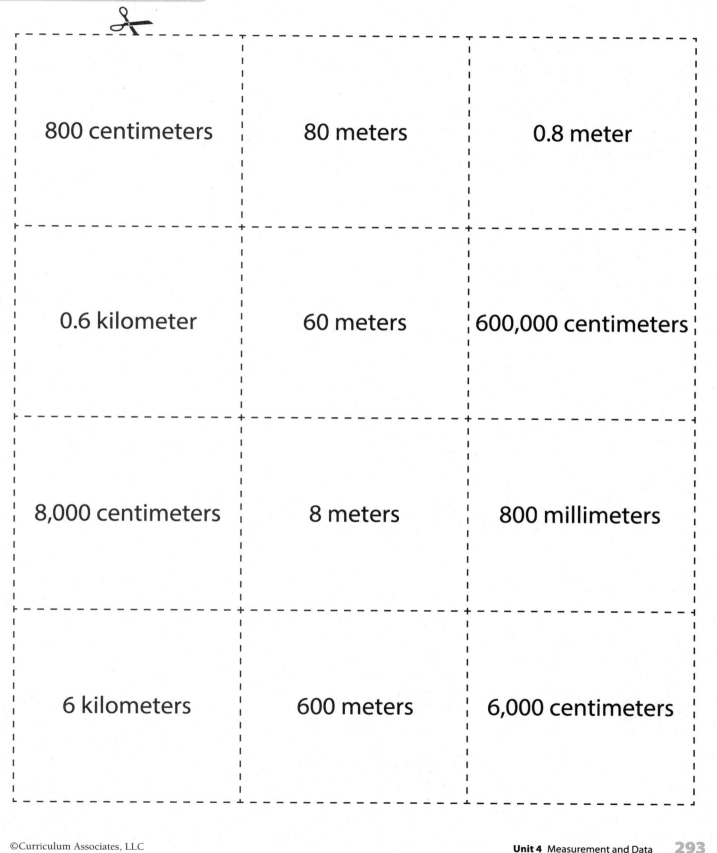

800 centimeters	80 meters	0.8 meter
0.6 kilometer	60 meters	600,000 centimeters
8,000 centimeters	8 meters	800 millimeters
6 kilometers	600 meters	6,000 centimeters

Measurement and Data

In this unit you learned to:	Lesson
convert from one measurement to another, for example: 4 ft = 48 in.	21, 22
make a line plot of data represented as fractions of measurements.	23
find volume by counting unit cubes.	24, 25
find volume by using a formula.	26
find volumes of composite figures .	27

Use these skills to solve problems 1–5 .

1 A standard fire hose is 50 feet long. What is the length of the hose in yards and feet?

(1 yard = 3 feet)

Show your work.

Solution: _____

2 Which expression can be used to find the volume of the rectangular prism below? Circle the letter for all that apply.

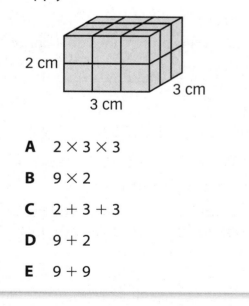

2 cm

3 cm

3 cm

A $2 \times 3 \times 3$

B 9×2

C $2 + 3 + 3$

D $9 + 2$

E $9 + 9$

Solve.

3 Jacinda and Priya are on the school swim team. Jacinda swims 0.956 kilometer during practice. Priya swims 987 meters. Circle the letter that shows which girl swam farther and correctly compares the distances in the same unit of measurement.

A Jacinda
9,560 meters > 987 meters

B Jacinda
0.956 kilometer > 0.0987 kilometer

C Priya
0.956 kilometer < 0.987 kilometer

D Priya
95.6 meters < 987 meters

4 The diagram shows two rectangular prisms joined together. What is the combined volume of these prisms?

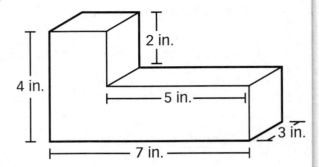

Show your work.

Solution: _____

5 Jorge wants to find out how many cubes will fill the box. He stacks some cubes in the box as shown.

Part A

How many more cubes does Jorge need to fill the box?

Solution: _____

Part B

What is the total volume of the box?

Solution: _____

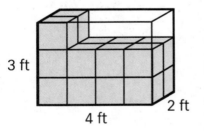

Part C

How could Jorge have found the volume of the box without filling the box with cubes? Explain.

Solution: _____

_____

_____

©Curriculum Associates, LLC   Copying is not permitted.

Name: _____

Answer the questions and show all your work on separate paper.

There's going to be a new swimming pool at the park! The pool will be used by everyone who lives nearby. This includes people of all ages. Some just want to play in the water, others will swim laps for exercise. There will even be an area for diving.

To meet everyone's needs, the pool will have 3 sections and each section will have a different depth:
- 2 ft deep for playing,
- 4 ft deep for lap swimming, and
- 15 ft deep for diving.

Each section of the pool will be a rectangular prism, but the lengths and widths do not have to be the same.

The 4-ft deep section should be at least 80 feet long and no more than 40 feet wide.

The other sections must be 20–50 feet wide and no more than 60 feet long.

The park supervisor has decided that the total volume of the pool must be between 35,000 and 46,000 cubic feet. This will help keep costs under control.

Make a plan for the pool. Include a chart and show that your plan meets all specifications. Draw a diagram of how the sections will fit together, as seen from above. Be sure to label the dimensions. Include 2 or 3 sentences to describe the pool design to the park supervisor.

Checklist

Did you . . .
- ☐ draw a diagram?
- ☐ use a formula?
- ☐ describe your plan?

Reflect on Mathematical Practices

1. **Make Models** What does your diagram tell you that your chart does not? Why is this important?

2. **Be Precise** Why is it important to write the units when working with measurement?

Word Bank Here are some words that you might use in your answer.

volume	length	width
depth	multiply	sum
product	total	

Models Here are some models that you might use to find the solution.

	Length	Width	Depth	Volume
Section 1				
Section 2				
Section 3				
Total				

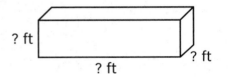

? ft
? ft
? ft

Sentence Starters Here are some sentence starters that might help explain your work.

The depth of section _____

The volume formula _____

The total volume _____

The pool has _____

  ©Curriculum Associates, LLC   Copying is not permitted.

Unit 4 Vocabulary

Name: _____

My Examples

metric system

the measurement system that measures length based on meters, capacity based on liters, and mass based on grams

customary system

the measurement system commonly used in the United States; it measures length in inches, feet, yards, and miles; capacity in cups, quarts, pints, and gallons; and weights in ounces and pounds

meter

the basic unit of length in the metric system

centimeter

one hundredth of a meter

©Curriculum Associates, LLC   Copying is not permitted.

millimeter

one thousandth of a meter

distribution

how spread out or how clustered pieces of data are

line plot

a graph that uses Xs above a number line to show data; useful for showing how data is grouped

scale

the increment by which the numbers along the axes of a graph change

©Curriculum Associates, LLC Copying is not permitted.

area

the amount of space a two-dimensional figure covers

cubic unit

a cube, 1 unit on each edge, used to measure volume

volume

the amount of space inside a solid figure

My Words

_____

_____

_____

_____

My Words

_____

_____

_____

_____

_____

_____

_____

_____

_____

_____

_____

_____

_____

_____

_____

_____

My Examples

©Curriculum Associates, LLC   Copying is not permitted.

Dear Family,

> This week your child is exploring the coordinate plane.

Your child is learning to use ordered pairs of numbers to find a location on the coordinate plane and to identify locations on the coordinate plane with ordered pairs.

The **coordinate plane** at the right has two axes, the *x*-axis and the *y*-axis.

- The **x-axis** is a horizontal number line.

- The **y-axis** is a vertical number line.

- The axes intersect, or meet, at a point called the **origin**.

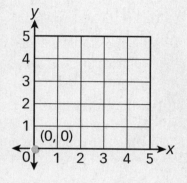

You can find any point on the coordinate plane if you know the *x*-coordinate and *y*-coordinate of the point. These coordinates are given in the **ordered pair** (*x*, *y*). The ordered pair (0, 0) tells where the origin is located. It marks a point on the coordinate plane. The point is located at 0 on the *x*-axis and 0 on the *y*-axis.

The ordered pair (3, 4) identifies point *J* on the coordinate plane at the right. Point *J* has an *x*-coordinate of 3 and a *y*-coordinate of 4. To locate point *J*, you start at the origin, move right 3 units on the *x*-axis, and move up 4 units.

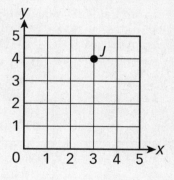

Invite your child to share what he or she knows about the coordinate plane by doing the following activity together.

NEXT

©Curriculum Associates, LLC   Copying is not permitted.

Coordinate Plane Activity

Materials: number cube

Work with your child to use ordered pairs to locate points on a coordinate plane.

- One person rolls a number cube to determine the *x*-coordinate of a point. The other person rolls the number cube to determine the *y*-coordinate.

- Write the coordinates in the table below in the row for Point *A*. This is the ordered pair for Point *A*.

  - Example: Roll a 2 and a 5 with the number cube. Write 2 in the *x* column and 5 in the *y* column of the table. The ordered pair for Point *A* is (2, 5).

- Use the ordered pair to locate the point on the coordinate grid below. Describe where you begin, how many units you move, and in which direction you move to locate the point. Mark and label the point as Point *A*.

- Repeat the activity three more times to determine coordinates for Points *B*, *C*, and *D*.

- Look at the points on the coordinate grid and identify any patterns that you see. (For example, the points might form a line.) Talk about the location of one point in terms of another point. (For example, Point *C* might be two units to the right and 3 units up from Point *B*.) What other things do you notice about the points?

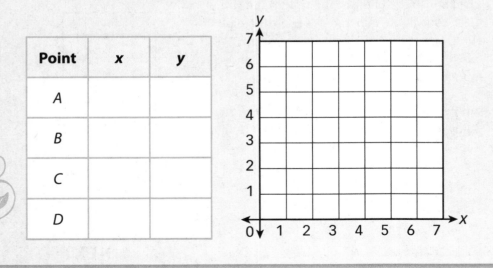

Point	x	y
A		
B		
C		
D		

©Curriculum Associates, LLC   Copying is not permitted.

Name: _____

Prerequisite: How do number lines show the
relationships among numbers?

**Study the example showing how to label fractions on
a number line. Then solve problems 1 and 2.**

Example

The rectangles show equal parts between 0 and 1 and
between 1 and 2 on the number line.

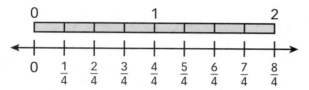

There are 4 equal parts between each pair of whole

numbers. Each part shows $\frac{1}{4}$. You can count by fourths on

the number line.

---

1 Look at the section between 0 and 1 on the number line.

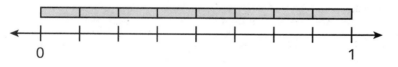

a. How many equal parts are there? _____

b. What fraction does each part show? _____

c. Label the number line with fractions.

2 Look at the number line in problem 1. What happens
to the numbers as you move from left to right on the
number line? From right to left?

_____

_____

_____

©Curriculum Associates, LLC   Copying is not permitted.

Solve.

Use the number lines to solve problems 3–8.

3　Which is at a greater number, point A or point B? Explain how you know.

_____

_____

_____

4　Which is farther from 0, point A or point B? _____

5　Which is at a lesser number, point C or point D? Explain how you know.

_____

_____

_____

6　Which is closer to 0, point C or point D? _____

7　Explain how a point's distance from 0 relates to the value of the number that it represents.

_____

_____

_____

8　Describe how the two number lines are alike and different.

_____

_____

_____

_____

_____

　　　©Curriculum Associates, LLC　Copying is not permitted.

Name: _____

Name and Locate Points on a Coordinate Plane

Study the example problem that shows how to name ordered pairs on a coordinate plane. Then solve problems 1–9.

Example

Each point is named with an *x*-coordinate and a *y*-coordinate.

The ordered pair for the origin is (0, 0).

The *x*-coordinate tells how many units from the origin the point is on the *x*-axis. It is the first number in the ordered pair.

The *y*-coordinate tells how many units from the origin the point is on the *y*-axis. It is the second number in the ordered pair.

The ordered pair for point *A* is (3, 1).

$$(x, y)$$

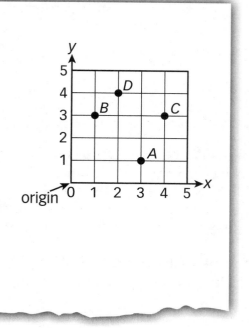

1   Point *B* is _____ unit(s) to the right of the origin and _____ unit(s) up from the origin.

The ordered pair for point *B* is (_____ , _____).

2   Point *C* is _____ unit(s) to the right of the origin and _____ unit(s) up from the origin.

The ordered pair for point *C* is (_____ , _____).

3   Write the ordered pair for point *D*. Explain how you got your answer.

_____

_____

_____

_____

4   Find the ordered pair (2, 3) on the coordinate plane. Mark and label this point "*E*."

Vocabulary

coordinate plane a space formed by two perpendicular number lines called axes.

ordered pair a pair of numbers, or coordinates, (*x*, *y*) describing the location of a point on the coordinate plane.

Solve.

Point	A	B	C	D	E	F
x				3	4	5
y				4	4	2

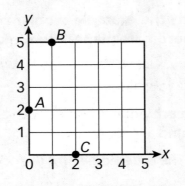

5 In the table, write the ordered pairs for points *A*, *B*, and *C* on the coordinate plane above.

6 Find and label points *D*, *E*, and *F* on the coordinate plane to represent the ordered pairs in the table.

7 Choose a point on the coordinate plane above. Describe its location compared to the origin.

_____

_____

Point	R	S	T
x	1	3	4
y	4	0	2

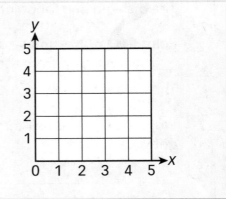

8 Find and label points *R*, *S*, and *T* on the coordinate plane to represent the ordered pairs in the table.

9 Describe the location of point *T* compared to point *S* on the coordinate plane.

_____

_____

    ©Curriculum Associates, LLC   Copying is not permitted.

Name: _____

Reason and Write

**Study the example. Underline two parts that you think make it
a particularly good answer and a helpful example.**

Example

Find the ordered pair (0, 4) on the coordinate plane. Label
the point *P*. Use point *P* as a corner, then draw a square.
Label the other corners with letters. List the coordinate
pairs for all corners.

Explain how you solved the problem and how you know
that you drew a square.

Show your work. Use pictures, words, or numbers to
explain.

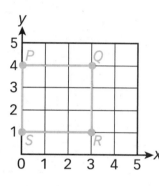

Coordinate pairs:
P(0, 4) *Q*(3, 4) *R*(3, 1) *S*(0, 1)

Where does the
example . . .

• label each point
  with a letter?

• connect points to
  draw a square?

• tell how you solved
  the problem?

• explain why the
  shape is a square?

I started at the origin and moved 4 units up. I labeled
it point *P*(0, 4). Then I drew a vertical segment from
point *P* 3 units down the *y*-axis. Then I drew a
horizontal segment starting at point *P*. Since all sides
of a square are equal, I made this segment 3 units
long. Opposite sides of a square are parallel. So, I
drew segments parallel to the horizontal and vertical
segments, each 3 units away.

I labeled the points at the corners of the square *P*, *Q*,
R, and *S*. Then I found the distance of each point from
the origin and wrote the coordinate pairs. I know the
shape is a square because it has 4 equal sides and
4 right angles. All of the sides are 3 units long, and the
angles are formed by the perpendicular lines in the
coordinate plane, and I know perpendicular lines form
right angles.

©Curriculum Associates, LLC   Copying is not permitted.

Solve the problem. Use what you learned from the example.

Find the ordered pair (1, 3) on the coordinate plane. Label it point *A*. Use point *A* as a corner, then draw a right triangle. Label the other corners with letters. List the coordinate pairs for all corners.

Explain how you solved the problem and how you know that you drew a right triangle.

Show your work. Use models, words, and numbers to explain your answer.

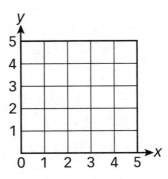

Did you . . .

• label each point with a letter?

• connect points to draw a triangle?

• tell how you solved the problem?

• explain why the shape is a right triangle?

   ©Curriculum Associates, LLC   Copying is not permitted.

Dear Family,

This week your child is learning to solve problems by graphing points on the coordinate plane.

Your child has already learned to use ordered pairs to locate and identify points on the coordinate plane. Now your child is learning how to solve problems involving points and figures on the coordinate plane.

Carla is saving money to buy a gift for her brother. The points on the coordinate plane at the right show Carla's savings. How many weeks does it take Carla to save $6?

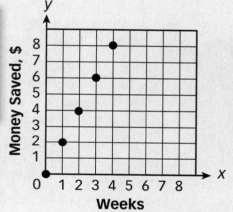

The *x*-axis represents the number of weeks that Carla saves. The *y*-axis represents the amount of money that Carla saves. To find the number of weeks it takes to save $6, find the point with a *y*-coordinate of 6. The point is (3, 6), so it takes Carla 3 weeks to save $6.

Your child is also learning to solve problems with plane figures on a coordinate plane. For example, you can find the perimeter of the rectangle *EFGH* on the coordinate plane at the right by counting the number of units on each side to find the side lengths of the rectangle. Then add the lengths to find the perimeter.

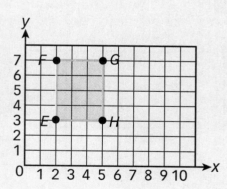

$$4 + 3 + 4 + 3 = 14$$

The perimeter of the rectangle is 14 units.

Invite your child to share what he or she knows about graphing points in a coordinate plane by doing the following activity together.

NEXT

©Curriculum Associates, LLC   Copying is not permitted.

Graphing Points on a Coordinate Plane Activity

Play a game to graph points and draw matching figures on coordinate planes with your child.

- Cut out the coordinate planes below or use separate paper, so each player can draw without the other player seeing.

  - Player 1 chooses 4 points, marks them, and labels them *A*, *B*, *C*, and *D*.

  - Connect the points with lines to draw a figure with 4 sides. Be sure the other player does not see you mark the points and draw your 4-sided figure.

  - List the ordered pair for each point in the table.

- Player 2 uses the table to graph the points on his or her own coordinate plane. Connect the points to form a 4-sided figure.

- Now compare the figures on your coordinate planes. Are they the same?

Point	*x*	*y*
A		
B		
C		
D		

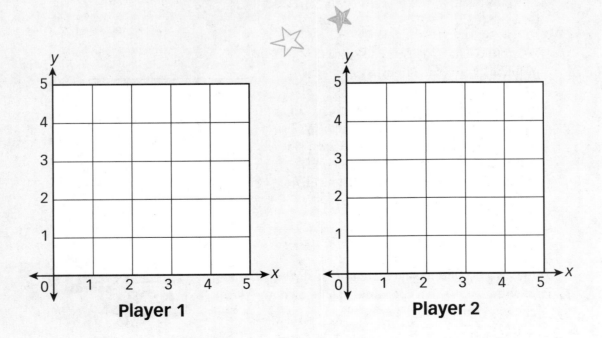

Player 1   Player 2

©Curriculum Associates, LLC   Copying is not permitted.

Graph Points in the Coordinate Plane

Name: _____

Prerequisite: Identify Ordered Pairs

Study the example showing how to name a point on a coordinate plane. Then solve problems 1–3.

Example

What is the ordered pair for point A?

The location of a point is named with an x-coordinate and a y-coordinate. The coordinates are written as an ordered pair, (x-coordinate, y-coordinate).

Start at the y-axis. Point A is 2 units to the right of the origin.

Start at the x-axis. Point A is 1 unit up from the origin.

The ordered pair for point A is (2, 1).

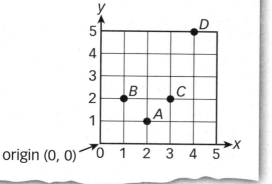

origin (0, 0)

1. Starting at the y-axis, point B is _____ unit(s) to the right of the origin.

   Starting at the x-axis, point B is _____ unit(s) up from the origin.

   The ordered pair for point B is (_____ , _____).

2. Write the ordered pairs.

   point C (_____ , _____)   point D (_____ , _____)

3. Explain how you found the ordered pair for point C or point D.

   _____

   _____

   _____

   _____

Vocabulary

x-coordinate a point's horizontal distance from the origin in units along the x-axis.

y-coordinate a point's vertical distance from the origin in units along the y-axis.

Use the coordinate plane to solve problems 4–6.

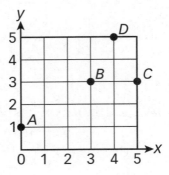

4 Complete the table to show the ordered pairs on the coordinate plane.

Point	A	B	C	D
x				
y				

5 Start at (0, 0). Move 3 units right and 0 units up. Label this point E. Write the ordered pair for E.

E (_____ , _____)

6 Find the ordered pair (1, 5) on the coordinate plane above. Label it point F.

7 Choose 4 points and draw a rectangle on the coordinate plane to the right. Label the points with letters. Write the letters and ordered pairs you used to draw your rectangle.

_____

_____

_____

_____

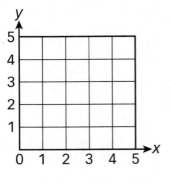

  ©Curriculum Associates, LLC   Copying is not permitted.

Name: _____

Show Relationships on a Coordinate Plane

Study the example problem showing how to represent and use relationships between quantities. Then solve problems 1–7.

Example

Holly is playing a crane game at the arcade. With each quarter, she gets 2 tries to grab a stuffed animal with the crane. Holly wants to know how many tries she will get using different numbers of quarters.

Show the relationship between quarters and numbers of tries.

You can use equations.   You can use a table.

$1 \times 2 = 2$ tries
$2 \times 2 = 4$ tries
$3 \times 2 = 6$ tries
$4 \times 2 = 8$ tries
$5 \times 2 = 10$ tries

Number of Quarters	1	2	3	4	5
Number of Tries	2	4	6	8	10

1 Use the table in the example above. Finish plotting the ordered pairs from the table in the coordinate plane to the right.

2 What is the meaning of the ordered pair (3, 6)?

_____

_____

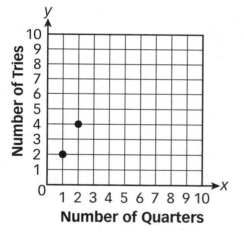

3 Describe a path from (1, 2) to (2, 4) and from (2, 4) to (3, 6). If you continue from point to point, what do you notice?

_____

_____

_____

_____

©Curriculum Associates, LLC   Copying is not permitted.

Solve.

> Holly plays a different game at the arcade. It takes
> 2 tokens to play the game. She starts with 10 tokens.

4 Write an equation that can be used to determine
how many tokens she has left after playing the
game each time. Fill in the blanks.

_____ tokens − (_____ tokens × number of _____) = number of tokens left

5 Use the equation to complete the table.

Number of Games Played	1	2	3	4	5
Number of Tokens Left					

6 Plot the ordered pairs from the table on the
coordinate plane. Choose a point on the coordinate
plane and tell what it means.

_____

_____

_____

_____

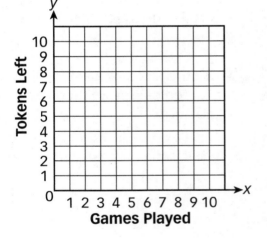

7 Compare the table and coordinate plane from this
problem with the problem on the previous page.
How are they different?

_____

_____

_____

_____

_____

316 **Lesson 29** Graph Points in the Coordinate Plane

©Curriculum Associates, LLC   Copying is not permitted.

Name: _____

Solve Measurement Problems on the Coordinate Plane

Study the example that shows how to solve a measurement problem with a shape on a coordinate plane. Then solve problems 1–6.

Example

The owner plans to add a new game room to the arcade. He draws a rectangle on the coordinate plane to represent the room. What is the area of the rectangle?

From point *G* to point *A*, go up 6 units.
From point *A* to point *M*, go right 5 units.
Length of $\overline{GA}$ is 6 units and length of $\overline{AM}$ is 5 units.

Area of a rectangle = length × width
Multiply the lengths of the sides to find the area of the rectangle: 6 × 5 = 30.
Area of rectangle *GAME* = 30 square units

1   Write ordered pairs for each point.

G (_____, _____)   A (_____, _____)   M (_____, _____)   E (_____, _____)

2   Find the lengths of $\overline{ME}$ and $\overline{EG}$. Explain how you can use the coordinates to find the distance between points *M* and *E* and between points *E* and *G*.

_____

_____

_____

_____

3   What is the perimeter of rectangle *GAME*? Tell how you found your answer.

_____

_____

_____

Lesson 29 Graph Points in the Coordinate Plane   **317**

Use the coordinate plane to solve problems 4 and 5.

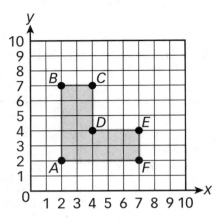

4 Write the coordinates of points *A*, *B*, *C*, *D*, *E*, and *F*.

A (_____, _____)   B (_____, _____)
C (_____, _____)   D (_____, _____)
E (_____, _____)   F (_____, _____)

5 What is the perimeter of shape *ABCDEF*?

Show your work.

Solution: _____

6 Draw a rectangle with an area of 12 square units in the coordinate plane to the right. Tell how you know the area is 12 square units.

_____

_____

_____

_____

_____

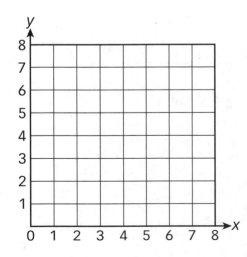

©Curriculum Associates, LLC   Copying is not permitted.

Graph Points in the Coordinate Plane

Solve the problems.

1 Look at rectangle *ABCD*. Tell whether each statement is *True* or *False*.

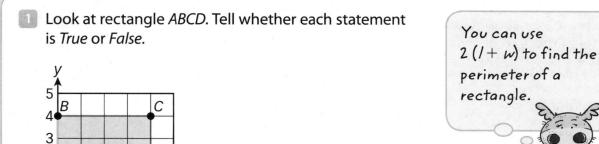

You can use $2(l + w)$ to find the perimeter of a rectangle.

a. The coordinates of the vertices of the rectangle are *A*(1, 0), *B*(4, 0), *C*(4, 4), and *D*(1, 4). ☐ True ☐ False

b. The coordinates of the vertices of the rectangle are *A*(0, 1), *B*(0, 4), *C*(4, 4), and *D*(4, 1). ☐ True ☐ False

c. The area of rectangle *ABCD* is 16 square units. ☐ True ☐ False

d. The perimeter of rectangle *ABCD* is 14 units. ☐ True ☐ False

2 Plot the following points on the coordinate plane.

K(2, 5)

L(0, 2)

M(4, 3)

Which is the first number in an ordered pair? The *x*-coordinate? The *y*-coordinate?

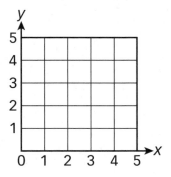

©Curriculum Associates, LLC   Copying is not permitted.

Solve.

3 Use the coordinate plane to the right. Start at (0, 1). Move 2 units right and 3 units up. Which point shows this location? Circle the letter of the correct answer.

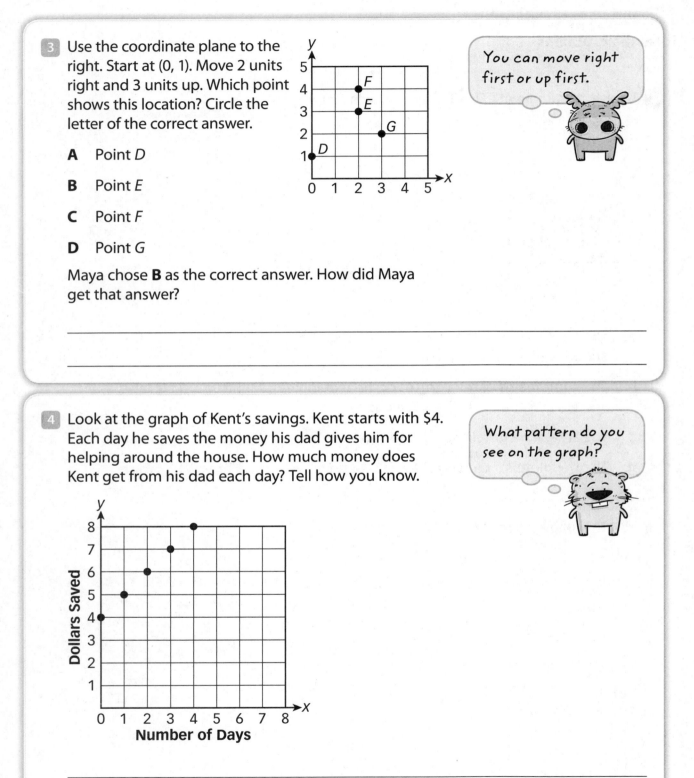

You can move right first or up first.

A Point *D*

B Point *E*

C Point *F*

D Point *G*

Maya chose **B** as the correct answer. How did Maya get that answer?

_____

_____

4 Look at the graph of Kent's savings. Kent starts with $4. Each day he saves the money his dad gives him for helping around the house. How much money does Kent get from his dad each day? Tell how you know.

What pattern do you see on the graph?

_____

_____

_____

©Curriculum Associates, LLC   Copying is not permitted.

Dear Family,

This week your child is learning to classify two-dimensional figures.

You can classify all polygons, or special two-dimensional figures, by their properties. Some properties of figures are the number of sides they have, whether the sides are perpendicular or parallel, and what kinds of angles they have.

You can use a hierarchy to rank categories of figures. At the top of the hierarchy is the category for the most general group. As you go down a hierarchy, you can see how more specific groups are related.

You can use a hierarchy to show how figures such as squares, rectangles, parallelograms, and other quadrilaterals (four-sided figures) are related. A useful way to show categories in a hierarchy is with a Venn diagram.

The Venn diagram at the right shows that quadrilaterals are the most general category. All figures that have four sides are quadrilaterals. Parallelograms, rectangles, and squares are kinds of quadrilaterals.

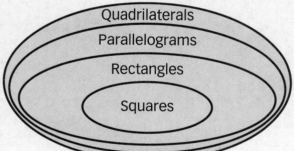

Another way that your child is learning to classify figures is with a flow chart. The flow chart below shows the hierarchy of quadrilaterals from left to right.

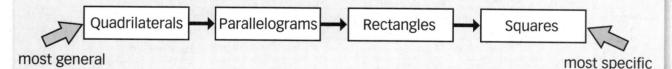

most general   most specific

Invite your child to share what he or she knows about classifying two-dimensional figures by doing the following activity together.

©Curriculum Associates, LLC   Copying is not permitted.

Classifying Two-Dimensional Figures Activity

Work together with your child to draw a figure based on a description of the figure's properties.

- Use the dot paper below. One person describes properties of a figure and the other person draws and names the figure based on the description of its properties.

- Here are some examples:

  - The figure is a quadrilateral that has at least 1 pair of parallel sides (trapezoid, parallelogram, rectangle, square, rhombus).

  - The figure has 4 sides of equal length, 2 pairs of parallel sides, and 4 right angles. (square)

  - The figure has 4 sides, its opposite sides are parallel, and it has four right angles. (rectangle or square)

©Curriculum Associates, LLC   Copying is not permitted.

Classify Two-Dimensional Figures

Name: _____

Study the example problem that shows how to sort shapes based on parallel and perpendicular sides. Then solve problems 1–6.

Example

Mark each shape that appears to have at least one pair of parallel sides with the symbol ∥. Mark each shape that appears to have at least one pair of perpendicular sides with the symbol ⊥.

Parallel sides are always the same distance apart and will never cross. Perpendicular sides form a right angle (90°).

triangle	rectangle ∥ ⊥	parallelogram ∥	trapezoid ∥	right triangle ⊥

1   Look at the shapes in the example. Write the name of the shapes that belong in each group shown in the table below.

parallel sides only	perpendicular sides only	parallel and perpendicular sides

2   Which group from problem 1 does each shape shown below belong in?

_____   _____

_____   _____

3   Draw a shape that does not belong to any of the groups in problem 1.

Solve.

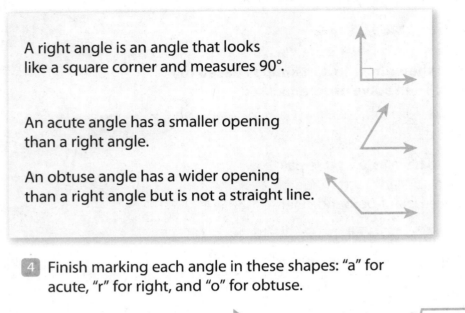

A right angle is an angle that looks like a square corner and measures 90°.

An acute angle has a smaller opening than a right angle.

An obtuse angle has a wider opening than a right angle but is not a straight line.

4 Finish marking each angle in these shapes: "a" for acute, "r" for right, and "o" for obtuse.

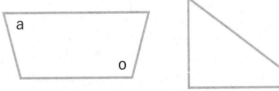

5 Write the name of each shape from problem 4 that belongs in each group shown in the table below.

acute and right angles	acute and obtuse angles

6 Where does each shape belong in the Venn diagram below? Write the letter of the shape in the section that it belongs in.

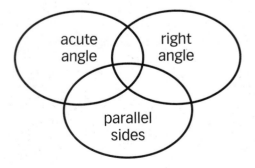

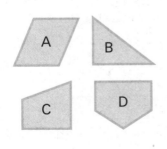

©Curriculum Associates, LLC   Copying is not permitted.

Name: _____

Order Shapes in a Hierarchy

Study the example showing how to order shapes in a hierarchy. Then solve problems 1–6.

Example

A hierarchy starts with the most general category and then shows how more specific groups are related. Draw a tree diagram relating the shapes in the table.

Shape	Description
plane figure	a two-dimensional shape
polygon	a closed plane figure with straight sides
triangle	a polygon with 3 sides
quadrilateral	a polygon with 4 sides
pentagon	a polygon with 5 sides

Polygons have all the properties that plane figures have. Polygons also have properties that plane figures don't have. Polygons appear right below plane figures in the hierarchy.

Triangles, quadrilaterals, and pentagons have all the properties that polygons have. They have other properties, too. Because triangles, quadrilaterals, and pentagons have different properties from each other, they appear side-by-side.

Tree Diagram

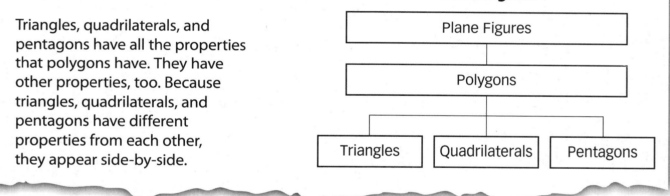

1. Fill in the blanks.
   Triangles are both _____ and _____.

2. A circle is a plane figure. It does not have straight sides, so it is not a polygon. Where in the hierarchy should "Circles" go? Explain.

   _____

   _____

   _____

   _____

   _____

Vocabulary

hierarchy a ranking of categories based on properties.

Lesson 30 Classify Two-Dimensional Figures   **325**

Solve.

3 Mark an X in the column if the shape always has that property.

Shape	4 sides	2 pairs of parallel sides	4 right angles
parallelogram			
rectangle			
quadrilateral			

4 Use the table in problem 3 to make a flow chart that shows the relationship between the three shapes. Order the shapes from general to specific going from left to right.

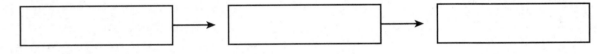

5 Where would you include squares in the flow chart in problem 4? Explain.

_____

_____

_____

6 Fill in the Venn diagram that shows the relationship between rectangles, squares, and rhombuses. Explain what the diagram shows about squares.

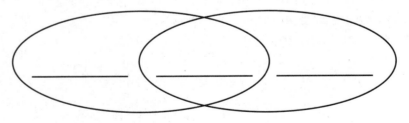

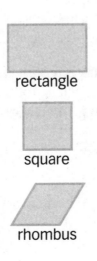

rectangle

square

rhombus

_____

_____

_____

_____

©Curriculum Associates, LLC   Copying is not permitted.

Name: _____

Classify Two-Dimensional Figures

Solve the problems.

1 Look at the flow chart below.

| Triangle | → | Isosceles | → | Equilateral |

Which statement is true? Circle the letter of all that apply.

A Equilateral triangles can be classified as isosceles triangles.

B Isosceles triangles have all the properties that equilateral triangles have.

C Isosceles triangles can be classified as equilateral triangles.

D Equilateral triangles have all the properties that isosceles triangles have.

Which is the most general category? The most specific?

2 Create a Venn diagram to show the hierarchy of triangles, quadrilaterals, isosceles triangles, and polygons.

In a Venn diagram, categories with nothing in common do not overlap.

3 Use the diagram in problem 2. Write two different statements that describe the relationships between the shapes.

Which shapes share properties?

Solution: _____

_____

_____

_____

©Curriculum Associates, LLC   Copying is not permitted.

Solve.

4 Look at the tree diagram below.

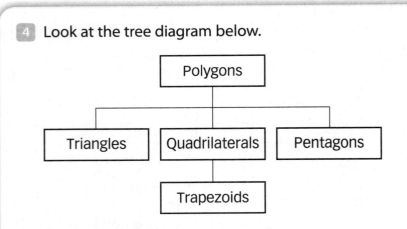

The most general category is at the top of the tree diagram.

Which statement is true? Circle the letter of the correct answer.

A All polygons are triangles, quadrilaterals, and pentagons.

B All quadrilaterals are trapezoids.

C All triangles and quadrilaterals are polygons.

D Triangles, quadrilaterals, and pentagons all have the same properties.

Dina chose **B** as the correct answer. How did she get that answer?

_____

_____

5 Chen wrote some names that can be used to classify this shape in order from LEAST specific to MOST specific.

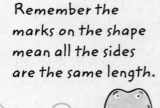

Remember the marks on the shape mean all the sides are the same length.

quadrilateral, parallelogram, square, rhombus

Do you agree with what he did? Explain.

Solution: _____

_____

_____

_____

©Curriculum Associates, LLC   Copying is not permitted.

Dear Family,

This week your child is exploring properties of two-dimensional figures.

Your child has already learned to use hierarchies to classify figures. Now your child is learning to use properties, or attributes, to classify figures.

Figures can be grouped into categories by their attributes, such as their number of sides or angles, the lengths of their sides, and their angle measures. All figures in a category share certain attributes. Figures in a subcategory have all the same attributes that figures in the category have.

A Venn diagram can show categories and subcategories of figures. The Venn diagram below shows ways to classify Triangles. Categories that do not overlap do not share attributes.

The category Right does not overlap Obtuse. A right triangle does not share all the properties of an obtuse triangle.

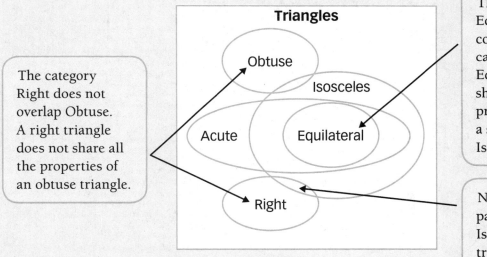

The category Equilateral is nested completely inside the category Isosceles. Equilateral triangles share all the same properties of, and are a subcategory of, Isosceles triangles.

Notice that Right partly overlaps Isosceles. A right triangle can share all the properties of an isosceles triangle.

Your child is also learning to classify figures by their properties in other ways, such as with flow charts and tree diagrams.

Invite your child to share what he or she knows about properties of two-dimensional figures by doing the following activity together.

NEXT

©Curriculum Associates, LLC   Copying is not permitted.   **Lesson 31** Understand Properties of Two-Dimensional Figures   **329**

Properties of Two-Dimensional Figures Activity

Work together with your child to describe how figures are classified in Venn diagrams.

- Look at the figures in the Venn diagrams below and talk about how the figures are related to each other.

- Work together to describe the properties of the figures. Tell what properties the figures do and do not share. The words in the box describe some properties of figures that you might use in your discussion.

triangle	equilateral	isoceles
equal side lengths	different side lengths	
right angle	acute angle	

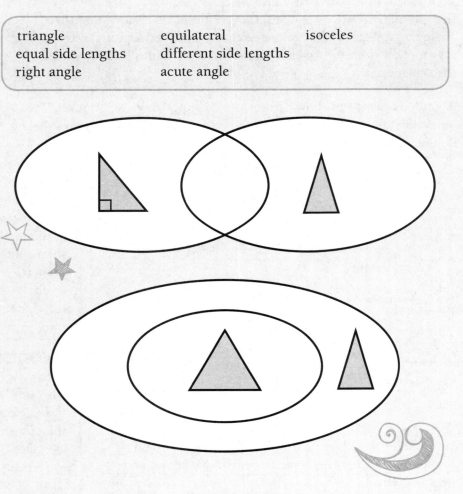

©Curriculum Associates, LLC   Copying is not permitted.

Understand
Properties of Two-Dimensional Figures

Name: _____

Prerequisite: How do you name triangles?

Study the example showing the different names that can be used for a triangle. Then solve problems 1–8.

Example

What is the name of this triangle?

You can name triangles based on their sides and angles.

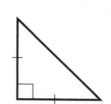

Name	Description of Sides
equilateral	3 equal sides
isosceles	at least 2 equal sides
scalene	0 equal sides

Name	Description of Angles
acute	3 acute angles
right	1 right angle
obtuse	1 obtuse angle

The triangle has a right angle, so it is a right triangle.

The triangle also has 2 equal sides, so it is also an isosceles triangle.

The name of the triangle is a right isosceles triangle.

1 Look at triangle A. How would you describe its sides?

_____

2 What kinds of angles does triangle A have?

_____

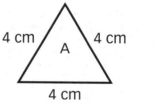

3 What are two names for triangle A?

_____

4 What are two names for triangle B? Explain.

_____

_____

_____

©Curriculum Associates, LLC   Copying is not permitted.

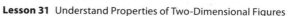

Solve.

5 Can triangle C be called an acute triangle? Why or why not?

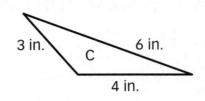

_____

_____

_____

_____

6 How are these triangles alike? How are they different?

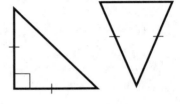

_____

_____

_____

_____

_____

7 Look at triangles D and E. Triangle D's sides are all different lengths. Triangle E has two sides of the same length. Write a letter D or E in the table below for all possible names of each triangle.

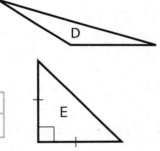

equilateral	isosceles	scalene	acute	right	obtuse

8 Kelly draws a triangle F, with 3 equal sides. She writes F under equilateral and acute in the table in problem 7. Did she forget any possible names for triangle F? Explain.

_____

_____

_____

_____

   ©Curriculum Associates, LLC   Copying is not permitted.

Name: _____

Understand Shared Properties

Study the example that uses a Venn diagram to show shared properties in triangles. Then solve problems 1–6.

Example

The Venn diagram shows how the properties of different triangles are related.

When two sections overlap, they sometimes share properties.

When one section is completely inside another section, they always share properties.

When two sections do not overlap at all, they never share properties.

An isosceles triangle has at least 2 equal sides. An equilateral triangle has 3 equal sides. So, an equilateral triangle has all the properties of an isosceles triangle. That's why the equilateral section lies completely inside the isosceles section.

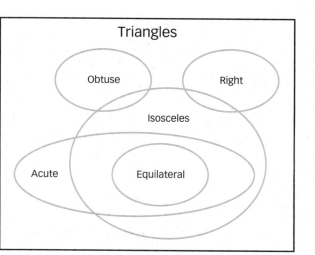

1 Complete each sentence with one of the words from the word bank in order to make each sentence true.

always
sometimes
never

a. An equilateral triangle _____ has all the properties of an isosceles triangle.

b. A right triangle _____ shares properties with an isosceles triangle.

c. A right triangle _____ shares properties with an obtuse triangle.

2 Look at the Venn diagram in the example. Describe what it shows about the relationship between acute and equilateral triangles.

_____

_____

_____

©Curriculum Associates, LLC   Copying is not permitted.

Solve.

3　Use the information in the table to fill in the tree diagram showing the hierarchy of the following quadrilaterals: parallelograms, squares, rhombuses, trapezoids, and rectangles. Remember, each category in the hierarchy has all the properties of the category above it.

Shape	Properties
parallelograms	2 pairs of parallel sides
squares	4 equal sides, 4 right angles
rhombuses	4 equal sides
trapezoids	at least 1 pair of parallel sides
rectangles	4 right angles

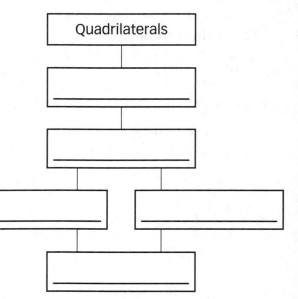

Quadrilaterals

4　Explain what the tree diagram in problem 3 shows about the relationship between trapezoids and parallelograms.

_____

_____

_____

_____

5　Describe a quadrilateral that cannot be placed in the hierarchy under trapezoids. Explain.

_____

_____

_____

6　Use the tree diagram in problem 3 to fill in the blanks to make the following sentence true.

The opposite sides of any parallelogram are equal. Therefore the opposite sides of any _____ , _____ , and _____ are equal.

Vocabulary

hierarchy　a ranking of categories based on properties.

Name: _____

Reason and Write

Study the example. Underline two parts that you think make it a particularly good answer and a helpful example.

Example

Use the information in the tree diagram.

Write a statement that is always true about the relationship between two different kinds of triangles. Write a statement that is sometimes true about isosceles triangles.

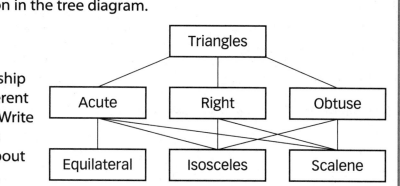

Show your work. Use pictures and words to explain.

Statement that is always true: Equilateral triangles are always acute. In the diagram above, "equilateral" branches only to "acute." If you draw different size equilateral triangles, the angles are always acute.

Statement that is sometimes true: An isosceles triangle is sometimes a right triangle. The diagram above shows isosceles triangles branching to acute, right, and obtuse triangles. The pictures show isosceles triangles that are both acute and right, so not every isosceles triangle is a right triangle.

> Where does the example . . .
> • make a statement that is always true?
> • make a statement that is sometimes true?
> • use words to explain?
> • use pictures to explain?

Solve the problem. Use what you learned from the example.

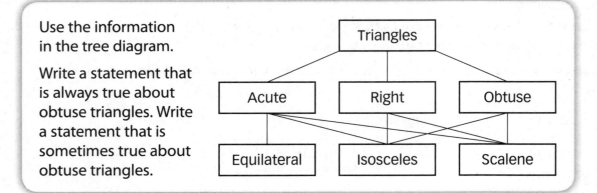

Use the information in the tree diagram.

Write a statement that is always true about obtuse triangles. Write a statement that is sometimes true about obtuse triangles.

Tree diagram:

Triangles
- Acute
- Right
- Obtuse

- Equilateral
- Isosceles
- Scalene

Show your work. Use pictures and words to explain.

Did you...

- make a statement that is always true?

- make a statement that is sometimes true?

- use words to explain?

- use pictures to explain?

©Curriculum Associates, LLC   Copying is not permitted.

Name: _____

Triangle Bingo

What you need: Recording Sheet, Game Board, Game Cards, 9 counters for each player

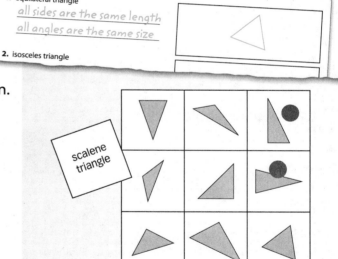

Directions

- Mix the game cards and put them in a pile face down.

- The first player draws a card. Find one triangle that matches the name on the card. Cover it with a counter.

- Draw a picture and write the attributes of the triangle on the recording sheet.

- If there are no matches on the board, skip a turn.

- Players take turns. The first player to place 3 counters in a row, across, up and down, or diagonally, wins.

Name: _Gia_

Triangle Bingo Recording Sheet

1. equilateral triangle
   all sides are the same length
   all angles are the same size

2. isosceles triangle

I put my counter on the scalene triangle in the upper right corner, so I would have two in a row.

Triangle Bingo Recording Sheet

1. equilateral triangle

_____

_____

2. isosceles triangle

_____

_____

3. scalene triangle

_____

_____

4. acute triangle

_____

_____

5. obtuse triangle

_____

_____

6. right triangle

_____

_____

©Curriculum Associates, LLC

Triangle Bingo Game Board

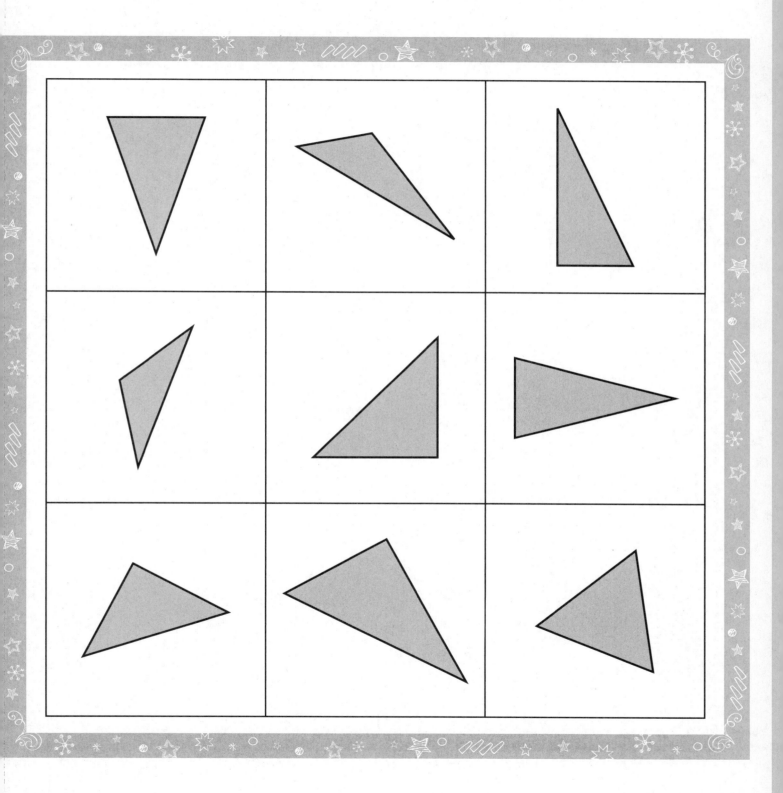

©Curriculum Associates, LLC   Copying is not permitted.

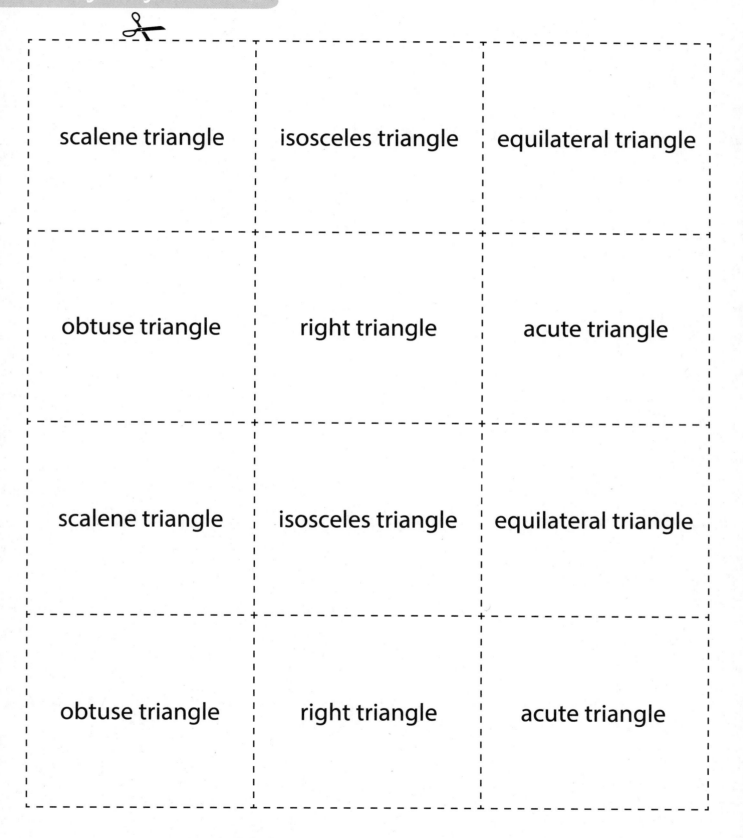

scalene triangle	isosceles triangle	equilateral triangle
obtuse triangle	right triangle	acute triangle
scalene triangle	isosceles triangle	equilateral triangle
obtuse triangle	right triangle	acute triangle

©Curriculum Associates, LLC

Name: _____

Geometry

In this unit you learned to:	Lesson
graph points in the first quadrant of the coordinate plane.	28
find the distance between two points on the coordinate plane.	29
graph real-world situations on the coordinate plane and interpret the meaning of the graph.	29
classify two-dimensional figures based on their properties, for example: a square is also a rhombus or rectangle, but not all rhombuses and rectangles are squares.	30, 31

Use these skills to solve problems 1–5.

1 Which figure has all the properties of a parallelogram? Circle the letter for all that apply.

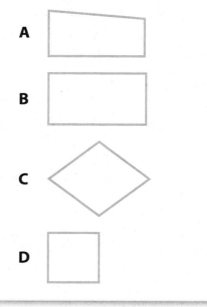

A

B

C

D

2 Write the letter of each point in the box next to the matching ordered pair.

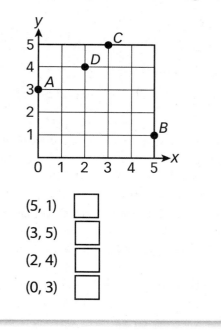

(5, 1) ☐

(3, 5) ☐

(2, 4) ☐

(0, 3) ☐

©Curriculum Associates, LLC   Copying is not permitted.

Solve.

3 Plot the points (1, 1), (1, 4), (3, 1), and (3, 4) on the coordinate plane to the right. Connect the points to form a quadrilateral.

Write all the names that can be used to classify the shape. List them in order from general to specific, starting with "quadrilateral." Justify how you came up with the specific shape name.

_____

_____

_____

_____

4 Look at the Venn diagram. Choose *True* or *False* for each statement.

a. An equilateral triangle is never a right triangle. ☐ True ☐ False

b. An isosceles triangle is always a right triangle. ☐ True ☐ False

c. An equilateral triangle is always an isosceles triangle. ☐ True ☐ False

Triangles

Isosceles

Right

Equilateral

5 Draw a rectangle on the coordinate plane with a perimeter of 16 units. Write the coordinates of the corners. Tell how you know the perimeter is 16 units.

_____

_____

_____

_____

_____

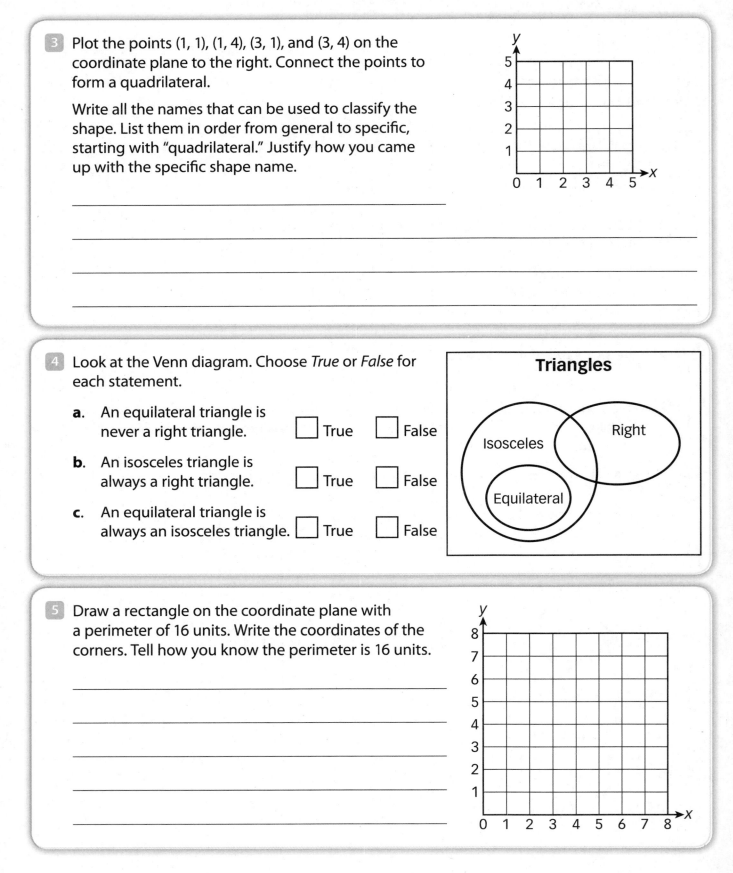

©Curriculum Associates, LLC   Copying is not permitted.

Name: _____

Answer the questions and show all your work on separate paper.

Your school is getting ready to plant a garden. You are using a field on the school property that is 25 yards long and 15 yards wide. There is a shed on the field and the field is fenced in.

You need to decide where to plant three sections of the garden for tomatoes, squash, and cucumbers. Each section needs to be rectangular and between 20 and 30 square yards in area.

A math teacher had students draw a diagram of the field on a coordinate grid. It's on the back side of this page.

Here is your task:

- Draw the three sections of vegetables where you want them to go. Label each section with the vegetable name.

- On a separate piece of paper, write the ordered pairs for the vertices of the three vegetable sections on your diagram.

- Explain how you decided on the arrangement of the sections. Show how your plan meets the requirements.

Reflect on Mathematical Practices

1 **Repeated Reasoning** What did you notice about the corresponding x-coordinates and y-coordinates of the vertices of the rectangles?

2 **Models** How did the coordinate plane help you complete this task?

Checklist

Did you . . .

☐ draw a diagram on the coordinate plane?

☐ write ordered pairs?

☐ show how to find the areas?

Word Bank Here are some words that you might use in your answer.

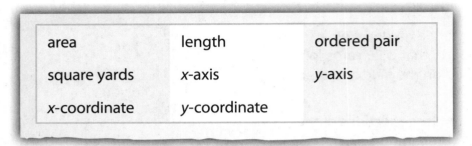

area	length	ordered pair
square yards	*x*-axis	*y*-axis
x-coordinate	*y*-coordinate	

Models Here is a model that you might use to find the solution.

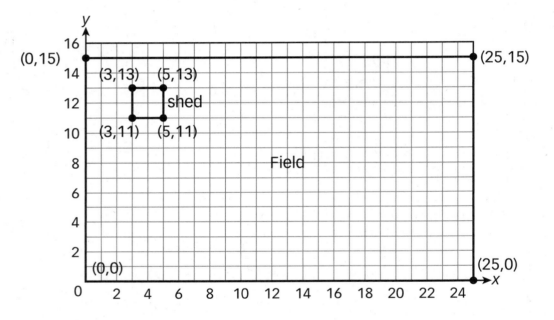

Sentence Starters Here are some sentence starters that might help explain your work.

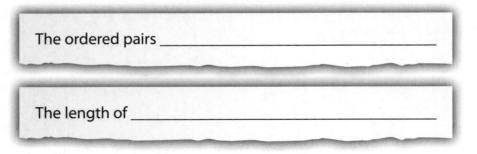

The ordered pairs _____

The length of _____

     ©Curriculum Associates, LLC   Copying is not permitted.

Unit 5 Vocabulary

Name: _____

My Examples

coordinate plane

    a two-dimensional space formed by two perpendicular number lines called axes

***x*-axis**

    the horizontal number line

***y*-axis**

    the vertical number line

axes

    the plural form of "axis"

origin

the point (0, 0) where the *x*-axis and *y*-axis intersect

ordered pair

a pair of numbers, or coordinates, (*x*, *y*) describing the location of a point on the coordinate plane

x-coordinate

a point's horizontal distance in units along the *x*-axis from the origin

y-coordinate

a point's vertical distance in units along the *y*-axis from the origin

©Curriculum Associates, LLC   Copying is not permitted.

attribute

a characteristic of a polygon (e.g., the number of sides)

subcategory

a category that is completely nested inside another category; it shares all the same properties as the category it is nested inside of

hierarchy

a ranking of categories based on properties

_____

_____

_____

_____

My Words

My Examples

©Curriculum Associates, LLC   Copying is not permitted.

Fluency Table of Contents

Multi-Digit Addition—Skills Practice

Name: _____

Add within 1,000,000.

Form A

1
$$\begin{array}{r} 4,699 \\ +209 \\ \hline \end{array}$$

2
$$\begin{array}{r} 733,633 \\ +5,678 \\ \hline \end{array}$$

3
$$\begin{array}{r} 5,050 \\ +5,049 \\ \hline \end{array}$$

4
$$\begin{array}{r} 35,009 \\ +21,991 \\ \hline \end{array}$$

5
$$\begin{array}{r} 123,321 \\ +987 \\ \hline \end{array}$$

6
$$\begin{array}{r} 806,515 \\ +14,372 \\ \hline \end{array}$$

7
$$\begin{array}{r} 97,342 \\ +728 \\ \hline \end{array}$$

8
$$\begin{array}{r} 150,225 \\ +145,225 \\ \hline \end{array}$$

9
$$\begin{array}{r} 28,403 \\ +26,910 \\ \hline \end{array}$$

10
$$\begin{array}{r} 5,146 \\ +5,915 \\ \hline \end{array}$$

11
$$\begin{array}{r} 915,412 \\ +15,412 \\ \hline \end{array}$$

12
$$\begin{array}{r} 42,963 \\ +8,825 \\ \hline \end{array}$$

13
$$\begin{array}{r} 188,888 \\ +222,222 \\ \hline \end{array}$$

14
$$\begin{array}{r} 670,780 \\ +9,564 \\ \hline \end{array}$$

15
$$\begin{array}{r} 16,275 \\ +36,334 \\ \hline \end{array}$$

16
$$\begin{array}{r} 7,741 \\ +2,260 \\ \hline \end{array}$$

17
$$\begin{array}{r} 10,864 \\ +864 \\ \hline \end{array}$$

18
$$\begin{array}{r} 642,002 \\ +80,999 \\ \hline \end{array}$$

19
$$\begin{array}{r} 22,987 \\ +44,789 \\ \hline \end{array}$$

20
$$\begin{array}{r} 47,247 \\ +8,747 \\ \hline \end{array}$$

©Curriculum Associates, LLC   Copying is permitted for classroom use.

Multi-Digit Addition—Skills Practice

Name: _____

Add within 1,000,000.

1
```
  3,597
+   307
```

2
```
  644,544
+   4,567
```

3
```
  2,020
+ 8,019
```

4
```
  42,991
+ 12,009
```

5
```
  234,432
+     876
```

6
```
  705,626
+  25,261
```

7
```
  64,751
+    429
```

8
```
  205,336
+ 204,336
```

9
```
  17,210
+ 15,801
```

10
```
  8,924
+ 8,157
```

11
```
  749,241
+  49,241
```

12
```
  53,854
+  9,945
```

13
```
  133,333
+ 777,777
```

14
```
  908,847
+   1,780
```

15
```
  28,764
+ 18,145
```

16
```
  6,632
+ 3,370
```

17
```
  22,552
+    552
```

18
```
  430,999
+  70,004
```

19
```
  33,678
+ 11,876
```

20
```
  76,356
+  7,626
```

©Curriculum Associates, LLC   Copying is permitted for classroom use.

Name: _____

Subtract within 1,000,000.

Form A

1
```
  11,223
−    311
```

2
```
   2,123
−  1,321
```

3
```
  432,765
−  43,276
```

4
```
  80,449
− 24,085
```

5
```
  184,234
−  93,517
```

6
```
  319,019
−   9,416
```

7
```
  62,626
−  6,262
```

8
```
  37,740
− 18,870
```

9
```
  7,347
− 5,182
```

10
```
  956,201
− 524,110
```

11
```
  476,747
−   9,696
```

12
```
  535
− 353
```

13
```
  90,000
−  1,234
```

14
```
  37,665
−    776
```

15
```
  215,451
−   8,795
```

16
```
  52,252
− 50,992
```

17
```
  602,602
− 444,444
```

18
```
  5,702
− 2,915
```

19
```
  877,007
−    525
```

20
```
  13,579
−  2,846
```

©Curriculum Associates, LLC   Copying is permitted for classroom use.

Multi-Digit Subtraction—Skills Practice

Name: _____

Subtract within 1,000,000.

1
$$\begin{array}{r} 13{,}445 \\ -522 \\ \hline \end{array}$$

2
$$\begin{array}{r} 8{,}789 \\ -7{,}987 \\ \hline \end{array}$$

3
$$\begin{array}{r} 654{,}631 \\ -65{,}432 \\ \hline \end{array}$$

4
$$\begin{array}{r} 70{,}338 \\ -13{,}074 \\ \hline \end{array}$$

5
$$\begin{array}{r} 162{,}478 \\ -81{,}759 \\ \hline \end{array}$$

6
$$\begin{array}{r} 518{,}018 \\ -8{,}515 \\ \hline \end{array}$$

7
$$\begin{array}{r} 71{,}717 \\ -7{,}171 \\ \hline \end{array}$$

8
$$\begin{array}{r} 51{,}120 \\ -25{,}560 \\ \hline \end{array}$$

9
$$\begin{array}{r} 6{,}536 \\ -5{,}372 \\ \hline \end{array}$$

10
$$\begin{array}{r} 833{,}021 \\ -312{,}110 \\ \hline \end{array}$$

11
$$\begin{array}{r} 596{,}454 \\ -9{,}393 \\ \hline \end{array}$$

12
$$\begin{array}{r} 626 \\ -262 \\ \hline \end{array}$$

13
$$\begin{array}{r} 70{,}000 \\ -2{,}345 \\ \hline \end{array}$$

14
$$\begin{array}{r} 28{,}776 \\ -887 \\ \hline \end{array}$$

15
$$\begin{array}{r} 437{,}673 \\ -9{,}895 \\ \hline \end{array}$$

16
$$\begin{array}{r} 32{,}131 \\ -30{,}881 \\ \hline \end{array}$$

17
$$\begin{array}{r} 501{,}501 \\ -333{,}333 \\ \hline \end{array}$$

18
$$\begin{array}{r} 6{,}803 \\ -4{,}806 \\ \hline \end{array}$$

19
$$\begin{array}{r} 966{,}006 \\ -414 \\ \hline \end{array}$$

20
$$\begin{array}{r} 14{,}568 \\ -3{,}725 \\ \hline \end{array}$$

©Curriculum Associates, LLC   Copying is permitted for classroom use.

Multi-Digit Multiplication—Skills Practice

Name: _____

Multiply. **Form A**

1   205
    × 33

2   6,660
    × 70

3   378
    × 12

4   1,221
    × 91

5   5,062
    × 25

6   829
    × 62

7   116
    × 46

8   7,256
    × 56

9   444
    × 99

10   3,136
    × 14

11   2,222
    × 55

12   761
    × 80

13   530
    × 28

14   142
    × 222

15   875
    × 305

16   250
    × 250

©Curriculum Associates, LLC   Copying is permitted for classroom use.

Name: _____

Multiply.

Form B

1   305
     × 22

2   7,770
     × 60

3   178
     × 32

4   2,332
     × 91

5   6,052
     × 25

6   629
     × 82

7   114
     × 44

8   5,256
     × 76

9   555
     × 99

10   1,136
     × 34

11   4,444
     × 55

12   861
     × 70

13   230
    × 58

14   142
    ×111

15   375
   ×805

16   125
   ×125

©Curriculum Associates, LLC   Copying is permitted for classroom use.

Multi-Digit Division—Skills Practice

Name: _____

Divide 3- and 4-digit dividends with mental math on some steps.

1 11)396

2 20)6,040

3 50)650

4 21)1,575

5 25)1,075

6 40)760

7 70)1,610

8 22)968

9 12)2,928

10 31)961

11 20)520

12 30)3,360

©Curriculum Associates, LLC   Copying is permitted for classroom use.

Multi-Digit Division—Skills Practice

Name: _____

Divide 3- and 4-digit dividends with mental math on some steps.　　　　　**Form B**

1

11)286

2

20)8,100

3

50)850

4

21)1,155

5

25)1,150

6

40)560

7

60)1,380

8

22)792

9

12)1,464

10

31)992

11

20)540

12

30)6,330

©Curriculum Associates, LLC   Copying is permitted for classroom use.

Name: _____

Divide 3-, 4-, and 5-digit dividends with mental math on some steps. Form A

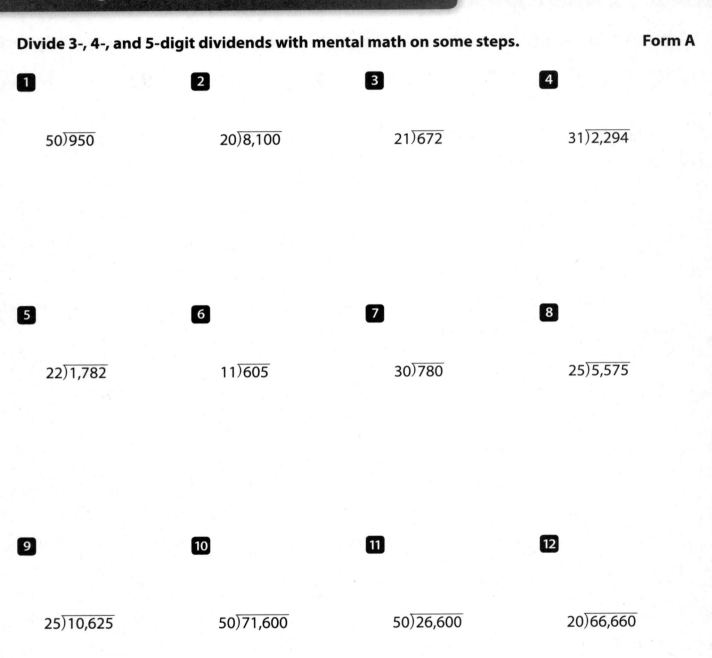

1

$50\overline{)950}$

2

$20\overline{)8{,}100}$

3

$21\overline{)672}$

4

$31\overline{)2{,}294}$

5

$22\overline{)1{,}782}$

6

$11\overline{)605}$

7

$30\overline{)780}$

8

$25\overline{)5{,}575}$

9

$25\overline{)10{,}625}$

10

$50\overline{)71{,}600}$

11

$50\overline{)26{,}600}$

12

$20\overline{)66{,}660}$

©Curriculum Associates, LLC   Copying is permitted for classroom use.

Multi-Digit Division—Skills Practice

Name: _____

Divide 3-, 4-, and 5-digit dividends with mental math on some steps.

1

$50\overline{)850}$

2

$20\overline{)6,100}$

3

$21\overline{)462}$

4

$31\overline{)1,674}$

5

$22\overline{)2,002}$

6

$11\overline{)715}$

7

$30\overline{)720}$

8

$25\overline{)8,350}$

9

$25\overline{)11,250}$

10

$50\overline{)61,700}$

11

$50\overline{)26,150}$

12

$20\overline{)44,440}$

©Curriculum Associates, LLC   Copying is permitted for classroom use.

Name: _____

Divide 3-, 4-, and 5-digit dividends.

Form A

1

$72\overline{)648}$

2

$30\overline{)2,880}$

3

$58\overline{)5,974}$

4

$18\overline{)828}$

5

$23\overline{)759}$

6

$40\overline{)960}$

7

$86\overline{)4,472}$

8

$12\overline{)7,632}$

9

$22\overline{)40,766}$

10

$15\overline{)10,875}$

11

$64\overline{)23,296}$

12

$20\overline{)91,340}$

©Curriculum Associates, LLC   Copying is permitted for classroom use.

Multi-Digit Division—Skills Practice

Name: _____

Divide 3-, 4-, and 5-digit dividends.

Form B

1

$74\overline{)592}$

2

$30\overline{)2{,}580}$

3

$56\overline{)5{,}936}$

4

$16\overline{)768}$

5

$33\overline{)825}$

6

$60\overline{)840}$

7

$88\overline{)4{,}488}$

8

$12\overline{)7{,}872}$

9

$42\overline{)59{,}010}$

10

$15\overline{)10{,}125}$

11

$62\overline{)21{,}452}$

12

$20\overline{)93{,}560}$

©Curriculum Associates, LLC   Copying is permitted for classroom use.

Multi-Digit Division—Repeated Reasoning

Name: _____

Find patterns with zeros.

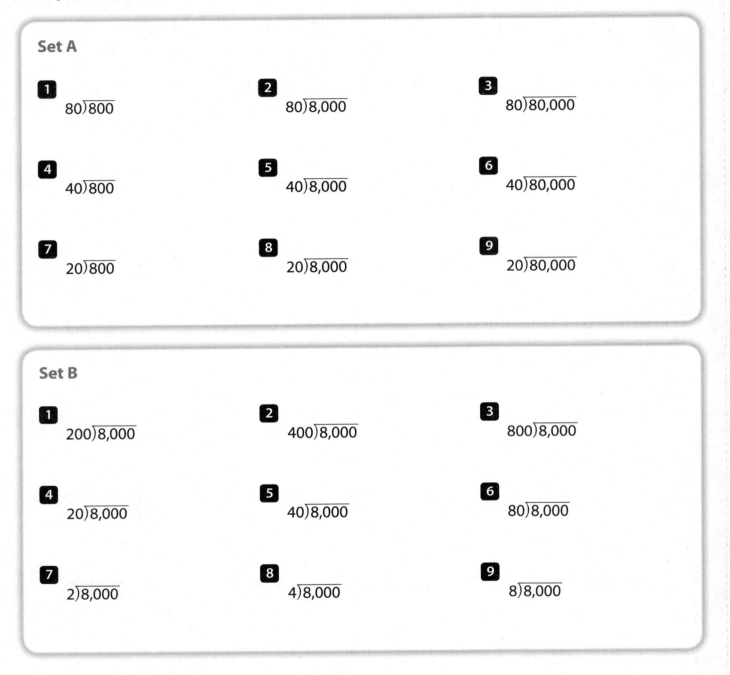

Set A

1
$80\overline{)800}$

2
$80\overline{)8,000}$

3
$80\overline{)80,000}$

4
$40\overline{)800}$

5
$40\overline{)8,000}$

6
$40\overline{)80,000}$

7
$20\overline{)800}$

8
$20\overline{)8,000}$

9
$20\overline{)80,000}$

Set B

1
$200\overline{)8,000}$

2
$400\overline{)8,000}$

3
$800\overline{)8,000}$

4
$20\overline{)8,000}$

5
$40\overline{)8,000}$

6
$80\overline{)8,000}$

7
$2\overline{)8,000}$

8
$4\overline{)8,000}$

9
$8\overline{)8,000}$

Describe a pattern you see in one of the sets of problems above.

_____

_____

_____

©Curriculum Associates, LLC   Copying is permitted for classroom use.

Name: _____

Find patterns in dividing by 25 or 50.

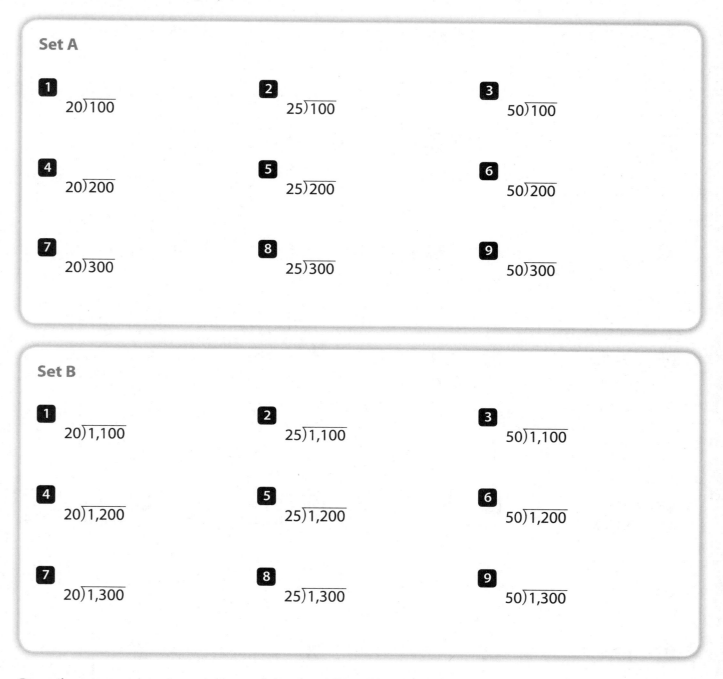

Set A

1 20)100

2 25)100

3 50)100

4 20)200

5 25)200

6 50)200

7 20)300

8 25)300

9 50)300

Set B

1 20)1,100

2 25)1,100

3 50)1,100

4 20)1,200

5 25)1,200

6 50)1,200

7 20)1,300

8 25)1,300

9 50)1,300

Describe a pattern you see in one of the sets of problems above.

_____

_____

_____

Name: _____

Add decimals through hundredths.

Form A

1 0.8 + 0.4 = _____

2 0.33 + 0.66 = _____

3 68.14 + 0.51 = _____

4 0.05 + 0.5 = _____

5 200.02 + 100.1 = _____

6 4.7 + 1.3 = _____

7 7.6 + 7.12 = _____

8 1.26 + 2.21 = _____

9 80.39 + 80.01 = _____

10
```
  54.17
+  4.92
```

11
```
  1.91
+ 0.09
```

12
```
  108.52
+ 258.01
```

13
```
  55.22
+ 22.55
```

14
```
  375.1
+ 525.7
```

15
```
  0.6
+ 0.6
```

16
```
  0.75
+ 0.45
```

17
```
  9.24
+ 4.26
```

18
```
  6.34
+ 3.6
```

19
```
  549.99
+  33.33
```

20
```
  4.84
+ 1.82
```

21
```
  48.4
+ 18.2
```

©Curriculum Associates, LLC   Copying is permitted for classroom use.

Decimal Addition—Skills Practice

Name: _____

Add decimals through hundredths.

Form B

1 0.5 + 0.8 = _____

2 0.22 + 0.77 = _____

3 46.12 + 0.31 = _____

4 0.09 + 0.9 = _____

5 500.05 + 300.3 = _____

6 6.2 + 1.8 = _____

7 9.6 + 9.31 = _____

8 2.36 + 3.32 = _____

9 70.02 + 70.28 = _____

10   64.23
    + 4.86

11   2.92
    + 0.08

12   209.71
    + 389.02

13   44.33
    + 33.44

14   250.5
    + 550.2

15   0.7
    + 0.7

16   0.75
    + 0.65

17   8.13
    + 4.17

18   5.42
    + 4.5

19   329.99
    + 22.22

20   2.52
    + 1.92

21   25.2
    + 19.2

©Curriculum Associates, LLC   Copying is permitted for classroom use.

Decimal Addition—Repeated Reasoning

Name: _____

Find place value patterns.

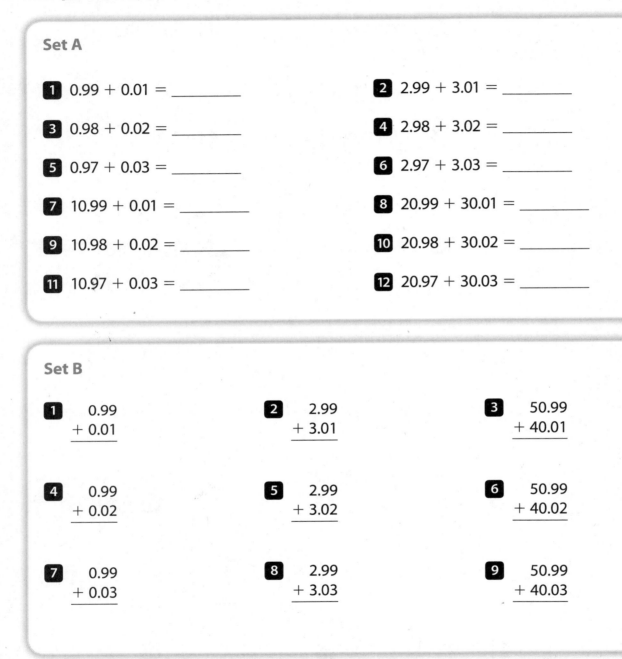

Set A

1 0.99 + 0.01 = _____

3 0.98 + 0.02 = _____

5 0.97 + 0.03 = _____

7 10.99 + 0.01 = _____

9 10.98 + 0.02 = _____

11 10.97 + 0.03 = _____

2 2.99 + 3.01 = _____

4 2.98 + 3.02 = _____

6 2.97 + 3.03 = _____

8 20.99 + 30.01 = _____

10 20.98 + 30.02 = _____

12 20.97 + 30.03 = _____

Set B

1   0.99
     + 0.01
    ‾‾‾‾‾‾‾

2   2.99
     + 3.01
    ‾‾‾‾‾‾‾

3   50.99
     + 40.01
    ‾‾‾‾‾‾‾

4   0.99
     + 0.02
    ‾‾‾‾‾‾‾

5   2.99
     + 3.02
    ‾‾‾‾‾‾‾

6   50.99
     + 40.02
    ‾‾‾‾‾‾‾

7   0.99
     + 0.03
    ‾‾‾‾‾‾‾

8   2.99
     + 3.03
    ‾‾‾‾‾‾‾

9   50.99
     + 40.03
    ‾‾‾‾‾‾‾

Describe a pattern you see in one of the sets of problems above.

_____

_____

_____

©Curriculum Associates, LLC   Copying is permitted for classroom use.

Decimal Subtraction—Skills Practice

Name: _____

Subtract decimals through hundredths.

1 25.25 − 0.11 = _____

2 0.4 − 0.04 = _____

3 200.4 − 100.04 = _____

4 0.7 − 0.5 = _____

5 70.18 − 10.09 = _____

6 9.5 − 9.05 = _____

7 3.42 − 1.32 = _____

8 0.88 − 0.33 = _____

9 1.25 − 0.75 = _____

10
$$\begin{array}{r} 1.42 \\ -\ 0.43 \\ \hline \end{array}$$

11
$$\begin{array}{r} 1.6 \\ -\ 0.8 \\ \hline \end{array}$$

12
$$\begin{array}{r} 352.52 \\ -\ 108.08 \\ \hline \end{array}$$

13
$$\begin{array}{r} 4.36 \\ -\ 3.6 \\ \hline \end{array}$$

14
$$\begin{array}{r} 725.7 \\ -\ 175.2 \\ \hline \end{array}$$

15
$$\begin{array}{r} 9.36 \\ -\ 5.36 \\ \hline \end{array}$$

16
$$\begin{array}{r} 99.88 \\ -\ 88.77 \\ \hline \end{array}$$

17
$$\begin{array}{r} 99.88 \\ -\ 88.99 \\ \hline \end{array}$$

18
$$\begin{array}{r} 59.1 \\ -\ 25.8 \\ \hline \end{array}$$

19
$$\begin{array}{r} 5.91 \\ -\ 2.58 \\ \hline \end{array}$$

20
$$\begin{array}{r} 802.11 \\ -\ 22.22 \\ \hline \end{array}$$

21
$$\begin{array}{r} 65.62 \\ -\ 2.81 \\ \hline \end{array}$$

©Curriculum Associates, LLC   Copying is permitted for classroom use.

Decimal Subtraction—Skills Practice

Name: _____

Subtract decimals through hundredths.

1 92.92 − 0.11 = _____

2 0.5 − 0.05 = _____

3 400.5 − 200.05 = _____

4 0.8 − 0.2 = _____

5 50.14 − 10.07 = _____

6 3.2 − 3.02 = _____

7 4.46 − 2.26 = _____

8 0.66 − 0.22 = _____

9 1.25 − 0.5 = _____

10
```
   1.61
 − 0.62
```

11
```
   2.4
 − 1.2
```

12
```
  591.91
 − 203.03
```

13
```
   6.58
 − 5.8
```

14
```
  955.9
 − 295.3
```

15
```
   4.72
 − 1.72
```

16
```
  77.66
 − 66.55
```

17
```
  77.66
 − 66.77
```

18
```
  89.1
 − 33.6
```

19
```
  8.91
 − 3.36
```

20
```
  603.22
 −  33.33
```

21
```
  43.48
 −  1.74
```

©Curriculum Associates, LLC   Copying is permitted for classroom use.

Decimal Subtraction—Repeated Reasoning

Name: _____

Find place value patterns.

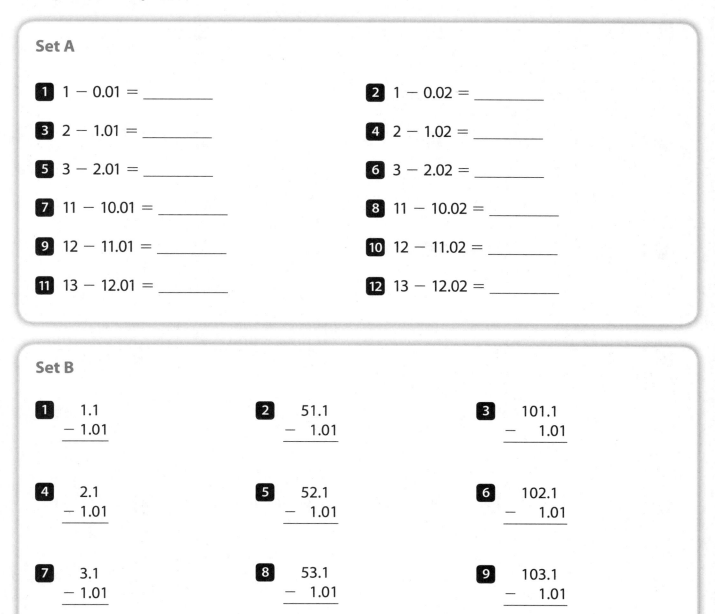

Set A

1 $1 - 0.01 = $ _____

2 $1 - 0.02 = $ _____

3 $2 - 1.01 = $ _____

4 $2 - 1.02 = $ _____

5 $3 - 2.01 = $ _____

6 $3 - 2.02 = $ _____

7 $11 - 10.01 = $ _____

8 $11 - 10.02 = $ _____

9 $12 - 11.01 = $ _____

10 $12 - 11.02 = $ _____

11 $13 - 12.01 = $ _____

12 $13 - 12.02 = $ _____

Set B

1
$$\begin{array}{r} 1.1 \\ -\ 1.01 \\ \hline \end{array}$$

2
$$\begin{array}{r} 51.1 \\ -\ 1.01 \\ \hline \end{array}$$

3
$$\begin{array}{r} 101.1 \\ -\ 1.01 \\ \hline \end{array}$$

4
$$\begin{array}{r} 2.1 \\ -\ 1.01 \\ \hline \end{array}$$

5
$$\begin{array}{r} 52.1 \\ -\ 1.01 \\ \hline \end{array}$$

6
$$\begin{array}{r} 102.1 \\ -\ 1.01 \\ \hline \end{array}$$

7
$$\begin{array}{r} 3.1 \\ -\ 1.01 \\ \hline \end{array}$$

8
$$\begin{array}{r} 53.1 \\ -\ 1.01 \\ \hline \end{array}$$

9
$$\begin{array}{r} 103.1 \\ -\ 1.01 \\ \hline \end{array}$$

Describe a pattern you see in one of the sets of problems above.

_____

_____

_____

©Curriculum Associates, LLC   Copying is permitted for classroom use.

Name: _____

Multiply.

Form A

1 $3 \times 0.6 =$ _____

2 $1.2 \times 1.2 =$ _____

3 $0.5 \times 4 =$ _____

4 $0.7 \times 0.2 =$ _____

5 $7 \times 0.02 =$ _____

6 $5.5 \times 0.1 =$ _____

7 $25 \times 0.01 =$ _____

8 $0.4 \times 0.08 =$ _____

9 $0.09 \times 10 =$ _____

10
$$\begin{array}{r} 3.7 \\ \times\ 0.4 \\ \hline \end{array}$$

11
$$\begin{array}{r} 1.8 \\ \times\ 4 \\ \hline \end{array}$$

12
$$\begin{array}{r} 6.12 \\ \times\ 0.5 \\ \hline \end{array}$$

13
$$\begin{array}{r} 3.06 \\ \times\ 2 \\ \hline \end{array}$$

14
$$\begin{array}{r} 0.31 \\ \times\ 0.6 \\ \hline \end{array}$$

15
$$\begin{array}{r} 1.75 \\ \times\ 2.5 \\ \hline \end{array}$$

16
$$\begin{array}{r} 0.11 \\ \times\ 14 \\ \hline \end{array}$$

17
$$\begin{array}{r} 4.1 \\ \times\ 5.2 \\ \hline \end{array}$$

18
$$\begin{array}{r} 3.33 \\ \times\ 2.2 \\ \hline \end{array}$$

19
$$\begin{array}{r} 33.3 \\ \times\ 0.22 \\ \hline \end{array}$$

20
$$\begin{array}{r} 0.5 \\ \times\ 15 \\ \hline \end{array}$$

21
$$\begin{array}{r} 11.1 \\ \times\ 0.09 \\ \hline \end{array}$$

©Curriculum Associates, LLC   Copying is permitted for classroom use.

Decimal Multiplication—Skills Practice

Multiply.

Form B

1 $4 \times 0.4 =$ _____

2 $1.1 \times 1.1 =$ _____

3 $0.5 \times 6 =$ _____

4 $0.6 \times 0.2 =$ _____

5 $6 \times 0.02 =$ _____

6 $8.8 \times 0.1 =$ _____

7 $15 \times 0.01 =$ _____

8 $0.9 \times 0.04 =$ _____

9 $0.03 \times 10 =$ _____

10
$$\begin{array}{r} 5.4 \\ \times\ 0.3 \\ \hline \end{array}$$

11
$$\begin{array}{r} 1.3 \\ \times\ 5 \\ \hline \end{array}$$

12
$$\begin{array}{r} 8.24 \\ \times\ 0.5 \\ \hline \end{array}$$

13
$$\begin{array}{r} 4.12 \\ \times\ 2 \\ \hline \end{array}$$

14
$$\begin{array}{r} 0.72 \\ \times\ 0.3 \\ \hline \end{array}$$

15
$$\begin{array}{r} 1.25 \\ \times\ 7.5 \\ \hline \end{array}$$

16
$$\begin{array}{r} 0.11 \\ \times\ 16 \\ \hline \end{array}$$

17
$$\begin{array}{r} 6.2 \\ \times\ 5.1 \\ \hline \end{array}$$

18
$$\begin{array}{r} 2.22 \\ \times\ 4.4 \\ \hline \end{array}$$

19
$$\begin{array}{r} 22.2 \\ \times\ 0.44 \\ \hline \end{array}$$

20
$$\begin{array}{r} 0.5 \\ \times\ 25 \\ \hline \end{array}$$

21
$$\begin{array}{r} 11.1 \\ \times\ 0.08 \\ \hline \end{array}$$

©Curriculum Associates, LLC   Copying is permitted for classroom use.

Decimal Multiplication—Repeated Reasoning

Name: _____

Find place value patterns.

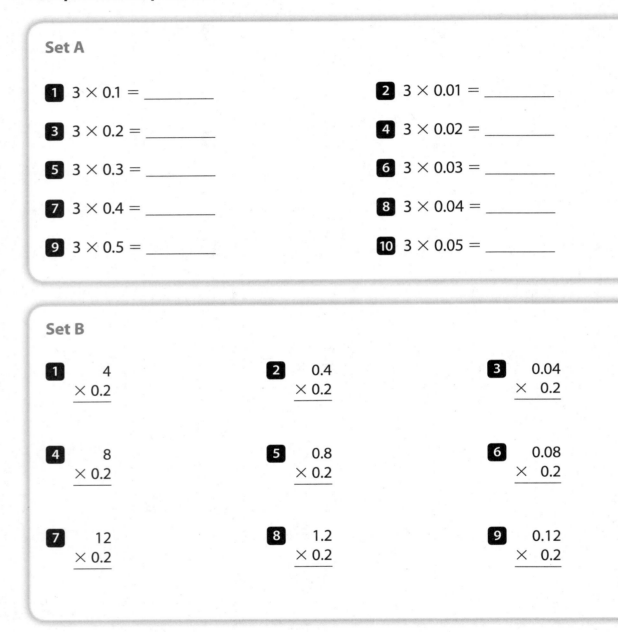

Set A

1 $3 \times 0.1 =$ _____

2 $3 \times 0.01 =$ _____

3 $3 \times 0.2 =$ _____

4 $3 \times 0.02 =$ _____

5 $3 \times 0.3 =$ _____

6 $3 \times 0.03 =$ _____

7 $3 \times 0.4 =$ _____

8 $3 \times 0.04 =$ _____

9 $3 \times 0.5 =$ _____

10 $3 \times 0.05 =$ _____

Set B

1
$$\begin{array}{r} 4 \\ \times\ 0.2 \\ \hline \end{array}$$

2
$$\begin{array}{r} 0.4 \\ \times\ 0.2 \\ \hline \end{array}$$

3
$$\begin{array}{r} 0.04 \\ \times\ 0.2 \\ \hline \end{array}$$

4
$$\begin{array}{r} 8 \\ \times\ 0.2 \\ \hline \end{array}$$

5
$$\begin{array}{r} 0.8 \\ \times\ 0.2 \\ \hline \end{array}$$

6
$$\begin{array}{r} 0.08 \\ \times\ 0.2 \\ \hline \end{array}$$

7
$$\begin{array}{r} 12 \\ \times\ 0.2 \\ \hline \end{array}$$

8
$$\begin{array}{r} 1.2 \\ \times\ 0.2 \\ \hline \end{array}$$

9
$$\begin{array}{r} 0.12 \\ \times\ 0.2 \\ \hline \end{array}$$

Describe a pattern you see in one of the sets of problems above.

_____

_____

_____

_____

©Curriculum Associates, LLC   Copying is permitted for classroom use.

Decimal Division—Skills Practice

Name: _____

Divide decimals through hundredths.

Form A

1 3.2 ÷ 4 = _____

2 12 ÷ 0.12 = _____

3 2.8 ÷ 0.7 = _____

4 0.9 ÷ 0.1 = _____

5 6 ÷ 0.3 = _____

6 1.15 ÷ 0.05 = _____

7 1.32 ÷ 12 = _____

8 1.32 ÷ 0.12 = _____

9 0.8 ÷ 4 = _____

10 1.04 ÷ 0.8 = _____

11 3.6 ÷ 0.9 = _____

12 30 ÷ 0.5 = _____

13 24 ÷ 0.04 = _____

14 1.2 ÷ 0.6 = _____

15 1.2 ÷ 0.06 = _____

16 0.15 ÷ 3 = _____

17 3.33 ÷ 0.3 = _____

18 28 ÷ 1.4 = _____

19 1.05 ÷ 5 = _____

20 1.05 ÷ 0.05 = _____

21 0.49 ÷ 0.7 = _____

22 0.8 ÷ 8 = _____

23 4.4 ÷ 11 = _____

24 0.36 ÷ 6 = _____

Decimal Division—Skills Practice

Name: _____

Divide decimals through hundredths.   **Form B**

1 2.4 ÷ 6 = _____

2 13 ÷ 0.13 = _____

3 3.5 ÷ 0.7 = _____

4 0.2 ÷ 0.1 = _____

5 8 ÷ 0.4 = _____

6 1.05 ÷ 0.05 = _____

7 1.44 ÷ 12 = _____

8 1.44 ÷ 0.12 = _____

9 0.6 ÷ 2 = _____

10 1.12 ÷ 0.8 = _____

11 4.2 ÷ 0.7 = _____

12 45 ÷ 0.5 = _____

13 36 ÷ 0.09 = _____

14 1.8 ÷ 0.6 = _____

15 1.8 ÷ 0.06 = _____

16 0.21 ÷ 3 = _____

17 2.22 ÷ 0.2 = _____

18 24 ÷ 1.2 = _____

19 1.25 ÷ 5 = _____

20 1.25 ÷ 0.05 = _____

21 0.64 ÷ 0.8 = _____

22 0.9 ÷ 9 = _____

23 3.3 ÷ 11 = _____

24 0.81 ÷ 9 = _____

©Curriculum Associates, LLC   Copying is permitted for classroom use.

Decimal Division—Repeated Reasoning

Name: _____

Find place value patterns.

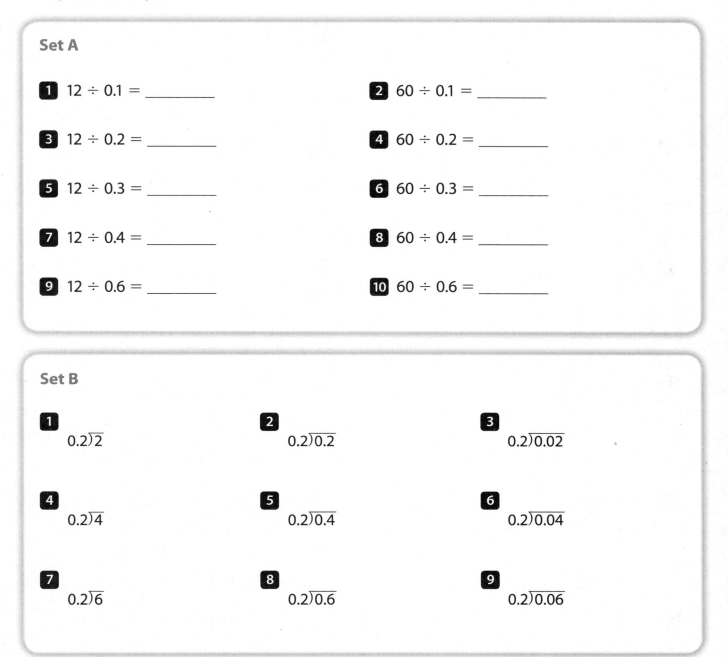

Set A

1 12 ÷ 0.1 = _____

2 60 ÷ 0.1 = _____

3 12 ÷ 0.2 = _____

4 60 ÷ 0.2 = _____

5 12 ÷ 0.3 = _____

6 60 ÷ 0.3 = _____

7 12 ÷ 0.4 = _____

8 60 ÷ 0.4 = _____

9 12 ÷ 0.6 = _____

10 60 ÷ 0.6 = _____

Set B

1 $0.2\overline{)2}$

2 $0.2\overline{)0.2}$

3 $0.2\overline{)0.02}$

4 $0.2\overline{)4}$

5 $0.2\overline{)0.4}$

6 $0.2\overline{)0.04}$

7 $0.2\overline{)6}$

8 $0.2\overline{)0.6}$

9 $0.2\overline{)0.06}$

Describe a pattern you see in one of the sets of problems above.

_____

_____

_____

©Curriculum Associates, LLC   Copying is permitted for classroom use.

Fraction Addition—Skills Practice

Add fractions or mixed numbers.

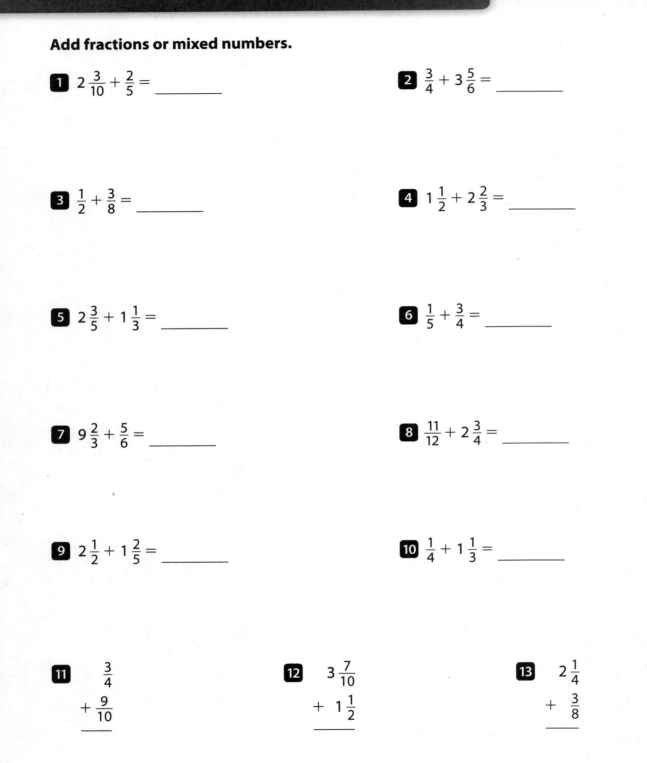

1 $2\frac{3}{10} + \frac{2}{5} = $ _____

2 $\frac{3}{4} + 3\frac{5}{6} = $ _____

3 $\frac{1}{2} + \frac{3}{8} = $ _____

4 $1\frac{1}{2} + 2\frac{2}{3} = $ _____

5 $2\frac{3}{5} + 1\frac{1}{3} = $ _____

6 $\frac{1}{5} + \frac{3}{4} = $ _____

7 $9\frac{2}{3} + \frac{5}{6} = $ _____

8 $\frac{11}{12} + 2\frac{3}{4} = $ _____

9 $2\frac{1}{2} + 1\frac{2}{5} = $ _____

10 $\frac{1}{4} + 1\frac{1}{3} = $ _____

11
$$\begin{array}{r} \frac{3}{4} \\ + \frac{9}{10} \\ \hline \end{array}$$

12
$$\begin{array}{r} 3\frac{7}{10} \\ + 1\frac{1}{2} \\ \hline \end{array}$$

13
$$\begin{array}{r} 2\frac{1}{4} \\ + \frac{3}{8} \\ \hline \end{array}$$

©Curriculum Associates, LLC   Copying is permitted for classroom use.

Name: _____

Add fractions or mixed numbers.

Form B

1 $1\frac{1}{3} + \frac{1}{6} =$ _____

2 $\frac{3}{5} + 3\frac{1}{2} =$ _____

3 $\frac{1}{2} + \frac{5}{12} =$ _____

4 $2\frac{9}{10} + 2\frac{1}{4} =$ _____

5 $1\frac{3}{8} + 1\frac{1}{6} =$ _____

6 $\frac{2}{3} + \frac{1}{8} =$ _____

7 $3\frac{7}{10} + \frac{4}{5} =$ _____

8 $\frac{3}{4} + 2\frac{1}{2} =$ _____

9 $4\frac{1}{4} + 3\frac{1}{3} =$ _____

10 $\frac{3}{5} + 1\frac{1}{4} =$ _____

11 $\begin{array}{r} \frac{4}{5} \\ + \frac{1}{3} \\ \hline \end{array}$

12 $\begin{array}{r} 5\frac{5}{8} \\ + 2\frac{3}{4} \\ \hline \end{array}$

13 $\begin{array}{r} 3\frac{1}{2} \\ + \frac{3}{10} \\ \hline \end{array}$

©Curriculum Associates, LLC   Copying is permitted for classroom use.

Fraction Addition—Repeated Reasoning

Name: _____

Find regrouping patterns.

Set A

1 $1\frac{3}{4} + \frac{1}{4} =$ _____

2 $1\frac{3}{4} + \frac{1}{2} =$ _____

3 $2\frac{3}{4} + \frac{1}{4} =$ _____

4 $2\frac{3}{4} + \frac{1}{2} =$ _____

5 $3\frac{3}{4} + \frac{1}{4} =$ _____

6 $3\frac{3}{4} + \frac{1}{2} =$ _____

7 $4\frac{3}{4} + \frac{1}{4} =$ _____

8 $4\frac{3}{4} + \frac{1}{2} =$ _____

Set B

1 $\quad 2\frac{7}{8}$
$+ \quad \frac{1}{8}$
_____

2 $\quad 2\frac{7}{8}$
$+ \quad \frac{1}{4}$
_____

3 $\quad 2\frac{7}{8}$
$+ \quad \frac{1}{2}$
_____

4 $\quad 3\frac{7}{8}$
$+ \quad \frac{1}{8}$
_____

5 $\quad 3\frac{7}{8}$
$+ \quad \frac{1}{4}$
_____

6 $\quad 3\frac{7}{8}$
$+ \quad \frac{1}{2}$
_____

7 $\quad 4\frac{7}{8}$
$+ \quad \frac{1}{8}$
_____

8 $\quad 4\frac{7}{8}$
$+ \quad \frac{1}{4}$
_____

9 $\quad 4\frac{7}{8}$
$+ \quad \frac{1}{2}$
_____

Describe a pattern you see in one of the sets of problems above.

_____

_____

©Curriculum Associates, LLC   Copying is permitted for classroom use.

Fraction Subtraction—Skills Practice

Subtract fractions or mixed numbers.

1 $3\frac{3}{4} - \frac{3}{8} =$ _____

2 $\frac{4}{5} - \frac{2}{3} =$ _____

3 $4\frac{1}{10} - 1 =$ _____

4 $4\frac{1}{4} - 2\frac{5}{12} =$ _____

5 $2\frac{1}{2} - \frac{3}{5} =$ _____

6 $5\frac{1}{3} - 1\frac{1}{6} =$ _____

7 $3 - \frac{3}{8} =$ _____

8 $\frac{5}{6} - \frac{5}{8} =$ _____

9 $5\frac{3}{10} - 4\frac{1}{2} =$ _____

10 $3\frac{3}{5} - 1\frac{3}{4} =$ _____

11 $\begin{array}{r} 5 \\ -\ 2\frac{1}{6} \\ \hline \end{array}$

12 $\begin{array}{r} 1\frac{1}{3} \\ -\ \frac{3}{12} \\ \hline \end{array}$

13 $\begin{array}{r} 3\frac{7}{8} \\ -\ 2\frac{2}{3} \\ \hline \end{array}$

©Curriculum Associates, LLC   Copying is permitted for classroom use.

Fraction Subtraction—Skills Practice

Name: _____

Subtract fractions or mixed numbers.

Form B

1 $4\frac{11}{12} - \frac{5}{6} =$ _____

2 $\frac{5}{6} - \frac{3}{4} =$ _____

3 $5\frac{1}{8} - 4 =$ _____

4 $5\frac{1}{5} - 2\frac{7}{10} =$ _____

5 $3\frac{2}{3} - \frac{1}{2} =$ _____

6 $2\frac{5}{12} - 2\frac{1}{4} =$ _____

7 $2 - \frac{3}{5} =$ _____

8 $\frac{3}{4} - \frac{2}{3} =$ _____

9 $4 - 2\frac{5}{12} =$ _____

10 $4\frac{1}{6} - 2\frac{5}{8} =$ _____

11 $\begin{array}{r} 4 \\ -\ 2\frac{5}{12} \\ \hline \end{array}$

12 $\begin{array}{r} 2\frac{3}{4} \\ -\ \frac{1}{12} \\ \hline \end{array}$

13 $\begin{array}{r} 8\frac{3}{10} \\ -\ 3\frac{1}{4} \\ \hline \end{array}$

382   **Fluency Practice**

©Curriculum Associates, LLC   Copying is permitted for classroom use.

Fraction Subtraction—Repeated Reasoning

Name: _____

Find regrouping patterns.

Set A

1 $1\frac{3}{4} - \frac{1}{2} =$ _____

2 $1\frac{1}{2} - \frac{3}{4} =$ _____

3 $2\frac{3}{4} - \frac{1}{2} =$ _____

4 $2\frac{1}{2} - \frac{3}{4} =$ _____

5 $3\frac{3}{4} - \frac{1}{2} =$ _____

6 $3\frac{1}{2} - \frac{3}{4} =$ _____

7 $4\frac{3}{4} - \frac{1}{2} =$ _____

8 $4\frac{1}{2} - \frac{3}{4} =$ _____

Set B

1
$$6\frac{1}{4}$$
$$-\ \frac{1}{4}$$
_____

2
$$6\frac{1}{4}$$
$$-\ \frac{1}{2}$$
_____

3
$$6\frac{1}{4}$$
$$-\ \frac{3}{4}$$
_____

4
$$7\frac{1}{4}$$
$$-\ \frac{1}{4}$$
_____

5
$$7\frac{1}{4}$$
$$-\ \frac{1}{2}$$
_____

6
$$7\frac{1}{4}$$
$$-\ \frac{3}{4}$$
_____

7
$$8\frac{1}{4}$$
$$-\ \frac{1}{4}$$
_____

8
$$8\frac{1}{4}$$
$$-\ \frac{1}{2}$$
_____

9
$$8\frac{1}{4}$$
$$-\ \frac{3}{4}$$
_____

Describe a pattern you see in one of the sets of problems above.

_____

_____

_____

©Curriculum Associates, LLC   Copying is permitted for classroom use.

Fraction Multiplication—Skills Practice

Name: _____

Multiply fractions and whole numbers.
Form A

1 $2 \times \frac{3}{8} =$ _____

2 $4 \times \frac{2}{3} =$ _____

3 $\frac{1}{2} \times 5 =$ _____

4 $\frac{2}{5} \times 6 =$ _____

5 $7 \times \frac{3}{10} =$ _____

6 $3 \times \frac{1}{5} =$ _____

7 $3 \times \frac{5}{8} =$ _____

8 $\frac{3}{4} \times 2 =$ _____

9 $\frac{2}{3} \times 2 =$ _____

10 $6 \times \frac{3}{5} =$ _____

11 $\frac{1}{6} \times 3 =$ _____

12 $4 \times \frac{4}{5} =$ _____

13 $\frac{7}{8} \times 5 =$ _____

14 $9 \times \frac{1}{3} =$ _____

15 $\frac{1}{20} \times 10 =$ _____

16 $8 \times \frac{1}{8} =$ _____

17 $\frac{5}{12} \times 4 =$ _____

18 $12 \times \frac{3}{4} =$ _____

©Curriculum Associates, LLC   Copying is permitted for classroom use.

Fraction Multiplication—Skills Practice

Name: _____

Multiply fractions and whole numbers.

Form B

1 $\frac{3}{8} \times 3 =$ _____

2 $\frac{2}{3} \times 6 =$ _____

3 $9 \times \frac{1}{2} =$ _____

4 $\frac{2}{5} \times 5 =$ _____

5 $\frac{3}{10} \times 3 =$ _____

6 $2 \times \frac{1}{5} =$ _____

7 $2 \times \frac{5}{8} =$ _____

8 $\frac{3}{4} \times 3 =$ _____

9 $4 \times \frac{2}{3} =$ _____

10 $\frac{3}{5} \times 8 =$ _____

11 $4 \times \frac{1}{6} =$ _____

12 $\frac{4}{5} \times 5 =$ _____

13 $\frac{7}{8} \times 2 =$ _____

14 $6 \times \frac{1}{3} =$ _____

15 $\frac{1}{20} \times 5 =$ _____

16 $6 \times \frac{1}{6} =$ _____

17 $\frac{5}{12} \times 3 =$ _____

18 $8 \times \frac{3}{4} =$ _____

©Curriculum Associates, LLC   Copying is permitted for classroom use.

Multiply fractions by fractions.   **Form A**

1 $\frac{3}{4} \times \frac{1}{4} =$ _____

2 $\frac{1}{5} \times \frac{1}{2} =$ _____

3 $\frac{2}{3} \times \frac{2}{5} =$ _____

4 $\frac{5}{12} \times \frac{1}{2} =$ _____

5 $\frac{3}{4} \times \frac{3}{8} =$ _____

6 $\frac{4}{5} \times \frac{5}{6} =$ _____

7 $\frac{7}{10} \times \frac{7}{10} =$ _____

8 $\frac{2}{3} \times \frac{2}{3} =$ _____

9 $\frac{9}{10} \times \frac{1}{2} =$ _____

10 $\frac{1}{3} \times \frac{1}{6} =$ _____

11 $\frac{5}{8} \times \frac{8}{5} =$ _____

12 $\frac{3}{10} \times \frac{3}{5} =$ _____

13 $\frac{3}{8} \times \frac{5}{8} =$ _____

14 $\frac{2}{5} \times \frac{4}{3} =$ _____

15 $\frac{1}{4} \times \frac{4}{1} =$ _____

16 $\frac{9}{10} \times \frac{3}{4} =$ _____

17 $\frac{1}{3} \times \frac{7}{10} =$ _____

18 $\frac{7}{8} \times \frac{2}{3} =$ _____

©Curriculum Associates, LLC   Copying is permitted for classroom use.

Fraction Multiplication—Skills Practice

Name: _____

Multiply fractions by fractions.

Form B

1 $\dfrac{2}{5} \times \dfrac{1}{5} =$ _____

2 $\dfrac{1}{4} \times \dfrac{1}{2} =$ _____

3 $\dfrac{3}{5} \times \dfrac{3}{8} =$ _____

4 $\dfrac{5}{8} \times \dfrac{1}{2} =$ _____

5 $\dfrac{2}{3} \times \dfrac{2}{8} =$ _____

6 $\dfrac{3}{4} \times \dfrac{4}{5} =$ _____

7 $\dfrac{3}{10} \times \dfrac{3}{10} =$ _____

8 $\dfrac{5}{8} \times \dfrac{5}{8} =$ _____

9 $\dfrac{9}{12} \times \dfrac{1}{2} =$ _____

10 $\dfrac{1}{4} \times \dfrac{1}{2} =$ _____

11 $\dfrac{4}{5} \times \dfrac{5}{4} =$ _____

12 $\dfrac{2}{5} \times \dfrac{2}{3} =$ _____

13 $\dfrac{3}{10} \times \dfrac{7}{10} =$ _____

14 $\dfrac{5}{6} \times \dfrac{10}{8} =$ _____

15 $\dfrac{1}{6} \times \dfrac{6}{1} =$ _____

16 $\dfrac{7}{8} \times \dfrac{5}{6} =$ _____

17 $\dfrac{1}{12} \times \dfrac{2}{3} =$ _____

18 $\dfrac{3}{4} \times \dfrac{5}{8} =$ _____

©Curriculum Associates, LLC   Copying is permitted for classroom use.

Fraction Multiplication—Repeated Reasoning

Name: _____

Multiply by a unit fraction to find patterns.

Set A

1 $12 \div 2 =$ _____

2 $12 \times \frac{1}{2} = \dfrac{\Box}{\Box} =$ _____

3 $12 \div 3 =$ _____

4 $12 \times \frac{1}{3} = \dfrac{\Box}{\Box} =$ _____

5 $12 \div 4 =$ _____

6 $12 \times \frac{1}{4} = \dfrac{\Box}{\Box} =$ _____

7 $12 \div 6 =$ _____

8 $12 \times \frac{1}{6} = \dfrac{\Box}{\Box} =$ _____

9 $12 \div 12 =$ _____

10 $12 \times \frac{1}{12} = \dfrac{\Box}{\Box} =$ _____

Set B

1 $6 \div 6 =$ _____

2 $6 \times \frac{1}{6} = \dfrac{\Box}{\Box} =$ _____

3 $60 \div 60 =$ _____

4 $60 \times \frac{1}{60} = \dfrac{\Box}{\Box} =$ _____

5 $600 \div 600 =$ _____

6 $600 \times \frac{1}{600} = \dfrac{\Box}{\Box} =$ _____

Describe a pattern you see in one of the sets of problems above.

_____

_____

_____

©Curriculum Associates, LLC   Copying is permitted for classroom use.

Fraction Division—Skills Practice

Name: _____

Divide a fraction by a whole number and divide a whole number by a fraction.   **Form A**

1 $2 \div \frac{1}{3} =$ _____

2 $3 \div \frac{1}{2} =$ _____

3 $5 \div \frac{1}{5} =$ _____

4 $\frac{1}{3} \div 3 =$ _____

5 $\frac{1}{4} \div 5 =$ _____

6 $\frac{1}{5} \div 4 =$ _____

7 $3 \div \frac{1}{4} =$ _____

8 $4 \div \frac{1}{3} =$ _____

9 $6 \div \frac{1}{5} =$ _____

10 $\frac{1}{5} \div 2 =$ _____

11 $\frac{1}{3} \div 6 =$ _____

12 $\frac{1}{6} \div 3 =$ _____

13 $2 \div \frac{1}{6} =$ _____

14 $5 \div \frac{1}{4} =$ _____

15 $4 \div \frac{1}{5} =$ _____

16 $\frac{1}{5} \div 2 =$ _____

17 $\frac{1}{2} \div 5 =$ _____

18 $\frac{1}{3} \div 2 =$ _____

Divide a fraction by a whole number and divide a whole number by a fraction.   **Form B**

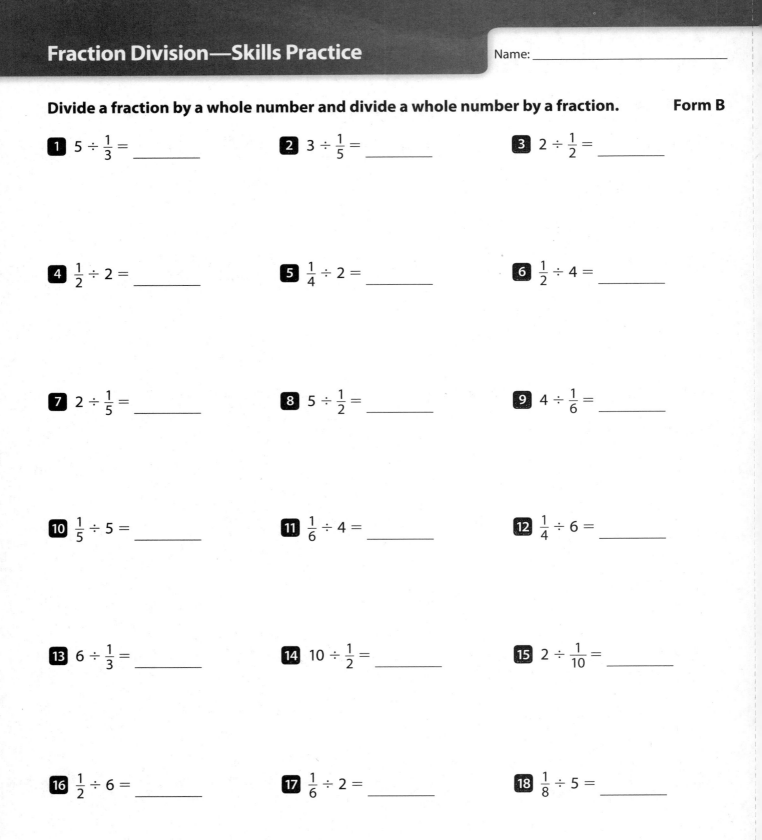

1 $5 \div \frac{1}{3} =$ _____

2 $3 \div \frac{1}{5} =$ _____

3 $2 \div \frac{1}{2} =$ _____

4 $\frac{1}{2} \div 2 =$ _____

5 $\frac{1}{4} \div 2 =$ _____

6 $\frac{1}{2} \div 4 =$ _____

7 $2 \div \frac{1}{5} =$ _____

8 $5 \div \frac{1}{2} =$ _____

9 $4 \div \frac{1}{6} =$ _____

10 $\frac{1}{5} \div 5 =$ _____

11 $\frac{1}{6} \div 4 =$ _____

12 $\frac{1}{4} \div 6 =$ _____

13 $6 \div \frac{1}{3} =$ _____

14 $10 \div \frac{1}{2} =$ _____

15 $2 \div \frac{1}{10} =$ _____

16 $\frac{1}{2} \div 6 =$ _____

17 $\frac{1}{6} \div 2 =$ _____

18 $\frac{1}{8} \div 5 =$ _____

©Curriculum Associates, LLC   Copying is permitted for classroom use.

Name: _____

Divide by a unit fraction to find patterns.

Set A

1 $6 \times 2 =$ _____

3 $6 \times 3 =$ _____

5 $6 \times$ _____ $= 24$

7 $6 \times$ _____ $= 30$

9 $6 \times$ _____ $= 36$

2 $6 \div \frac{1}{2} =$ _____

4 $6 \div \frac{1}{3} =$ _____

6 $6 \div \dfrac{\square}{\square} = 24$

8 $6 \div \dfrac{\square}{\square} = 30$

10 $6 \div \dfrac{\square}{\square} = 36$

Set B

1 $7 \times 10 =$ _____

3 $8 \times 10 =$ _____

5 $9 \times 10 =$ _____

7 $10 \times 10 =$ _____

2 $7 \div \frac{1}{10} =$ _____

4 $8 \div \frac{1}{10} =$ _____

6 $9 \div \frac{1}{10} =$ _____

8 $10 \div \frac{1}{10} =$ _____

Describe a pattern you see in one of the sets of problems above.

_____

_____

_____

©Curriculum Associates, LLC   Copying is permitted for classroom use.